Sexuality and Aging:

an annotated bibliography

by
George F. Wharton III

THE SCARECROW PRESS, INC.
METUCHEN, N.J. & LONDON
1981

Library of Congress Cataloging in Publication Data

Wharton, George F.
    Sexuality and aging.

    Previously published as: A bibliography on
sexuality and aging. 1978.
    Includes indexes.
    1. Aged--Sexual behavior--Bibliography.
I. Title.
Z7164.S42W48 1981   016.3067'0880565   81-5097
ISBN 0-8108-1427-7   AACR2

Ref.
Z
7164
S42W48
1981

To my father,

George F. Wharton, Jr.

CONTENTS

PREFACE

The demography of the United States is changing. The population as a whole is increasingly shifting in age from younger to older. Each year a larger proportion of the population reaches 65 and as this happens society needs to become more aware of the needs and problems of older people.

Human sexuality is natural and should continue into old age. However, aging brings about changes in the human body which in turn may bring about sexual problems. Basic facts about the changes that occur in the sexual organs and activity of older persons need to be integrated and disseminated. This annotated bibliography is an attempt to do just that. Although it is impossible to include all the works ever published pertaining to sexuality and aging, most of the major ones will be found here. There is some overlapping of topics. Also, many more citations exist for a topic such as the climacteric but only the most relevant ones with respect to sexuality and aging were included.

The bibliography was compiled using a number of computer searches. Among those included were Biological Abstracts, Index Medicus, Psychological Abstracts, Sociological Abstracts, and a search by the National Clearinghouse for Mental Health Information. Dissertation Abstracts and the Cumulative Index to Nursing and Allied Health Literature (from 1974 to 1979) were also used. When possible, the following abstract references are given within citations:

B. A.	Biological Abstracts
D. A.	Dissertation Abstracts International
E. M.	Excerpta Medica
I. M.	Index Medicus
P. A.	Psychological Abstracts
P. I.	Population Index
S. A.	Sociological Abstracts

In addition, the research collections of the Institute for Sex Research at Indiana University were used (as presented in their bibliography on Aging and Sex Behavior) to obtain and verify certain journal articles.   Other foundational works implemented included the Andrus Gerontology Center's Sexuality and Aging: A Selected Bibliography and SIECUS's Sexuality and the Aging: A Selected Bibliography.   The latter bibliography contains citations from Nathan Wetherill Shock's "Current Publications in Gerontology and Geriatrics" published in each issue of the Journal of Gerontology from 1974 to 1980.   The Andrus bibliography covered the same from 1959-1974.

The unclassified section of this work includes citations that are foreign, very dated, hard to obtain, out of print, or of little professional value.   The bibliography was originally published by the Rutgers Intra-University Program in Gerontology in an unannotated form.   However, many additions and corrections have been made to make the present annotated version an entirely revised work.

I wish to thank Marsel A. Heisel of the Rutgers Intra-University Program in Gerontology for her support and encouragement.   It is hoped that this work will be of use to adult educators, gerontologists, physicians, counselors, nurses, psychiatrists, or any older adult who wishes to learn more about sexuality and aging.

George F. Wharton III
New Brunswick, N. J.
May 1980

GENERAL WORKS ON SEXUALITY AND AGING

1   Allen, Andra J.   "All American Sexual Myths, " in American
          Journal of Nursing, Vol. 75, No. 10, 1770-1771, October
          1975.
          Presents 17 myths about sex and the actual reality about sex.
One of those myths is that the older one gets, the more one should
lose interest in sex.   The author suggests that people can be sexually active until death.

2   Allen, Gina, and Martin, Clement G.   Intimacy: Sensitivity,
          Sex and the Art of Love.   pp. 167-168; 259-260, Chicago:
          Cowles Book Co., Inc., 1971.
          A general discussion of intimacy and sexuality in the later
years including adjustment to the climacteric and impotence and the
importance of health to insure good sexual relations.

3   Amulree, (Lord) B. W. S.   "Sex and the Elderly, " in Practitioner,
          Vol. 172, No. 1030, 431-435, April 1954.
          A somewhat negative presentation of sex in the elderly.   Top-
ics covered include sexual activity in the elderly, the male climacteric, impotence in the elderly, and sexual offences in the elderly.   14
selected bibliographic items.

4   Anderson, Barbara G.   The Aging Game.   Success, Sanity and
          Sex After 60.   New York: McGraw-Hill, 1980.   (There is
          a short book review of this in Journal of Gerontology, Vol.
          35, No. 2, 281, March 1980.)
          A general discussion on sex after 60.

5   Anderson, Catherine J.   "Sexuality in the Aged, " in Journal of
          Gerontological Nursing, Vol. 1, No. 5, 6-10, November-
          December 1975.
          Sexuality in the aged is still misunderstood, mythologized,
and stereotyped.   The basic studies on human sexuality with reference to aging are summarized, namely 1) Kinsey studies, 2) Masters
and Johnson studies, and 3) Duke University studies.   Sexuality
should be considered in the nursing assessments of geriatric patients.
Study of human sexuality should be integrated into nursing curriculum.
24 references

6   Anderson, Helen, and Cote, Paul.   "Sexuality and the Socially
          Active Aged, " in Gerontologist, Vol. 15, No. 5, part 2, 47,
          1975.   (A paper presented at the 28th annual meeting of the

Gerontological Society, Louisville, Kentucky, October 1975.)
Interviews were conducted with 66 socially active adults aged
60 to 94. The instrument contained 25 direct, short, structured
questions. It was concluded that sexual activity continues into the
eighties. Helping professionals need to consider sexuality as an important issue and on the same level as physical, emotional, and
mental health issues.

7   Angelino, Henry R. "Sex and Aging," Paper presented at the
        85th Annual Convention of the American Psychological Asso-
        ciation. San Francisco, CA, August 30, 1977.
        A general discussion covering negative attitudes toward the
aged enjoying sexuality, their right to professional counseling in
these matters, the ability for physically fit human beings to have un-
limited sexuality, and some sex problems that occur with aging.
Suggestions are made to help the aging to be sexually active, including polygyny, coupling, nonmarital cohabitation, communes or
homosexual companionships. No references

8   Armstrong, Eunice Burton. "The Possibility of Sexual Happiness
        in Old Age," in Beigel, Hugo G. (ed.), Advances in Sex Re-
        search, pp. 131-137, New York: Hoeber-Harper, 1963.
        (S. A., Vol. 12, No. 6, B2225, 1964.)
        The counterpart theory states that the sexual pattern in the first
half of life usually determines the sexual pattern of the second half.
It is usually illness rather than age which leads to the decline in
sexual activity for persons over 65. Social and biological pressures
may also be factors in the decline. Healthy older people can continue to have sex into their ninth decade.

9   Auerback, Alfred. "Sexual Patterns in Later Years of Life," in
        Arizona Medicine, Vol. 27, 13-16, July 1970.
        A general discussion suggesting that men and women are cap-
able of satisfying sexual activity even into their later years. They
must have a healthy attitude toward aging and a sexually responsive
partner. Physicians should counsel patients concerning the use of
masturbation in the absence of intercourse. 9-item bibliography

10 Avant, W. Ray. "Sexuality and Older Persons," Paper presented
        at the annual meeting of the Georgia Gerontological Society,
        September 1975.
        The paper begins by emphasizing the increasing numbers of
older people in our society and of biased negative attitudes which
exist toward the sexuality of older people. The point is stressed
that not much research has been done on sexuality and aging but the
author summarizes the findings from three major research studies
which serve as cornerstones of our information on the topic, namely the Kinsey studies, the Duke University longitudinal study, and
the Masters and Johnson study. Contains a section entitled "Policy
and Program Implications" which makes mention of the importance
of taking into account nursing home residents when considering sexual expression in older people. The paper concludes that every person over 60 cannot hope to find a new intimacy and fulfillment and

that there is a great need for planning for the generations of older persons yet to come.   28 references

11   Barrett, J. C.   "An Analysis of Coital Patterns, " in Journal of Biosocial Science, Vol. 2, 351-357, 1970.
     Incidence of coitus was examined based on data from 241 married couples.   These couples had looked for advice on the basal body temperature (BBT) method of birth control from the Catholic Marriage Advisory Council.   The six days of the post-ovulatory phase were thought to be least affected by intentional birth control and therefore were analyzed.   Coital frequencies were tabulated by age of the wife.   The researcher's hypothesis was that probability of coitus on any day does not matter whether coitus occurred the day before or not.   There were a number of alternators, i. e. , couples whose probability of coitus decreased if it occurred the day before.   Coitus increased for some, called persistors, and other couples seemed to be unaffected in their pattern of coitus, i. e. , probability of coitus did not change whether coitus had occurred the day before or not.   13 references

12   Bastani, Jehangir B.   "Sexuality in Later Life, " in Nebraska Medical Journal, Vol. 62, No. 3, 62-64, March 1977.
     A general discussion of the topic.   9 references

13   Beach, Frank Ambrose (ed.)   Sex and Behavior.   New York: John Wiley, 1965.   (Reprint 1974, New York: Robert E. Krieger Publishing Co. , Inc. , 1974.)
     This book is a product of conference proceedings held in 1961 and 1962 at the University of California at Berkeley.   The Committee for Research in Problems of Sex, National Academy of Sciences--National Research Council sponsored and organized the meetings.   Three main topics were covered: 1) human sexuality and sex differences, 2) sex in animals, and 3) hormonal controls and control of hormones with respect to sexuality.

14   Beigel, Hugo G.   "Sex After 60: Is It Lechery?" in OP/The Osteopathic Physician, Vol. 44, No. 1, 68-70, 74-75, 77, 89, January 1977.
     A general discussion of the need for positive thinking about sex after 60 among society, the elderly, and the medical profession.

15   Berezin, Martin A.   "Masturbation and Old Age, " in Marcus, Irwin M. , and Francis, John J. (eds.), Masturbation from Infancy to Senescence, pp. 329-347, New York: International University Press, 1975.
     Many myths and misconceptions still exist about masturbation in old age as well as sexuality in old age.   Facts about masturbation in old age are presented and suggestions are given that more longitudinal studies need to be made.   23 references

16   _____ .   "Sex and Old Age: A Review of the Literature, " in Journal of Geriatric Psychiatry, Vol. 2, 131-149, 1969.   A paper presented at the Seventh Annual Scientific Meeting of

the Boston Society for Gerontological Psychiatry, September 23, 1967. Also in Zinberg, Norman Earl, and Kaufman, Irving (eds.), Normal Psychology of the Aging Process, (revised edition). New York: International University Press, Inc., pp. 217-236, 1978.

In his review of the literature, Berezin concludes that many myths, misconceptions and taboos exist about sexuality and the aged. We need to know more about the emotional and psychological aspects of sexuality and the aged. Studies reported so far have not touched upon love, affection, tenderness, and other kinds of sexual relationships. Sexuality is discussed with too limited a scope. Homosexuality in the aged and sexuality in institutions is not discussed in this review. 44 references

17 _____. "Sex and Old Age: A Further Review of the Literature," in Journal of Geriatric Psychiatry, Vol. 9, No. 2, 189-209, 1976. A paper presented at the Fifteenth Anniversary Annual Scientific Meeting of the Boston Society for Gerontologic Psychiatry, November 1, 1975. Also in Zinberg, Norman Earl, and Kaufman, Irving (eds.), Normal Psychology of the Aging Process, (revised edition). New York: International University Press, Inc., pp. 237-256, 1978.

According to the author, not much change has taken place since the first review was made in 1967. The level of sexual activity is not greatly changed from youth although it may slow down a bit. Those who study the subject of sexuality and aging are somewhat defensive about it. Much more popular literature on sex in old age is appearing on the scene (although the author doesn't specifically cite any). The physical aspects of sexuality and aging have been emphasized without much mention of love and romance. Loss of a partner through death or divorce is a problem. Public awareness on sexuality and aging has increased. 18 references

18 Berman, Ellen M., and Lief, Harold I. "Sex and the Aging Process," in Oaks, Wilbur W.; Melchiode, Gerald A.; and Ficher, Ilda (eds.), Sex and the Life Cycle, pp. 125-134, New York: Grune and Stratton, 1976. (A paper presented at the 35th Hahnemann Symposium, Philadelphia, PA.)

Stresses common to aging which relate to sexuality include loss of a meaningful companion and loss of physical power and health. There are two principal problem areas in the treatment of sexual dysfunction: 1) dysfunction in the marital relationship, and 2) lack of knowledge about changing physiology. 21 references

19 Blazer, Dan. "Adding Life to Years: Late Life Sexuality and Patient Care," in Nursing Care, Vol. 10, No. 7, 28-29, 42-43, July 1977.

A general article aimed at nurses and health care personnel, it was written by a physician who has summed up the general points about patient care and late life sexuality. He stresses individual differences in late life sexuality and the importance of nurses to be sensitive and receptive to the sexual problems of their patients. The main cause of marital problems in later life may be sexual.

Certain medications may cause sexual problems so efforts should
be made to change or reduce them.   Staff should encourage openness among themselves to discuss sex issues and problems which
may crop up in their institution.   Continuing education programs in
this area should be encouraged.   No references

20   Botwinick, Jack.   "Drives, Expectancies, and Emotions," in
        Birren, James E. (ed.), Handbook of Aging and the Individ-
        ual, pp. 739-768, Chicago: University of Chicago Press,
        1959.
        Covers changes in sexual responsiveness which occur with
aging as well as changes in general responsiveness.   Sexual behavior and age are discussed by quoting the Kinsey, et al., studies of
1948.   More cultural restrictions exist on female sexuality than on
male sexuality.   The effects of aging on the sexuality of male rats
and male guinea pigs are touched upon briefly.

21   _____.   "Sexuality and Sexual Relations," in his Aging and
        Behavior: A Comprehensive Integration of Research Findings,
        pp. 35-49, New York: Springer, 1973.
        Sexuality is characteristic for the young and the aged and
should continue until late in life.   Sexual response and vigor does
decline somewhat with age.   Because women live longer than men
and because they usually marry men who are older than themselves
widowhood is common.   This leaves them without a sanctioned sexual partner.   Widows find it harder to remarry than widowers.
Pressures of career and economic responsibilities can decrease
sexual interest.   Mental strain can reduce sexuality more than
physical strain.   Other factors responsible for sexual decline in men
include self doubt, alcohol abuse, boredom, or the loss of interest
of the wife toward him.   The menopause in women may cause trauma
regarding their sexuality.   Good health, regular sexual activity, and
an available partner can help maintain sexual ability into later life.
13 references

22   Bowman, Karl M.   "The Sex Life of the Aging Individual," in
        DeMartino, Manfred F. (ed.), Sexual Behavior and Person-
        ality Characteristics, pp. 372-375, New York: Citadel, 1963.
        (from Geriatrics, Vol. 9, 83-84, 1954.)
        A review of the literature on the sex activity of middle and
old age.   An active sex life can help preserve good mental health.

23   Boyarsky, Rose E.   "Sexuality," Chapter 26 in Steinberg,
        Franz U. (ed.), Cowdry's The Care of the Geriatric Patient,
        5th edition, pp. 393-400, St. Louis, MO: C. V. Mosby Co.,
        1976.
        A general discussion of sexuality for the elderly person.   The
chapter is broken down into several sections including male physiologic changes, female physiologic changes, cultural influences,
psychologic influences, and other factors.   28 references

24   Brenton, Myron.   "The (Sensual) Spirit of Seventy-Six," in
        Forum: The International Journal of Human Relations, Vol.
        7, No. 5, 50-53, February 1978.

A man tells a personal story of how he retained his sensuality into old age and how he felt about it.   A good article for people at this age to read.

25   Brier, Judith, and Rubenstein, Dan.   "Sex for the Elderly?
       Why Not?" in Perspective on Aging, Vol. 6, No. 1, 7-11,
       1977.   (Excerpted from a paper presented at the American
       Sociological Association Meeting in September 1976, New
       York City.)
       Contains sections on the following: no time limit drawn for
sexual performance; impotency can be reversible; why the role is
lost; the cultural seeds of human sexual response; the climacterium;
the double standard of aging; "machismo" expected in males; economic security and sexual response; marriage; widowhood; and a
section on congregate care.   17 references

26   Brock, Anna Marie; O'Neal, Daniel J. III; and Walker, Marcus L.   "Demythologizing the Issues," in Journal of Gerontological Nursing, Vol. 4, No. 6, 26-33, December 1978.
       The myth that sex is only for the young is discussed.

27   Broderick, Carlfred.   "Sexuality and Aging: An Overview," in
       Solnick, Robert Lewis (ed.), Sexuality and Aging (revised),
       pp. 1-8, Los Angeles: University of Southern California,
       1978.   (Also in Burnside, Irene Mortenson (ed.), Sexuality
       and Aging, pp. 1-6, Los Angeles: University of Southern
       California, 1975.)
       A general overview on sexual development is presented here.
It is exactly the same as presented in the Burnside book.   Two interesting points stand out.   One is that older women in depression
have been brought out of it by taking them to a beauty parlor.
Another is that the privacy of older people in nursing homes needs
to be stressed.   1 reference listed in Solnick but not in Burnside.

28   Brotman, Herman B.   "Who Are the Aging?" in Busse, Ewald
       W., and Pfeiffer, Eric (eds.), Mental Illness in Later Life,
       pp. 19-39, Chapter 2, Washington, D.C.:   American Psychiatric Association, 1973.
       Tables of sex ratios are presented as well as tables on the
marital status of older persons.

29   Brower, H. Terri, and Tanner, Libby A.   "A Study of Older
       Adults Attending a Program on Human Sexuality: A Pilot
       Study," in Nursing Research, Vol. 28, No. 1, 36-39, January-February 1979.
       Report of a study which attempted to determine if significant
changes took place in older adults' knowledge and attitudes about
human sexuality after a two-session course on the subject.   Of the
30 participants who took the pretest, only 4 took the posttest even
though most of the 30 attended the second session.   The review of
the literature includes sections on physiologic sexual aging, physical
and sexual impairment, sex in the older adult, sex education for the
elderly, and the nurse's role in the sexual education of the elderly.

There is a great need for the education of staff who work with the aged in both day care and institutional settings. 19 references

30 Bumagin, Victoria E. , and Hun, Kathryn F. Aging Is a Family Affair. New York: Thomas Y. Crowell Co. , 1979. (Reviewed by Herman T. Blumenthal in Journal of Gerontology, Vol. 35, No. 1, 127, January 1980.)
Covers a number of topics including sex and marriage.

31 Burnside, Irene Mortenson (ed.), Sexuality and Aging. Los Angeles: University of Southern California, 1975.
Many different disciplines have contributed to this book. Each chapter has been annotated separately in this bibliography.

32 _____. "Sexuality and the Aged," pp. 452-464, Chapter 32, in her Nursing and the Aged. New York: McGraw-Hill, 1976. (An expanded version of "Sexuality and Aging," in her Sexuality and Aging, pp. 42-53, Los Angeles: University of Southern California, 1975. Reprinted by permission of Medical Arts and Sciences, Vol. 27, No. 3, 13-27, 1973. Parts of this chapter were delivered at the Mary L. Monteith Lecture at Loma Linda University in Loma Linda, CA, on April 1973, for a conference entitled "Human Sexuality." Parts of it were also discussed on a CBS television show entitled "Sex After Sixty," which was produced by Irina Posner, October 22, 1974.)
An article relevant to health care personnel. It discusses the lack of information on sexuality and aging, the importance of touch to aged individuals, sex and the aging woman, and sex and the aging male. Additional topics covered included sex and the institutionalized aged, love, romance and marriage of older patients, peer and family reactions, and implications for nursing. 29 references and a 19-item bibliography

33 _____. "Sexuality and the Older Adult: Implications for Nursing," in her Sexuality and Aging, pp. 26-34, Los Angeles: University of Southern California, 1975. (Based on speeches given for the American Nurses' Association Conference, "Therapeutic Strategies with the Aged," at Los Angeles, CA, September 28, 1974, and Burlingame, CA, October, 1974.)
Contains a summary of a major study on sexuality which included older people, i.e., Masters and Johnson (1966). Covers illness and sexuality, sexuality in nursing homes, the importance of physical examinations, and suggested interventions. 12 references

34 Busse, Ewald W. "Sex After Fifty (discussion by Goldfarb, Alvin I. , M.D. , follows)," Chapter 11 in Adelson, Edward T. (ed.), Sexuality and Psychoanalysis, pp. 215-229, New York: Brunner/Mazel, 1975.
Topics of discussion in this chapter include: 1) the sex taboo in old age, 2) the aging male and female--anatomic and physiological changes, 3) sex endocrine changes and replacement, 4) the

Duke University longitudinal study, 5) marriage in late life and 6) the
single woman--widowed or divorced. In the future, sexual activity
among the elderly will increase according to the author. 14 references

35 _____, and Pfeiffer, Eric. Behavior and Adaptation in Late
        Life, p. 49, Boston: Little, Brown, and Co., 1969.
        A small paragraph on sexual activity and interest pointing
to the Kinsey survey and the Duke University longitudinal study indi-
cating that a large number of older adults continue to have interest
in and engage in sexual activity. Page 49 is in the section written
by Erdman Palmore entitled "Sociological Aspects of Aging."

36 _____; Barnes, Robert H.; Silverman, Albert J.; Shy, G.
        Milton; Thaler, Margaret; and Frost, Laurence L. "Studies
        of the Process of Aging: Factors That Influence the Psyche
        of Elderly Persons," in American Journal of Psychiatry,
        Vol. 110, No. 12, 897-903, June 1954. (This was a paper
        presented at the 109th annual meeting of The American Psy-
        chiatric Association, Los Angeles, CA, May 4-8, 1953.)
        All subjects of this study were above 60 years of age and
divided into 4 groups; three as community groups and one as a hospitalized group. Group A (52 women, 48 men) had an average age of
70.9 years. Group B (28 women, 22 men) had an average age of
72.2 years. Group C (18 men, 12 women) had an average age of
71.5 years. Sexual activity and interest increased progressively
from Group A through Group C. Some elderly people have sexual
drives but no satisfactory outlet. People who had made a poor
sexual adjustment in early life had virtually no sex interests in
older age. 11-item bibliography

37 Butler, Robert N. Why Survive? Being Old in America. New
        York: Harper and Row, Inc., 1975.
        Older people are concerned about sexual abilities but the only
two requirements for sexual activity are good health and an interesting and interested partner. There are many myths about impotence
and menopause that need to be dispelled by physicians. Doctors
need to understand that sexuality can be very important to a person
in later life. Older people can take advantage of sexual counseling
and therapy. Alcohol can have a detrimental effect on sex. Sexual
activity can be an exercise to relieve tension, for emotional well-
being, and good for the muscles and circulation. Problems of an
individual's capacity for intimacy and of marital choice need more
exploration.

38 _____, and Lewis, Myrna I. Sex After Sixty: A Guide for
        Men and Women for Their Later Years. New York: Harper
        and Row, Inc., 1976.
        Written specifically for older individuals with positive en-
couragement toward sexuality in the later years. Much factual information is presented on places to write or call concerning information on sex or related topics. An easy to read and helpful guide.
Paperback edition was published in 1977 under the title Love and

Sex After Sixty. A short adaptation of the hardcover book appears in Landers, Ann. The Ann Landers Encyclopedia A to Z, pp. 957-961, Garden City, N.Y.: Doubleday and Co., 1978. In addition, there is a book review of the Landers book by Lorna Brown in SIECUS Report, Vol. 8, No. 1, 15, September 1979.

39   Calderone, Mary Steichen. "Middle-Age Sex: Myths and Mis-
         conceptions" (an interview), in Dynamic Maturity, Vol. 9,
         40-43, November 1974.
         Dr. Calderone's interviewer was Glen Evans, a regular
writer for Dynamic Maturity on health subjects. A series of general
questions were asked of Dr. Calderone with most of them dealing
with myths and misconceptions about sexuality in old age. No references

40   _____. Release from Sexual Tensions. New York: Random
         House, 1960.
         Chapter 15 entitled "Love Can Be Ageless" discusses just
that. A resource useful to both physicians and patients and easy to
read.

41   _____. "Sex and the Aging," in Gross, Ronald; Gross, Bea-
         trice; and Seidman, Sylvia (eds.), The New Old: Struggling
         for Decent Aging, pp. 205-208, Garden City, NY: Anchor
         Books, 1978.
         A general discussion on the topic.

42   _____. "Sexuality and the Later Years," Chapter 13 in
         Grabowski, Stanley, and Mason, W. Dean (eds.), Education
         for the Aging, pp. 284-292, Syracuse, NY: ERIC Clearing-
         house on Adult Education at Syracuse University, 1974.
         The aging homosexual is discussed as are attitudes of others
on aging and sexuality. Sexuality among the aged varies widely.
Caring and sexual relationships should be continued throughout the
lifespan. We don't know much about the sexual images of old people.

43   _____. "Sexuality and the Later Years" (an interview), in
         Managing the Disturbed Elderly Patient in Family Practice,
         Vol. 2, pp. 39-49, Fort Washington, PA: McNeil Labora-
         tories, Inc., 1976. (Formerly no. 10 in the series Managing
         the Elderly Patient in Family Practice, 1975.)
         A question and answer format. Covers sexual and emotional
needs of older people, the need for the intimacy and warmth of
sexuality for older people, ways a family physician can help older
people develop a sexual lifestyle and help patients overwhelmed with
guilt and shame about their sexual desires, the major causes of
decline in sexual activity, and parasexual ways of expressing affection as a substitute for direct sexual expression. In addition, it
covers advice for physicians on obtaining a sexual history from patients, the part masturbation plays in the life of older people, and
the importance of privacy for expression of sexuality whether the
person is in an institution or not.

44 _____ . "The Sexuality of Aging, " in SIECUS Newsletter,
    Vol. 7, No. 1, 1-2, October 1971.
        A short essay on the importance of knowing that the emotional
or sexual needs of older people are exactly the same as the young--
with individual variation in kinds of expression and intensity.   A
mention is made of the lack of privacy in institutions.   10 suggestions for further reading

45 Cameron, Paul.   "Note on Time Spent Thinking About Sex, " in
    Psychological Reports, Vol. 20, No. 3, Part I, 741-742,
    June 1967.
        Residents of Boulder, Colorado (N= 238) were asked what per-
centage of time was spent thinking about sex each day.   Both males
and females were equally interested in sex but the interest declined
with age.   1 reference

46 _____ , and Biber, Henry.   "Sexual Thought Throughout the
    Life-Span, " in Gerontologist, Vo. 13, 144-147, Summer 1973.
        When 4, 420 persons were asked "What were you thinking
about over the past five minutes?" sex as a focal or peripheral
thought was found to be highest in teen and young adult years.   The
range in age of people asked was from 8 to 99, and when interrupted
to be asked the question, they were in a variety of different situations.   No matter what age level, male thought was found to be
"sexier" than female thought.   Mental thought of sex is much higher
than the action which really occurs.   14 references

47 Cauldwell, D. O.   "When Does Sex Life End?" in Sexology, Vol.
    25, 250-253, November 1958.
        Age need not be the decisive factor in terminating sexual ac-
tivity and interest.   Several examples are given of men who fathered
children rather late in their lives.   Sometimes sex interest declines
in one partner before the other and unless they seek counseling from
a physician, the unhappy situation will continue.   No references

48 Chapman, Ruth H.   "Comment and Controversy.   No Longer at
    Risk: Sex Among the Elderly, " in Family Planning Perspec-
    tives, Vol. 8, No. 5, 253, September-October 1976.
        A general article on aging and sexuality.   All that is needed
for sex among the aged to occur is a reasonable state of health, and
an interested and interesting partner.   Physicians should encourage
sexuality in the elderly.   3 references

49 Charatan, Fred B.   "Sexual Function in Old Age, " in Medical
    Aspects of Human Sexuality, Vol. 12, No. 9, 150-151, 155,
    159, 163-164, 169, September 1978.
        Dr. Charatan presents facts on sexual decline with age (but
not termination), common problems interfering with sexual function
including menopausal problems, hysterectomy and prostatectomy,
diabetes mellitus, heart disease, drugs and medications, and other
conditions.   In addition, he presents two cases to illustrate psychological problems affecting sexual function.   The geriatric patient can
and should enjoy sexuality in later life.   Commentary follows by
William A. Frosch, M. D.   6 references

50   Chartham, Robert. Sex and the Over-Fifties. Chatsworth, CA:
        Brandon Books, 1972. (London: Leslie Frewin, 1969.)
        This book uses the case study approach to show that middle-
aged and elderly can have an active sex life. Common problems of
the aged are discussed.

51   _____. "You Are Never Too Old to Make Love," in Forum:
        The International Journal of Human Relations, Vol. 4, No. 6,
        30-33, March 1975.
        A discussion of some letters received by Dr. Chartham from
widows, widowers and single people over the age of 60 and their
problems in achieving sexual satisfaction. He quotes from a number
of the letters. He suggests that we must teach younger people that
the elderly have emotional and physical needs which they have a right
to satisfy and secondly, to arrange for older people to be sexually
satisfied without embarking on marriage. No references

52   Chernick, Beryl, and Chernick, Avinoam. As Sexuality Matures.
        London, Ontario: Sound Feelings, Ltd. , n. d.
        There are some physiological changes in sexuality with age
but sexuality can also get richer. The Chernicks discuss some of
the common myths about sex after forty in this 88-minute cassette
with diagrams. The sexual problems of two couples are used to illustrate positive and negative attitudes toward sex and aging.

53   Chew, Peter. "The Perils of the Midlife Affair," in Dynamic
        Maturity, Vol. 12, No. 3, 23-26, 1977.
        Suggestions are made that extra-marital affairs are becoming
acceptable, even fashionable. Affairs may be bad, good, or indif-
ferent depending on the people involved. One of the most interesting
suggestions made in this article is the report of studies about mammals stating that only 3 percent are monogamous. Although monog-
amy is considered a Western norm, polygyny is the common practice.
Sociobiologists have suggested "the male may be programmed genet-
ically to spread his genes among a great number of sexual partners
and to keep other males away from them so that he can be certain
of his parenthood."

54   Chisholm, Lloyd W. How to Grow Young After Forty and Main-
        tain and Develop Sexual Power. Hicksville, NY: Exposition
        Press, 1975. (Book review of this on p. 365 of Journal of
        Gerontology, Vol. 30, No. 3, May 1975.)
        The author is a chiropractor who emphasizes the importance
of sexual knowledge. A general book meant for non-professionals.

55   Clark, LeMon. "Sex Life of the Middle Aged," in Marriage
        and Family Living, Vol. 11, No. 2, 58-60, Spring 1949.
        (P.A., Vol. 23, No. 4718, 1949.) (This also appears in
        DeMartino, Manfred F. (ed.), Sexual Behavior and Personality
        Characteristics, pp. 365-371, New York: Citadel Press,
        1963.)
        A discussion of changes which occur in middle age. These
changes can be physiological, psychological, and emotional, and can

affect sexual life in the middle age.   The changes can bring about problems and suggestions are given as to how these problems can be dealt with.

56   Clayton, Paula J., and Bornstein, Philipp E.   "Widows and
         Widowers," in Medical Aspects of Human Sexuality, Vol. 10,
         No. 9, 26-27, 31, 35-38, 43-44, 46, 48, 51-53, September
         1976.
         This article discusses the main problems and adjustments a
widower or widow must make, namely, dating, sex, and remarriage.
9 references.   Commentaries by Robert S. Weiss, Ph.D., Garfield
Tourney, M.D., and C. William Briscoe, M.D.

57   Clistier, Adeline (pseudonym).   "You're Over Sixty and You're
         in Love...," in Forum: The International Journal of Human
         Relations, Vol. 7, No. 9, 40-43, June 1978.
         This article was written to encourage older adults about their
sexuality.   The author states that with an enthusiastic partner, good
health, and privacy, an active sex life is possible through the seventies and beyond.   A general article, easy to understand and encouraging.

58   Cole, Theodore M.   "The Physician's Role in Working with the
         Sexuality of the Elderly," in Kelly, J.T., and Weir, J.
         (eds.), Perspectives on Human Aging, pp. 95-98, Minneapolis,
         MN: Craftsman Press, 1977.
         Physicians should include sexuality in their questioning of a
patient.   Even though the first question might elicit embarrassment,
the physician should make the patient comfortable in talking about
sexuality by exhibiting ease when talking about it.   Older people have
had many years to learn about themselves as sexual people.   It is
important to discuss sex with older patients in the context of the
aging experience.   The physician can provide approval and reinforce-
ment for sexuality in the older person.   No references

59   Comfort, Alex.   A Good Age, pp. 192-199, New York: Crown
         Publishers, 1976.
         Sexual desires and capacity extend throughout the entire life.
Changes occur through aging which may affect performance.   Several
studies are quoted to illustrate this.   Several steps for preserving
sexuality into later years are presented.   Several examples of people
who were or continue to be sexually active in their later years are
given.   Residential homes for older people would have much happier
atmospheres if sexual mores were less stringent.

60   _____.   The Joy of Sex, (paperback), p. 224, New York:
         Simon and Schuster, 1972.
         A page is devoted to age and sexuality.   Men and women do
not lose sexual needs or function with age.   When people continue
their sexual activity over 50, the activity keeps the hormone levels
up.   People who stop having sex could find it harder restarting.

61   _____.   More Joy of Sex, (paperback--pp. 210-214, 219)
         (hardcover--pp. 148-151, 156-157), New York: Simon and

Schuster, 1973, (paperback) and Crown Publishers, Inc., 1974, (hardcover).
Gentle sex should be started again after a heart attack as sex is an important part of rehabilitation. Disablement and disablement practicalities are discussed. A small section is included on the prostate and related problems.

62 _____. "Sex and Aging," in British Journal of Sexual Medicine, Vol. 4, No. 26, 22-24, June 1977. (This article is
from a taped interview with Dorothy M. Easton, Multi Media
Resource Center, San Francisco, CA.)
Sexuality changes in humans from about 50 on, but it changes more in the male than in the female. Males are not so easily stimulated and do not achieve orgasm at every act of intercourse. Although it takes longer for the male to achieve an erection, he can hold it longer. Therefore, sexual performance can improve considerably for older men who can have more sex per orgasm than younger men. No references

63 _____. "Sex and Aging," in Resource Guide, Vol. 1, No. 1,
4-7, 1976. (Published by Multi Media Resource Center, San
Francisco, CA.)
Changes in the sexual responses of men and women with age are presented. Impotence in men is usually the result of thinking that it may occur. Women seem to retain their interest and ability for sex more than men do.

64 _____. "Sexuality and Aging," in SIECUS Report, Vol. 4,
No. 6, 1, 9, July 1976.
Human sexual performance is altered by aging. Several studies are quoted to show that older people have the capacity and ability for sex in their later years. There is a great deal of individual variation in sexual activity. Sexuality in institutions is touched upon. We need to encourage and support sexuality in older people. 4 references

65 _____. "Sexuality in Old Age," in Journal of the American
Geriatrics Society, Vol. 22, No. 10, 440-442, 1974.
Geriatricians need to know that the aged can and want to experience sexual pleasure. Sexual experiences should be encouraged as they result in generally good effects. Sexuality of aged in nursing homes and other institutions is wrongly suppressed. No references

66 _____. "Sexuality in Old Age," in OP/The Osteopathic Physician, Vol. 41, 112-116, November 1974.
Age can be a factor which can reduce human sexual performance but the changes are minimal. Support and encouragement should be given to older adults who wish to continue sexual expression. The need for the right to privacy in nursing homes is emphasized.

67 Costello, Marilyn K. "Sex, Intimacy and Aging," in American
Journal of Nursing, Vol. 75, No. 8, 1330-1332, August 1975.
A case study is presented to illustrate the problems geriatric patients have in the quest for sexual gratification. Nurses need to re-

member that the elderly have sexual needs too. 18 references

68 Cuber, John Frank, and Harroff, Peggy B. The Significant
    Americans: A Study of Sexual Behavior Among the Affluent.
    New York: Appleton-Century-Crofts, 1965; Baltimore: Pen-
    guin Books, 1965.
    A search for truth about sexual and emotional relationships of
upper middle class men and women. It is presented as it looks and
feels to the people actually involved in the relationships. Much sexual activity occurs before and outside of marriage.

69 Daniel, Ronald S. Human Sexuality Methods and Materials for
    the Education, Family Life and Health Professions: An An-
    notated Guide to the Audiovisuals. Vol. I. Brea, CA:
    Heuristicus Publishing Company, 1979.
    Topic 15, entitled Geriatric Sexuality, includes 72 titles of
audiovisuals. Intended for use by health care professionals.

70 Dean, Stanley R. "Geriatric Sexuality: Normal, Needed, and
    Neglected," in Geriatrics, Vol. 29, No. 7, 134-37, July
    1974.
    Patients should be assured and counseled about sexual prob-
lems so that sex can continue after 60. 10 references

71 _____. "Sexual Behavior in Middle Life," in American
    Journal of Psychiatry, Vol. 128, No. 10, 1267, April 1972.
    Dr. Dean, in this discussion, suggests mental status com-
parisons between sexually satisfied and sexually unsatisfied, investi-
gations of solitary sexual practices, and changing patterns of sexual
behavior with age. 3 references

72 de Beauvoir, Simone. The Coming of Age. New York: G. P.
    Putnam's Sons, 1972.
    The author states that women are second class citizens in a
patriarchal society and that this has affected the sexual relations between men and women. Some areas covered without a specific focus
on sexuality and aging include intercourse frequency, masturbation,
homosexuality, and the effects of aging on men and women.

73 De Lora, Joann S., and Warren, Carol A. B. "Sexuality in the
    Middle and Later Years," Chapter 9 in their Understanding
    Sexual Interaction, pp. 218-237, Boston: Houghton Mifflin
    Co., 1977.
    Topics covered include monogamy (functions, problems, per-
sistence), sex and the unmarried (including the divorced, widowed,
never married), sexuality and aging, and the sexual problems of
aging.

74 De Nigola, Pietro, and Peruzza, Marino. "Sex in the Aged,"
    in Journal of the American Geriatrics Society, Vol. 22, No.
    8, 380-382, 1974. (P.A., Vol. 53, No. 00984, 1975.)
    Observations on 53 males and 32 females as well as litera-

ture sources are used to look at sexuality and the aged.   The range
of ages was from 62 to 81 years.   Factors influencing sexuality in
the aged include social, psychological, and environmental factors as
well as diseases.   Counseling is important in order to give a supportive atmosphere for continued sexual activity.   14 references

75   Dickinson, Peter A.   The Fires of Autumn: Sexual Activity in
      the Middle and Later Years.   New York: Drake Publishers,
      Inc. , 1974.
      Sexual myths are dispelled here in this easily readable book.
Common physical problems of illness and surgery and their effects
on sexuality are explained.   The book explains to the older layman
how he or she might retain a sexually active life.

76   Dobrowolski, L. A.   "Sexuality in the Later Years: Roles Be-
      haviour, " in Medicina geriatrica   (Florence), Vol. 11, 1-7,
      1979.
      The author begins the article with a general discussion of
later life marriages.   Other topics covered in a general way include sex and aging, sexual problems, and the range of sexual alternatives.   No references

77   Dresen, Sheila E.   "The Sexually Active Middle Adult, " in
      American Journal of Nursing, Vol. 75, No. 6, 1001-1005,
      June 1975.   (P. A. , Vol. 56, No. 04534, 1976.)
      A nurse's attitude about sexuality will be an important factor
in influencing his or her counseling ability with people with sexual
problems.   The author talks of the purposes of intercourse and the
patterns of sexuality in middle age.   Menopause in women and the
possibility of a menopause in men are discussed.   Sexual dysfunction,
the state of marriage and chronic health problems round out the discussion in this article.   18 references

78   Ehrmann, Winston.   "Some Knowns and Unknowns in Research
      into Human Sex Behavior, " in Marriage and Family Living,
      Vol. 19, No. 1, 16-24, February 1957.
      Except for age, the frequency of marital coitus shows little
or no relationship to other variables including marital happiness or
adjustment according to the author.   Most concern has focused on
quantity of premarital sex and the quality of marital sex.   Eight essential tasks that need to be completed or kept in mind for the future are summarized.   Comments follow by Clifford Kirkpatrick.
11 items in a selected bibliography

79   Estes, M. Diane.   Aging and Sexuality: A Physiological Ap-
      proach.   Omaha, NE: The Gerontology Program, University
      of Nebraska at Omaha, n. d.   (Reviewed in SIECUS Report,
      Vol. 7, No. 6, p. 6, July 1979 by Deryck Calderwood, Ph. D.)
      A slide-cassette program (54 slides, audio cassette) present-
ing the human sexual response cycle in men and women over 60.
The presentation is based on Masters and Johnson.   Narration includes male and female voices presenting a positive review of the
facts on aging and sexuality.   The slides are in color and the program runs $11\frac{1}{2}$ minutes.

80   Eymann, Kenneth. "Sexual Desires in the Aging," in Geriatric
       Care, Vol. 4, No. 10, 1, October 1972. (From Blumberg,
       Bernard, "Aging, A Philosophy of Care," published by West-
       ern Center for Continuing Education in Administration of
       Health Care Facilities, UCLA Extension, Los Angeles, CA)
         There is no other part of human behavior which is more mis-
understood than sex, especially sex and the aged. Sex in old age
can be potentially fulfilling and bring happiness to the senior citizen.
Questions for thought are suggested: 1) How do you feel about nursing home weddings? 2) A majority of married couples between 60
and 70 have sex; without data on this would you have believed it?

81   Falk, Gerhard, and Falk, Ursula, A. "Sexuality and the Aged,"
       in Nursing Outlook, Vol. 28, No. 1, 51-55, January 1980.
         Negative attitudes toward sexuality in the aged are due partly
to the culture which is youth oriented, age differences in spouses,
and cultural conditioning. Adult children sometimes fear financial
loss when the idea of their parents' remarriage comes up. Sexuality
in the aged is repressed and condemned in our society. Those responsible for the care of the aged need to become more knowledgeable
about sexual expression among the aged.

82   Feigenbaum, Elliott M.; Lowenthal, Marjorie Fiske; and Trier,
       Mella L. "A Report of a Study," in Geriatric Focus, Vol.
       5, No. 20, 2, 1967. (Paper presented at the Gerontological
       Society, New York, 1966.)
         As a part of another study, this study concerned 273 San
Francisco community residents from age 62 to 96 (133 men and 140
women). The question asked was "How much sex do you think a
person of your age should have?" The authors admit the study has
limitations because the data were too scanty for rigid analysis.
However, older persons are very interested in information about sex.
They are also somewhat confused about how much sex does or should
occur in the later years. No references

83   Finkle, Alex Louis. "Sexual Aspects of Aging," Chapter 6, pp.
       63-74 in Bellak, Leopold, and Karasu, Toksoz B. (eds.),
       Geriatric Psychiatry: A Handbook for Psychiatrists and Pri-
       mary Care Physicians. New York: Grune and Stratton, Inc.,
       1976.
         A general discussion of the following topics: 1) sexual interest
and competency in aging men, 2) classifications and treatments of
sexual impotency, 3) the sexual role of aging women, 4) organic
causes for impotency, 5) socio-psychologic influences on potency,
6) urological counseling of the impotent male, and a summary. 51
references

84   _____. "Sexual Function During Advancing Age," in Ross-
       man, Isadore (ed.), Clinical Geriatrics, pp. 473-479, Phila-
       delphia: J. B. Lippincott Co., 1971.
         Topics of discussion include the importance of eliciting a
sexual history from a patient, organic bases for impotency, extra-
organic influences on sexual function, sexuality of advancing age,

causes of impotency in aging males, and aids to potency in men.
Most cases of impaired sexual intercourse are psychogenic in origin.
In order to bring back sexual competency, a willing partner and an
assuring physician are needed.   33 references

85   Fleishman, Joseph J.   Manual of Human Relations for People
     Working with the Elderly: Theory and Practice.   Philadelphia:
     Geriatric Coordinators, Ltd. , 1976.
       The author provides a definition of sexuality, norms on sex-
uality for the aged, and physical aspects of sexuality and aging.
There is an exercise presented to enable the reader to understand
the myth of "the dirty old man. "

86   Fox, Nancy Littel; Garland, Anne M. ; Hanss, Joseph W. , Jr. ;
     and Pettid, Dennis E.   "Sexuality Among the Aging, " in
     Journal of Practical Nursing, Vol. 28, No. 8, 16-18, 41,
     August 1978.   (Abstract in Aged Care and Service Review,
     Vol. 1, No. 5 and 6, 14, 1978-79.)
       This was a presentation at the 1978 NAPNES Convention.
The author explains that there are many facets of sexuality.   There
are many labels that mislead such as "dirty old men. "   Sex after
sixty is possible and is desired by many older people and data are
presented to support this.   It is the responsibility of those who work
with older people to help them validate their sexuality.   There is a
need for changing attitudes and approaches toward sexuality among
the elderly and suggestions for changes are given.   Sex in nursing
homes is discussed by Anne M. Garland, the passion to love and be
loved is discussed by Dr. Joseph W. Hanss, Jr. , and the negative
connotations that our society holds about sex among the aging is discussed by Dennis E. Pettid.   No references

87   Francoeur, Robert T. , and Francoeur, Anna K.   "The Pleasure
     Bond: Reversing the Antisex Ethic, " in The Futurist, Vol.
     10, No. 4, 176-180, August 1976.   (Also in Reflections, Vol.
     12, 42, 1977.)
       Contains a small section on the sexual needs of the aged.

88   Freeman, Joseph T.   "Sexual Aspects of Aging, " in Cowdry,
     Edmund Vincent, and Steinberg, Franz U. (eds.), The Care
     of the Geriatric Patient, (4th edition), pp. 174-188, St. Louis,
     MO: C. V. Mosby Co. , 1971.   (3rd edition), pp. 130-146,
     1968.
       The decline in sexual activity in men is homogeneous and
physiologic according to the author.   He states that sexual decline in
women is heterogeneous and is more dependent on social forces.
Some influences on sexual function include marital status, customs
and personal mobility.   It is hard to separate sexual properties ac-
quired through marriage and social conditioning from properties due
to aging.   28 references

89   Freese, Arthur S.   "Meet Mary Calderone, " in Modern Maturity,
     Vol. 21, No. 4, 55-56, August-September 1978.
       A short biography on Dr. Mary Steichen Calderone precedes a

section of short questions and answers taken from an interview.
Among those questions discussed include sexual freedom of older
people, responsibility and sexual freedom, sexuality in institutions,
homosexuality and the elderly, the regard of religion for sexuality
and homosexuality, comparison of mature sex with young sex, where
to look for sexual advice, where you can find specialists, the effects
of the new sexual life-style on older people, where older people can
get more information on sexual questions, and advice to older people:
"Don't ossify mentally, emotionally, sexually or creatively...." No
references

90   Fried, Edrita.   "Clinical Aspects of Adult Therapy. II.
        Some Connections Between Sexuality and Ego Organization,"
        in American Journal of Orthopsychiatry, Vol. 29, 391-401,
        1959.
        The author states that disturbances in interpersonal relations
(object relations) which are not accompanied by physical malfunctioning are more easily corrected than disturbances associated with some
somatic malfunctioning.   Sexual problems can be improved a lot
faster than problems of multiple forms of somatic functioning.   Several case studies are presented.   Primary forms of sexual malfunctioning, especially partial or total frigidity, premature ejaculation,
and impotence, can be caused by ego defects according to the author.
Discussion follows by William V. Silverberg, M. D.

91   Friedeman, Joyce Sutkamp.   "Factors Influencing Sexual Expres-
        sion in Aging Persons: A Review of the Literature," in
        Journal of Psychiatric Nursing and Mental Health Services,
        Vol. 16, No. 7, 34-47, July 1978.
        A review of the literature which presents a conceptual frame-
work for looking at the system of variables which can affect the
sexual expression of older people.   Variables examined include: 1)
value system, 2) sexual knowledge, 3) previous patterns of sexual
activity, 4) demographic factors, 5) physical health, 6) emotional
health, and 7) social and economic resources.   Researchers have
focused on physical health and the demographic factors of age and
marital status.   More attention needs to be placed on the value
system and sexual knowledge.   The author evaluates the research
methods in these studies and makes suggestions for future research.
39 references

92   _____. "Sexuality in Older Persons: Implications for Nurs-
        ing Practice," in Nursing Forum, Vol. 18, No. 1, 92-101,
        1979.
        Presents factors influencing sexual expression in aging per-
sons, research findings on sexual behavior in aging persons, changes
in sexual function with age, and implications for the nursing process.
11 references

93   Gadpaille, Warren J.   The Cycles of Sex.   New York: Charles
        Scribner's Sons, 1975.
        The book presents psychosexual development in three cycles.
The first cycle covers development in the womb through childhood.

The second cycle covers adolescent sexual development. The third cycle is most relevant to this bibliography in that it covers sexual development in young adulthood, parenthood, and the middle and later years. Illness and sexuality are also discussed.

94 Gaydos, Jeff. "Love Won't Retire," in Parade, p. 9, December 16, 1979.
     People can continue to have gratifying love lives into their 80's and 90's. Personnel in nursing homes and retirement communities often have questions on dating and sex among older adults. Older people in retirement communities date much more than their children think. People should be supportive so that older people can enjoy themselves in romance and sex.

95 Genevay, Bonnie. "Age Is Killing Us Softly ... When We Deny the Part of Us Which Is Sexual," in Burnside, Irene Mortenson (ed.), Sexuality and Aging, pp. 67-75, Los Angeles: University of Southern California, 1975.
     Bonnie Genevay uses her experiences with geriatric group therapy to provide us with examples of touching as social or affectional expression in the nursing home setting. She suggests that touch, as a therapeutic intervention, should be explored. Many older people face a sexual identity problem. The chapter of the same title in the Solnick book is similar but is more detailed. Nursing home sexuality is discussed here in one of the few writings to touch on the subject.

96 _____. "Age Kills Us Softly When We Deny Our Sexual Identity," in Solnick, Robert Lewis (ed.), Sexuality and Aging (revised), pp. 9-25, Los Angeles: University of Southern California, 1978.
     As mentioned in the annotation on the similar chapter in the Burnside book Sexuality and Aging, this chapter discusses the need for expression of intimacy and affection throughout life. A romantic relationship can add zest to life that was previously thought to be over. She sets the stage for further discussion by delineating the double bind for older women, agism and sexism. Heterosexual affection and sexual choice without societal punishment are other topics which she covers. Nursing home sexuality is also mentioned again as it was in the Burnside book. 16 references

97 Gillman, Ruth. "Human Sexuality and Adult Education," in Lifelong Learning: The Adult Years, Vol. 2, No. 2, 20-23, October 1978.
     Several sections presented on this topic include assumptions, sexuality and the adult, psychological changes, physiological changes with aging, sexuality is for everyone, handicapped and terminally ill, the victim of sexual assault, sexual minorities, and relevance to adult education. Adult educators should promote the study of human sexuality to aid people in making decisions based on rational problem-solving instead of emotions or guilt feelings. Love, intimacy, and affection help promote mental health and fulfillment.

98 Greenblatt, Robert Benjamin, and Leng, Jean-Joël. "Factors
      Influencing Sexual Behavior," in Journal of the American
      Geriatrics Society, Vol. 20, No. 2, 49-54, February 1972.
      (This paper was presented in part at the 28th Annual Meeting
      of The American Geriatrics Society, Chicago, Illinois, April
      23-24, 1971.)
      Some of the factors influencing human sexuality include: 1)
chromosomal determinants, 2) external genital adequacy, 3) socioeconomic influences, 4) dependency on exogenous and endogenous
hormones, 5) gonadal integrity and hypothalamic sensitization during
fetal life. Overt sexual behavior is greatly influenced by hormones.
Testosterone can increase male and female sex drive. Illustrated
cases are presented to show that age need not be the cause of changing sexual activity. 9 references

99 _____; Pfeiffer, Eric; Masters, William H.; Johnson, Vir-
      ginia E.; and Comfort, Alex. Sexuality and Aging. East
      Hanover, NJ: Sandoz Pharmaceuticals, 1974. (A cassette
      tape of highlights of a panel discussion presented at the An-
      nual Meeting of the American Geriatrics Society.)
      Highlights of a panel discussion on general aspects of sexu-
ality and aging.

100 Greengross, Wendy. Sex in the Middle Years. London: Na-
      tional Marriage Guidance Council, 1969.
      Questions are answered on the topics of menopause, sexual
activity, male changes, and women's emotions in sex. An easy to
read publication.

101 Griggs, Winona. "Stay Well While Growing Old: Sex and the
      Elderly," in American Journal of Nursing, Vol. 78, No. 8,
      1352-1354, August 1978.
      A general discussion of the topic covering the areas of effects
of aging on sexuality, teaching about sex, the social effects on sex,
illness and sex, and sexuality and the nurse. 16 references

102 Group for the Advancement of Psychiatry. Assessment of
      Sexual Function: A Guide to Interviewing, Report No. 88,
      pp. 809-813, New York: The Group, 1973.
      Chapter 5 is entitled "Interviewing the Older Person."
Covers the persistence of sexual interest in older people, the possibility of overprotection by the children, sexual activity after illness,
and points for the interviewer of older patients. A case example is
included. Appendix A contains an outline which indicates the lines
of inquiry to be considered in obtaining a sexual history.

103 Hegeler, Sten; and Mortensen, Mei-Mei. "Sexuality and Ageing,"
      in British Journal of Sexual Medicine, Vol. 5, No. 32, 16-
      19, January 1978.
      (Abstract in Excerpta Medica, Vol. 22, Section 20, No. 236,
      1979.)
      Data from 1,000 questionnaires returned from Danish men
from 51-95 years of age were used to write this article. There

were 107 questionnaires from men 91 to 95 years of age. Information on the questionnaires consisted of sexual debut, frequency of
coitus both formerly and presently, incidence of venereal diseases,
and frequency of masturbation. Most of the men were interested in
sex up to 75 after which only every second to third man was positively interested in sex.

104   Herrick, E. H. "Sex Changes in Aging," in Sexology, Vol.
      24, 248-253, November 1957.
      The life span of the average adult is increasing, thus creat-
ing an interest and importance in studying the aging process. Sexual changes that occur at various stages of life are covered in a
simple, general manner. 6 references

105   Hiatt, Harold. "Dynamic Psychotherapy in Later Life," in
      Current Psychiatric Therapies, Vol. 15, 117-122, 1975.
      A discussion of the use of dynamic psychotherapy with the
senescent patient. Transference/countertransference is stressed.
Sexual transference was one of four overlapping transference reactions found. 14 references

106   Hinkley, Nancy E. "Sexuality and Aging." Paper presented
      at the Adult Education Bicentennial Congress, New York,
      November 20, 1976. ED 137 568, CE 010 551 (Synopsis
      of this appears in Educational Gerontology, Vol. 3, No. 2,
      201, April-June 1978. Also listed in ERIC's Resources in
      Education, Vol. 12, No. 9, 18-19, September 1977.)
      Maslow's hierarchy of needs (physiological needs, safety and
security needs, belongingness needs, esteem needs, and the need
for self-actualization) and literature on sexuality and aging are used
to pair needs of aging individuals derived from sexuality with each
of Maslow's levels. Sexual needs over the life cycle need to be
understood. Included in the discussion are a definition of sexuality,
social control mechanisms and stereotypes, sexual needs of older
people, and implications for the adult educator. 52 references

107   Horn, Patrice, and the editors of Behavior Today. "Rx: Sex
      for Senior Citizens," in Psychology Today, Vol. 8, 18, 20,
      June 1974.
      A very short report on a speech by Victor Kassel of Salt
Lake City to New England hospital and nursing home administrators.
Emphasis is made on personal and medical benefits of sex for elderly patients. Orgasm relieves anxiety and most nursing home patients suffer from chronic anxiety. According to Kassel, a few
nursing homes which have encouraged sexual liaisons in their homes
have lost their licenses. Nursing home practices should be geared
to the desires of the patients. A rare thing is shown on page 18:
a close-up picture of an elderly couple kissing.

108   Howells, John G. Modern Perspectives in the Psychiatry of
      Old Age. Vol. 6, New York: Brunner/Mazel, 1975.
      Sexual behavior in old age is treated in depth.

109 Hurdle, J. Frank. "You Can Enjoy Sex After Seventy," in
        Sexology, Vol. 37, 49-51, April 1971.
        Presents a positive approach to helping older people achieve
sexual fulfillment. Dr. Alfred Kinsey is referred to in order to
substantiate the fact that even though sexual capacity gradually declines throughout life, most healthy older men and women continue
to enjoy sex. No references

110 James, William H. "The Reliability of the Reporting of Coital
        Frequency," in Journal of Sex Research, Vol. 7, No. 4,
        312-314, November 1971.
        Error in reporting of coital rate is random and is perhaps
due to failure of memory. Humans are very likely to accurately
report the truth about their sex lives. 8 references

111 Johnson, Linda. "The Middle Years: Living Sensibly," in
        American Journal of Nursing, Vol. 75, No. 6, 1012-1016,
        June 1975.
        During the middle years there can be a gradual decrease in
sexual function which can vary depending on the individual and the
quality of intimacy the couple enjoys. Readjustments in life-style
which can change this are diet, physical activity, drug and tobacco
use, and preventive health care. Women who haven't entered menopause are less likely than men of the same age to have heart attacks. 10 references

112 Jones, David R. "You're Never Too Old for Sex," in Sexology,
        Vol. 40, No. 4, 56-60, November 1973.
        If an elderly person continues to feel and think young, they
can remain sexually active. The author points out that older women
want sex. Also mentioned are some sex problems after 50. Hormones are suggested to restore interest in persons in whom definite
glandular problems are present. No references

113 Jones, Dorothy M. "Sex! Not for Youngsters Only," in
        Journal of Practical Nursing, Vol. 26, No. 3, 30-31, March
        1976.
        Older people have sexual needs and often express them in
long term care facilities. Nurses and other health care professionals do not know how to deal with sexual expression of the residents.
5 references

114 Kaplan, Helen Singer. "The Effects of Age on Sexuality,"
        Chapter 6 in her The New Sex Therapy, pp. 104-114, New
        York: Brunner/Mazel, 1974. (Also appeared in an article
        in Medical Aspects of Human Sexuality, entitled "Sexual Pat-
        terns at Different Ages," by Kaplan, Helen Singer, and
        Sagar, Clifford J., Vol. 5, No. 6, 10-11, 14-16, 19, 23,
        June 1971.)
        The chapter presents gender differences in aging including
effects of age on the different phases of sexual response, age-related changes in male sexual functioning, discussion on whether there
is a male menopause, age-related changes in female sexual function-

ing, and clinical implications.   The entire book is reviewed by
Hugo G. Beigel in Journal of Sex Research, Vol. 11, No. 1, 67-
68, February 1975.

115   Kasner, Kenneth Harold.   "The Influence of Age and Sexuality
      on Attitude Formation," a dissertation done at Washington
      State University, 1975.   (D. A. , Vol. 36, (7-B) 3612-B,
      1976.)
      This study focuses on the effects that information concerning
a person's age and sexuality might have on attitudes formed about
that person.   Subjects for study consisted of 328 male and female
undergraduates.   Based on the results of the study, there was no
evidence to support a taboo against sexuality in old age.   Given
certain conditions, according to the author, age affected inferences
made by young persons concerning an individual who had sex.

116   Kastenbaum, Robert J.   Growing Old: Years of Fulfillment.
      New York: Harper and Row, 1979.   (Reviewed in Journal
      of Gerontology, Vol. 35, No. 2, 281, March 1980.)
      Contains a chapter entitled "Love and Intimacy in Later Life. "

117   _____.   "Loving, Dying and Other Gerontologic Addenda, "
      in Eisdorfer, Carl, and Lawton, M. Powell (eds.), The
      Psychology of Adult Development and Aging, pp. 699-708,
      Washington, D. C. :   American Psychological Association,
      1973.
      Love-sex-intimacy dynamics in old age are important for
psychological gerontologists to know about but not much research
has been focused on this.   Gerontologists often assume that older
people don't have sexual thoughts and we usually avoid any intimate
contact with the aged.   Love is not necessarily related to the number of sexual interests and activities.   Love and sex in later life
are important but the loss of intimate sharing may be more critical
than orgasm deprivation.   11 references

118   Katchadourian, Herant A. , and Lunde, Donald T.   Fundamen-
      tals of Human Sexuality, pp. 75-79, 91, 95, 136, New York:
      Holt, Rinehart and Winston, Inc. , 1972.   (2nd edition paper-
      back, 1975, pp. 79-81, 102, 106, 316, 371, 373-374, 566-
      567.)
      Contains a section on the effects of aging on sexual functions.

119   Kellogg, John Harvey.   Plain Facts for Young and Old, pp.
      123-124, Burlington, IA: Segner, 1882.
      "Senile sexuality--as with childhood, old age is a period in
which the reproduction functions are quiescent unless unnaturally
stimulated.   Sexual life begins with puberty, and, in the female
ends at about the age of forty-five years, the period known as the
menopause, or turn of life.   At this period, according to the plain-
est indications of nature, all functional activity should cease.   If
this law is disregarded, disease, premature decay, possible local
degenerations, will be sure to result.   Nature cannot be abused
with impunity.

"The generative power of the male is retained somewhat
longer than that of the female, and by stimulation may be indulged
at quite an advanced age, but only ... if he would render himself
guilty of shortening his days of sensuality."

120 Kent, Saul. "Sex Education Is for Physicians, Too," in
     Geriatrics, Vol. 30, No. 2, 177-178, 182, 1975.
       Great benefits would occur if physicians participated in
human sexuality programs.   A list of available programs is given.
Minnesota's Sexual Attitude Reassessment (SAR) seminar is discussed.   No references

121 Kimmel, Douglas C. Adulthood and Aging: An Interdiscipli-
     nary, Developmental View, pp. 204-217, New York: John
     Wiley and Sons, 1974.
       Contains information on sexual behavior and age, sexual be-
havior of divorced persons, the family cycle and sex, impotence,
sex after menopause, sexual behavior of widowed women, and age-
sex roles.

122 Kirkendall, Lester A., and Rubin, Isadore. Sexuality and the
     Life Cycle: A Broad Concept of Sexuality. Study Guide No.
     8. New York: Human Sciences Press, 1969.
       Covers sexuality throughout the life cycle.   Short sections of
relevance to this bibliography include sexuality in adulthood, menopause and aging, sexuality in the family life cycle, and parent-child
relations.   There needs to be a separation of reproductive outcomes
from sexual functioning so that sexuality can be emphasized for intimacy, communication and enjoyment.   13-item selected bibliography

123 Knopf, Olga. Successful Aging: The Facts and Fallacies of
     Growing Old. New York: Viking Press, 1975.
       Sexual adaptation in later life is covered.

124 Krippene, Arleen. "Today's Facts About Senior Sex," in
     Harvest Years, Vol. 7, 6-10, June 1967.
       A general article for the layperson which cites the Duke Uni-
versity studies and presents effects of sex life on health, myths
about sex, keeping "sexy" longer, sex appeal, and marriage after
sixty.   Results of a survey done by the Langley Porter Neuropsy-
chiatric Institute on "Sexual Attitudes of the Elderly" are presented.
No references

125 Kurlychek, Robert T., and Trepper, Terry Steven. "Sex
     Education for the Middle and Later Years: Rationale, Sug-
     gested Content, and Consideration of Approaches," in Educa-
     tional Gerontology, Vol. 4, No. 4, 333-340, October-Decem-
     ber 1979. (Based on a presentation delivered at the 23rd
     Annual Meeting of the Western Gerontological Society, March
     21, 1977, Denver, Colorado.)
       Interpersonal closeness, intimacy, and a positive self-concept
are important factors needed for a healthy personality.   It is important that later life sexuality be recognized.   The article presents

reasons for developing sex education courses for older adults and
explores areas of curriculum development as well as strategies of
implementation.   21 references

126   Lamb, Lawrence E.   "Sex in Later Years, " Chapter 15 in
          his Dear Doctor: It's About Sex ..., pp. 272-286, New
          York: Walker and Co. , 1973.
          The author, a medical columnist, presents sexual questions
he has received in a readable way.   The publication is intended for
non-medical readers.   Topic categories include sex variety, anti-
sex women, sex after surgery, diminished fluid and desire and frequency.

127   Lane, Andrea.   "'We Can Still Enjoy It': The Surprising Truth
          About Sex After 50, " in Sexology, Vol. 41, No. 7, 39-43,
          February 1975.
          Older people have erotic capacity.   Some sex problems which
occur in older adults are presented.   Lack of a mate interferes
with the sexual satisfaction of many elderly women.   Some problems
of sex in institutions for older people are discussed.   An active sex
life keeps a person physically fit.

128   Laury, Gabriel V.   "Aging and Sex, " in OP/The Osteopathic
          Physician, Vol. 43, 42-43, 47, 103, October 1976.
          Advanced age should be no deterrent to sexual activity and
fulfillment.   It is important for the physician to accept as normal
the sexual interests of his or her patients.   The physician should
be able to advise the patients so that they can continue their sexual
activity as they grow older.   15 references

129   _____.   "Foreplay in Old Age, " in Medical Aspects of
          Human Sexuality, Vol. 11, No. 3, 92-93, March 1977.
          Older people have different responses to growing older as
far as sex is concerned.   Some couples decrease their precoital
activities in old age and some increase their activity.   It is impera-
tive that a physician counsel older couples with care as to prevent
them from being ashamed or guilty while encouraging sexual growth
and pleasure.   The couple must be mutually supportive, patient, and
take advantage of hormone therapy when necessary.   4 references

130   _____.   "Sensual Activities of the Aging Couple, " in Medical
          Aspects of Human Sexuality, Vol. 14, No. 1, 32-37, Janu-
          ary 1980.
          There are many myths of the aged which portray them as
being sexless.   The physician has an important role in presenting
the fact that advanced age should provide no obstacle in the seeking
of sexual gratification.   The article presents a general discussion
of how older people can remain sensual.   Commentary follows by
Alex Comfort, Stanley H. Cath, and Susan G. Krinsky.   6 references

131   Lazarus, Lawrence W.   "Psychodynamics of Sexual Humor:
          Old Age, " in Medical Aspects of Human Sexuality, Vol. 14,
          No. 3, 146, 150, 152, March 1980.
          Presents an analysis of typical jokes about sex and old age.

132   Leaf, Alexander. "Every Day Is a Gift When You Are Over
      100," in National Geographic, Vol. 143, No. 1, 92-119,
      January 1973.
          Dr. Alexander Leaf studied centenarians in the Ecuadorean
village of Vilcabamba, the people of Hunza in Kashmir, and those
in the Caucasus. With very few exceptions, only individuals who
were married reached very old age. An interest in the opposite
sex persisted in most of the individuals studied. Workday vigor
was present in the old people of all three cultures. Many colorful
pictures accompany this article. No references

133   Leiblum, Sandra R., and Kopel, Steven A. "Screening and
      Prognosis in Sex Therapy: To Treat or Not to Treat," in
      Behavior Therapy, Vol. 8, No. 3, 480-486, June 1977.
      (P. A., Vol. 59, No. 06050, 1978.)
          A middle-aged couple with a rigid religious belief system
displayed an unstable and unsatisfying marriage. They were successfully treated of a chronic sexual dysfunction (primary orgasmic
dysfunction and premature ejaculation). Innovative treatments used
included the assistance of a Roman Catholic priest, modeling of attitudes, home assignments, therapist feedback and encouragement,
sex education and film presentations, and by presenting the couple
with a constructive problem-solving atmosphere. There is great
need for an open-mindedness during the screening of potential clients
for sexual counseling.

134   Levin, Sidney. "Some Comments on the Distribution of Nar-
      cissistic and Object Libido in the Aged," in International
      Journal of Psycho-Analysis, Vol. 46, 200-208, 1965. (Pre-
      sented at the panel on "Psychoanalytical Considerations of
      Old Age" at the Annual Meeting of the American Psychoana-
      lytic Association, May 3, 1963.)
          The ability to redistribute libido to new objects and new aims
will determine whether normal aging will occur. Narcissistic libido
must be withdrawn from the ego ideal. The withdrawn libido can
be channeled to other forms of narcissistic satisfaction. To avoid
emotional problems a certain amount of redistribution of libido to
other objects must occur. 19 references

135   Lewin, Samuel Aaron, and Gilmore, John. Sex After Forty.
      New York: Medical Research Press, 1952. (P. A., Vol.
      27, No. 3400, 1953.)
          A discussion of hormones, romance and sex after forty.
The anxieties which usually accompany sex after forty are also discussed.

136   Lewis, Myrna I. "Sex and Aging," in Goldstein, Kenneth K.;
      Salisbury, Paul A.; and Davison, W. Phillips (eds.), Aging:
      Research and Perspectives. A Briefing for the Press.
      Center for the Advanced Study of Communication and Public
      Affairs, Graduate School of Journalism, Columbia University,
      New York, 1979. Monograph No. 3, pp. 28-36. (This
      monograph is based on the proceedings of a one-day confer-

ence, made possible by the support of the National Institute on Aging, Department of Health, Education and Welfare, Washington, D. C. The Conference was held at Columbia University on September 28, 1979.)

Presents normal physical changes with age of both men and women, the effects of physical illness or disability on sexuality, common emotional problems and sex, recent developments in treatment of sexuality problems of older men, medical developments regarding sexuality problems in older women, changing attitudes toward the sexuality of later life, and some directions for future research. No references

137   LeWitter, Maximilian, and Abarbanel, Albert. "Aging and Sex, " in Ellis, Albert, and Abarbanel, Albert (eds.), The Encyclopedia of Sexual Behavior, pp. 75-81, New York: Hawthorn Books, 1961. (2nd edition 1973, J. Aronson.)

Sex has two main functions: 1) procreation, and 2) stimulation of the body. Good health is important in maintaining proper sexual functioning in old age. A change of life occurs for both men and women in the middle years. Anxiety during this time can bring about impaired sexual function. Physical changes at middle age can cause changes in sexuality. Sexual activity and aging is discussed as well as impotence and behavior changes, nutrition, aphrodisiacs, and "rejuvenation. " 23 references

138   Lief, Harold I. , and Broderick, Carlfred B. "Interview: Sex in Older People, " in Sexual Behavior, Vol. 1, No. 7, 72-74, October 1971.

Dr. Harold I. Lief is interviewed by Dr. Carlfred B. Broderick on the topic of sex in older people. Specific topics which are discussed include the possibilities of sex for older people, menopause and sex, male menopause, production of seminal fluid, ability to sustain an erection, impotence, source of sex drive, meanings attached to sex, and nutrition. Other topics included vitamins and sexuality, attitudes of health care professionals toward older people and sex, complaints about lack of sexual outlets, and the need for a warm close and intimate relationship with another person. Efforts should be made to have older people satisfy their sexual needs. No references

139   Lobsenz, Norman M. "Sex and the Senior Citizen, " in Moss, Gordon, and Moss, Walter (eds.), Growing Old, pp. 94-109, New York: Simon and Schuster, Inc. , 1975. (This was reprinted from The New York Times Magazine, January 20, 1974. Also developed from this article was Sex after Sixty-Five, New York: Public Affairs Pamphlet No. 519, 1975.)

Our culture does not take sexuality of the aged seriously. Sometimes very positive psychological and physical effects occur from sexual activity in old age. The author contends that even more positive effects might occur if societal attitudes were to change, thus resulting in a supportive atmosphere for such activity. A small but poignant section on sexuality in institutions is included.

140   Long, Irene. "Human Sexuality and Aging," in Social Case-
        work, Vol. 57, No. 4, 237-244, April 1976. (P. A. , Vol.
        58, No. 01012, 1977.)
        The aged need psychological support to deal with sex.   Phys-
ical ability and psychosocial influences are interdependent.   In the
male, impotence can be caused by lack of self-confidence and regular sexual outlets.   Fear of immorality in the female may also
lead to sexual dysfunction.   Intimacy and potency are needed in old
age but are stifled by societal ignorance and overemphasis on youth.
There is a need for professionals to be educated in sexuality and
aging.   54 references

141   Lowry, Herbert.   "Why Single Adults Should Masturbate," in
        Forum: The International Journal of Human Relations, Vol.
        8, No. 4, 64-65, January 1979.
        Herbert Lowry, a clergyman, suggests masturbation as a
vehicle for relieving sexual tension in the later years.   He says it
enriches the single person's solitude with physical pleasure.   It also
is the moral sex activity available to most older single adults.

142   McCarthy, Patricia. "Geriatric Sexuality: Capacity, Interest,
        and Opportunity," in Journal of Gerontological Nursing, Vol.
        5, No. 1, 20-24, February 1979.
        An article on sexuality and aging aimed at gerontological
nurses but informative for most any reader.   Mentions several research study conclusions including some clinical experiences at a
rural nursing home.   She suggests that health care professionals
should respect all forms of sexual expression among consenting
adults.   6 references

143   McCary, James Leslie. Human Sexuality: Physiological,
        Psychological, and Sociological Factors. New York: Van
        Nostrand Reinhold Co. , 1973.
        Contains a small section on the climacteric and sexual activ-
ity of men and women in the later years of their life.

144   _____. "Quiz: A Monthly Feature," in Medical Aspects of
        Human Sexuality, Vol. 9, No. 2, 139-140, February 1975.
        A question is posed regarding important considerations in
understanding sexual expressions in later years.   The answer is
given to the question.

145   McCary, Stephen Paul. "The Interrelationships Between Rele-
        vant Sex Variables and Individuals' Reported Ages and Sources
        of Information for Learning and Experiencing Sexual Concepts,"
        doctoral dissertation done at University of Houston, 1976.
        (D. A. , Vol. 37, (3-B), 1442, 1976.)
        Data collected from 348 university students were analyzed in
this study.   Among the information gathered included the students'
mean ages for learning sexual concepts and mean ages for experiencing sexual concepts.   Those individuals who learned about sexual
concepts when they were at a younger age had more liberal sexual
behaviors.   Individuals who experienced sexual concepts at younger

ages had lower levels of overall self esteem and had more liberal
sexual behaviors. Those students who had learned about sex from
schools or books knew more about sex, had more orthodox sexual
behaviors, and had more orthodox sexual attitudes. The author
concludes that there is a need for formal sex education programs
in schools.

146 Machida, Takeo; Nomura, Tetsuro; and Matsumoto, Kazuko.
     "Changes in Open-Field Behavior with Increasing Age in
     Mice," in Annual of Animal Psychology, (Tokyo), Vol. 26,
     No. 1, 59, 1976. (A paper read to the 36th Symposium of
     Japanese Animal Psychologists held in June 1976 at Osaka
     University.)
     A report on the effects of increasing age on male (ICR
strain) mice from 45 to 770-days-old. An increasing age leads to
a decrease in the weight of the gonads. Previous experiments had
shown a decrease in behavior in castrated rats. Normal levels of
behavior were restored with the introduction of sexual hormones.

147 McKenzie, Sheila C. Aging. Glenview, IL: Scott, Foresman
     and Co., 1980.
     Contains a section on sexual behavior.

148 Manney, James D., Jr. Aging in American Society, pp. 27,
     44-45, 88-89, 115, Ann Arbor, MI: Institute of Gerontology,
     The University of Michigan--Wayne State University, 1975.
     A short section is included on decline in sexual activity with
age. The end of sexual activity for some people could speed up or
begin a withdrawal from all intimacy and emotional involvement. A
barrier to some late-life marriages is due in part to our denial of
older people's sexuality. In one study of San Francisco's crime
statistics, only 1 percent involved sexual offenses. Sex crimes in
old age, violent or otherwise, are extremely uncommon.

149 Marshall, Donald Stanley, and Suggs, Robert Carl (eds.),
     Human Sexual Behavior: Variations in the Ethnographic
     Spectrum. New York: Basic Books, 1971.
     Covers sexual behavior in a variety of cultures. The age
factor is considered and broken down into prepubertal, puberty,
maturation, menopause, and old age phases.

150 Masters, William H., and Johnson, Virginia E. "Geriatric
     Sexual Response," Chapters 15 and 16 in their Human Sexual
     Response, pp. 221-270, Boston: Little, Brown and Co.,
     1966.
     Detailed sexual changes in the aging male and female are
described. Changes discussed include reproductive viscera, external
genitalia, extragenital reactions, sexual monotony, overeating, alcohol abuse, fear of failure, and mental or physical fatigue.

151 _____, and _____. "Human Sexual Response: The Aging
     Female and the Aging Male," in Neugarten, Bernice L. (ed.),
     Middle Age and Aging, pp. 269-279, Chicago: University of

Chicago Press, 1968.
This is abridged from Masters, William H., and Johnson,
Virginia E. Human Sexual Response. Boston: Little, Brown and
Co., 1966, Chapter 15, pp. 238-247, and Chapter 16, pp. 260-270.

152 _____, and _____. "Sex After Sixty," in Medical World
     News, (special issue on Geriatrics), 74, 76, 1971.
     A general discussion of problems and vital ingredients for
sexual activity after sixty.   No references

153 Merritt, C. Gary; Gerstl, Joel E.; and LoSciuto, Leonard A.
     "Age and Perceived Effects of Erotica-Pornography: A
     National Sample Study," in Archives of Sexual Behavior,
     Vol. 4, No. 6, 605-621, November 1975.
     A national survey of 2486 adults (ages 20 to 80) was done in
the Spring of 1970.   The purpose of the study was to determine public attitudes in the United States and experience of the public with
erotic materials.   The oldest adults felt that pornography had mostly
undesirable effects on its consumers.   5 references

154 Miller, M. "Sexuality in the Aged," in Forum, Wisconsin
     Psychiatric Institute, University of Wisconsin--Madison,
     1972, No. 2.
     Presents some specific suggestions for sexual counseling of
the aged.   Some arrangement should be made for the privacy of
older couples who are institutionalized.   By and large this is a
general discussion of the topic.

155 Miller, Michael B.; Bernstein, Herbert; and Sharkey, Harold.
     "Family Extrusion of the Aged Patient: Family Homeostasis
     and Sexual Conflict," in Gerontologist, Vol. 15, No. 4, Part
     2, 291-296, 1975.   (A paper presented at the Annual Meeting
     of the American Geriatrics Society, held in Toronto on April
     18, 1974.)
     The question tackled by this paper was why some ill or older
patients were displaced from the family while others were not.
Three case studies were presented which showed that chronic sexual
conflict usually resulted in nursing home placement unless there was
a death in the family or overt psychiatric disability.   8 references

156 Millet, J. A. P. "Sexuality After 60: Unmasking the Myths,"
     in Medical Insight, Vol. 4, 24-27, 1972.
     Actual medical and psychological facts are presented to dispel
common myths and misconceptions with respect to sexuality and the
aged.   An important sign of healthy aging is continuing sexual activity.

157 Monea, Helen Elena. "The Experiential Approach in Learning
     About Sexuality in the Aged," in Burnside, Irene Mortenson
     (ed.), Sexuality and Aging, pp. 76-80, Los Angeles: Uni-
     versity of Southern California, 1975.
     See the annotation on the same author in Solnick's Sexuality
and Aging.   The chapter in the Solnick book is much more detailed.
There are 6 references in this chapter.

158 _____ . "The Experiential Approach in Learning About
        Sexuality in the Aged," in Solnick, Robert Lewis (ed.),
        Sexuality and Aging (revised), pp. 115-131, Los Angeles:
        University of Southern California, 1978.
        The author presents a much more detailed description of the
topic here than was previously presented in Burnside's Sexuality and
Aging.   The media experience is described.   The theories and concepts related to experiential learning are reviewed, namely 1) body
relaxation, 2) mental imagery, 3) multi-media, and 4) sharing.   The
author describes how she learned to teach experientially.   15 references

159 Money, John. "Determinants of Human Sexual Identity and
        Behavior," in Sager, Clifford J., and Kaplan, Helen Singer
        (eds.), Progress in Group and Family Therapy, pp. 564-
        586, New York: Brunner/Mazel, 1972.
        Sexual behavior is dimorphic, its growth being a process of
both differentiation and development.   There is a limited period of
time whereby the genetic coding of a fertilized human egg can be
changed and after which no change can occur.   In the case of the
differentiation of human gonads this critical period is the sixth week
after conception.   Androgen must be present for a fetus to differ-
entiate externally as a male, and if not present, the fetus will dif-
ferentiate externally as a female regardless of chromosomal sex.
Menopause does not signal the end of a woman's sexual life which
may actually even improve into old age.   A male's sexual life may
also continue in old age and impotence due to low androgen levels
can be controlled by the use of testosterone.   39 references

160 Monks, Richard C. "Sexuality and the Elderly," in Canadian
        Welfare (Ottawa), Vol. 51, No. 5, 19-20, 1975.
        A discussion of factors influencing sexuality in older people.
A steady decline in interest and activity occurs with age.   Factors
influencing this decline include age, marital status, and sex (male
or female).   Early attitude of older people toward sexuality can be
an important determinant of sexual activity.   Physical well-being is
also paramount in determining sexual activity.   Sexual problems can
result from systematic physical illness, certain environmental factors, and emotional disorders.   The majority of older people have
the desire and ability to continue their sexual functioning.   5 references

161 Moran, Joyce. "Sexuality After Sixty," in ARN Journal, Vol.
        2, 19-21, July-August 1977.
        Sexuality is an indigenous part of the total person and nurses
should be better prepared to offer support to the aged about their
sexuality.   The author mentions that no provisions are made for
privacy for the aging in nursing homes.   Social pressures can cause
older people to doubt their sexuality at a time when their sexual
needs may be different and more diffuse.   Nurses have a responsibility to dispel myths about sexuality and aging.   They should also
examine their own attitudes and feelings about sexuality.   7 references, 16 bibliographic items

162 _____ . "Sexuality: An Ageless Quality, a Basic Need," in
      Journal of Gerontological Nursing, Vol. 5, No. 5, 13-16,
      September-October 1979.
         A general article on the sexual needs of older people.   Sex-
ual expression in older people includes an emotional intimacy that
is important to have in life.   Many happy older people are ones who
have been involved in one or several personal relationships.   Companionship may be the most important reason for remarriage later
in life.   6 references

163 Neugarten, Bernice L. (ed.).   Middle Age and Aging.   Chicago:
      University of Chicago Press, 1968.
         Three relevant articles are included.   The first is entitled
"Disenchantment in the Later Years of Marriage," by Peter C.
Pineo.   The second is entitled "Human Sexual Response: The Aging
Female and the Aging Male," by William H. Masters and Virginia E.
Johnson.   The third is entitled "Women's Attitudes Toward the Meno-
pause," by Bernice L. Neugarten, Vivian Wood, Ruth J. Kraines,
and Barbara Loomis.   All three are annotated separately in this
bibliography.

164 Newman, Gustave, and Nichols, Claude R.   "Sexual Activities
      and Attitudes in Older Persons," in Journal of the American
      Medical Association, Vol. 173, 33-35, 1960.   (This also ap-
      pears in DeMartino, Manfred F. (ed.), Sexual Behavior and
      Personality Characteristics, Chapter 24, pp. 384-391, New
      York: Citadel Press, 1963.   It also appears in Palmore,
      Erdman (ed.), Normal Aging, Chapter 8, pp. 277-281, Dur-
      ham, NC: Duke University Press, 1970.   It also appears in
      Wagner, Nathaniel N. (ed.), Perspectives on Human Sexuality,
      Chapter 23, pp. 501-508, New York: Behavioral Publications,
      Inc., 1974.)
         Sexual activity and attitudes of older people living in Durham,
N.C. were studied.   The average age of the subjects was 70 and
ages ranged from 60 to 93 years.   Black and white men and women
were studied.   There was little correlation of sexual activity with
age but blacks were more active than whites and men were more
active than women.   A constancy of sexual drive throughout life was
found.   Some decline occurs in sexual activity and drive in older
people but good health and interested partners are all that are needed
to continue sex into the 90's.   3 references

165 O'Connor, John F., and Flax, Carol C.   "The Effects of Aging
      on Human Sexuality," in Nursing Care, Vol. 10, No. 7, 22-
      24, 26, 43, 1977.
         As the title suggests, this is a general article on the effects
of aging on human sexuality.   Although sexual activity may not be
as frequent or vigorous in the later years, it is still desired and
performed by many older people.   The female climacteric has some
effects on the woman's sexuality but need not alter sexual expression.
Male changes in response rate need not alter sexuality either.   Cultural and psychological influences are much stronger than physical
ones.   Continuous sexual expression throughout marriage will ensure

its maintenance into old age.   Feelings of well-being can be experienced by older patients who resume sexual activity and this may contribute to the recovery of the individual.   No references

166   Orr, John G.   "Care of the Elderly Patient in Hospital," in
       Nursing Times (London), Vol. 73, No. 27, 1028-1032, 1977.
An evaluation of hospital services in England for geriatric patients.   Maslow's pyramid of needs was used as a guide.   Sexuality was one of the points evaluated.   Suggestions were given to facilitate changes in order to bring about a higher compassionate quality of geriatric care in hospitals.

167   Palmore, Erdman.   "Facts on Aging: A Short Quiz," in
       Gerontologist, Vol. 17, No. 4, 315-320, 1977.
       This short quiz is helpful in identifying aging biases.   Question 3 is of importance to this annotated bibliography.   The question states, "True or False   3.   Most old people have no interest in, or capacity for, sexual relations."   The answer, of course, is false. Documentation is provided to back up the validity of the questions and and several uses of the quiz are suggested.   40 references

168   _____ (ed.).   "Leisure and Sexual Behavior," Chapter 7 in
       his Normal Aging II, pp. 232-262, Durham, NC: Duke
       University Press, 1974.
       The article on leisure is not relevant to sexuality and aging. Articles of interest include: 1) "Sexual Behavior in Middle Life," by Eric Pfeiffer, Adriaan Verwoerdt, and Glenn C. Davis--reprinted from American Journal of Psychiatry, Vol. 128, No. 10, 1262-1267, April 1972, and 2) "Determinants of Sexual Behavior in Middle and Old Age," by Eric Pfeiffer and Glenn C. Davis--reprinted from Journal of the American Geriatrics Society, Vol. 20, No. 4, 151-158, 1972.   These are annotated separately in this bibliography.

169   _____ (ed.).   "Marriage, Family and Sexual Behavior,"
       Chapter 8 in his Normal Aging, pp. 266-303, Durham, NC:
       Duke University Press, 1970.
       Three articles are included in this chapter: 1) "Two Thousand Years of Married Life," by Ewald W. Busse; 2) "Family Structure and Social Isolation of Older Persons," by Robert G. Brown--reprinted from Journal of Gerontology, Vol. 15, 170-174, 1960; 3) "Sexual Activities and Attitudes in Older Persons," by Gustave Newman and Claude R. Nichols--reprinted from the Journal of the American Medical Association, Vol. 173, 33-35, 1960; 4) "Sexual Behavior in Senescence," by Adriaan Verwoerdt, Eric Pfeiffer, and Hsioh-Shan Wang--reprinted from Geriatrics, Vol. 24, 137-154, 1969; and 5) "Sexual Behavior in Aged Men and Women," by Eric Pfeiffer, Adriaan Verwoerdt, and Hsioh-Shan Wang--reprinted from Archives of General Psychiatry, Vol. 19, 756-758, Dec. 1968.   All except 1 and 2 are reviewed separately in this bibliography.

170   _____, and Kivett, Vira.   "Change in Life Satisfaction: A
       Longitudinal Study of Persons Aged 46-70," in Journal of

Gerontology, Vol. 32, No. 3, 311-316, 1977.
A longitudinal analysis was performed on changes in life
satisfaction among a sample of 378 community residents from ages
46 to 70.   Life satisfaction at the end of a four-year period was
significantly related to a number of factors with one of them being
sexual enjoyment.   11 references

171   , and   . "Predictors of Life Satisfaction Among
      Middle Aged Persons," in Gerontologist, Vol. 15, No. 5,
      Part 2, 66, 1975.   (This was a paper given at the 28th an-
      nual meeting of the Gerontological Society, Louisville, Ken-
      tucky, October 1975.)
      Changes in life satisfaction were accounted for by changes in
health.   Also significant among the men were changes in employment
and contacts.   For the women changes in sexual enjoyment and social hours were significant.

172   Pengelley, Eric T.   "Sexuality and Aging," Chapter 8 in his
      Sex and Human Life, pp. 127-135, Reading, MA: Addison-
      Wesley Publishing Co., 1974.
      A general and easy to understand discussion on the effects of
aging on the reproductive system (for both male and female), sex
problems of older women, and sex problems of older men.   Two
suggestions given for further reading.

173   Peterson, James Alfred.   "Sexual Success in the Mid-Years,"
      Chapter 5, pp. 81-101, in his Married Love in the Middle
      Years.   New York: Association Press, 1968.
      The chapter stresses the importance of sexual success in the
mid-years.   Problems and the roots of the problems which occur at
this time are touched upon.   A case study is included.   Many problems which occur at this time had their root long before they begin
to surface.

174   , and Payne, Barbara.   "Sexual Achievement for the
      Single Person in the Later Years," Chapter 6 in their Love
      in the Later Years, pp. 81-101, New York: Association
      Press, 1975.   (Abstract of this in Journal of Gerontology,
      Vol. 31, 108, 1976.)
      The chapter concerns women as they disproportionately out-
number men over the age of 55 in the "singles" category.   Older
single women are less likely to marry than older single men.   A
situation is described in which two residents of a nursing home
married and subsequently took a cut in social security payments.
In women, marital status had an effect on sexual activity but not interest.   Therefore, the older single woman's lack of sexual activity
is due to lack of a sanctioned partner.   Courtship and marriage for
older single men and women is usually disapproved of by the adult
children.   Alternatives to the traditional family are presented including: 1) the swinging model, 2) the cocktail lounge model, 3) the
Berkeley, Campus, or Companionship model, 4) the Hippie model,
5) the One Sex Community model.   The nursing home resident is
given special emphasis.

175 Pfeiffer, Eric. "Geriatric Sex Behavior," in Medical Aspects
     of Human Sexuality, Vol. 3, No. 7, 19, 22-23, 26, 28,
     July 1969.
        A general article on sexuality in old age mentioning taboos
against sex for the elderly, the Kinsey data, Masters and Johnson
data, the Duke University longitudinal data, and factors in the decline of female sexuality. Implications for practice are presented.
15 references

176 _____. "Sex and Aging," in Gross, Leonard (ed.), Sexual
     Issues in Marriage: A Contemporary Perspective. New
     York: Spectrum Publications, 1975.
        The author stresses the importance of sexual expression in
the aged and the social taboos that prevent this expression. The
Masters and Johnson study as well as the Duke University study
are summarized and discussed. Because interest and ability persists even into very old age, older people should be able to express
their sexuality with dignity.

177 _____. "Sex and Aging," in Sexual Behavior, Vol. 2, No.
     10, 17-21, October 1972.
        Even after other taboos are struck down, the taboo of sex
after sixty still remains. The taboo even extends to the scientific
community. The old may lose sexual interest because they are expected to lose it. The studies at Duke University concerning sexual
activity during old age are briefly and generally discussed. Comments are provided by Harold Hiatt, M. D. , Richard Connelly, Ph. D. ,
Sharon Price Bonham, Ph. D. , and Ruby H. Gingles, M. S. No
references

178 _____. "Sex in Old Age," in North Carolina Journal of
     Mental Health, Vol. 4, No. 1, 34-42, 1970.
        There are many stereotypes of sexual behavior in old age.
There are great differences of sexual behavior in old age between
men and women. Two implications are given: 1) data regarding
sexual activity should be examined separately for men and women
and 2) unequal sexual drives can lead to sexual conflicts in some
individuals. The Duke University study is summarized. The physician shouldn't push sexual activity on all of his or her patients but
rather give concerned attention to the older person's sexual needs.
9 references

179 _____. "Sexual Activity Among the Elderly," in OP/The
     Osteopathic Physician, Vol. 41, 95-100, November 1974.
        Sexual activity among older people is normal and does exist.
Studies are cited to illustrate this. Suggestions are made to help
physicians to be supportive in the sexual needs of their patients.
Freedom of choice and privacy are very important in sexual matters
of older people.

180 _____. "Sexual Behavior," in Howells, John G. (ed.),
     Modern Perspectives in Psychiatry. No. 6. Modern Per-
     spective in the Psychiatry of Old Age, pp. 313-325, New
     York: Brunner/Mazel, Inc. , 1975.

Sections of this chapter include 1) the quality of survival,
2) the taboo against sex in old age, 3) stereotypes of sexual behavior in old age, 4) studies in human sexual behavior (Kinsey, Masters and Johnson, and the Duke Longitudinal Studies), 5) the reliability of interview data on sexual behavior, 6) sexual behavior in
middle life, and 7) implications for the practitioner.   22 references

181 _____ . "Sexual Behavior in Old Age," in Busse, Ewald W.,
      and Pfeiffer, Eric (eds.), Behavior and Adaptation in Late
      Life, Chapter 8, pp. 151-162, Boston: Little, Brown and
      Co., 1969; 2nd edition, 1977, pp. 130-141.
      This chapter discussion is partly based on "Geriatric Sex
Behavior," in Medical Aspects of Human Sexuality, Vol. 3, No. 7,
19, 22-23, 26, 28, July 1969.   The taboo of sex in old age begins
the chapter.   The three main studies which provide us data on
sexuality and the aged are summarized, namely Kinsey's findings,
Masters and Johnson's studies, and the Duke University Longitudinal
data.   Practical implications are presented.   18 references

182 _____ . "Sexuality in the Aging Individual," in Solnick,
      Robert Lewis (ed.), Sexuality and Aging (revised), pp. 26-
      32, Los Angeles: University of Southern California, 1978.
      (Same as Journal of the American Geriatrics Society, Vol.
      22, No. 11, 481-484, November 1974.   Originally presented
      as part of the Symposium on Sexuality in the Aging Individual,
      at the 31st Annual Meeting of the American Geriatrics Society,
      Royal York Hotel, Toronto, Canada, April 17-18, 1974.)
      Sex is important to older people.   Seventy percent of men at
age 68 have regular sex and one-fourth of those at 78 still do.
Marriage isn't important to men for the regular sexual activity but
it is important for the women.   If an older woman isn't married
she rarely reports having any sexual activity.   A sanctioned partner
is the main reason for having sex.   The ratio of men to women may
be 4:1 in some environments.   Privacy, necessary for sexual expression, is not always afforded the aged.   Physicians should be
aware of sexual problems of their older patients.   10 references

183 _____ , and Davis, Glenn C. "Determinants of Sexual Be-
      havior in Middle and Old Age," in Journal of the American
      Geriatrics Society, Vol. 20, No. 4, 151-158, April 1972.
      (Presented at the 28th Annual Meeting of the American Geri-
      atrics Society, Chicago, Illinois, April 23-24, 1971.)
      Men and women from 46 to 71 years of age were studied to
determine the factors which might determine their sexual behavior.
Independent variables such as psychologic, social, and physical
measures were analyzed in stepwise multiple regression analyses.
Independent contributions to sexual behavior included objective health
ratings, subjective health ratings, sex of the subject, and the age
of the subject.   Men were influenced by more variables than women
were.   Such variables as age, past sexual enjoyment, and marital
status were important determinants for women.   For women a sanctioned partner was critical.   21 references

184 _____; Verwoerdt, Adriaan; and Davis, Glenn C. "Sexual
      Behavior in Middle Life," in American Journal of Psychiatry,
      Vol. 128, No. 10, 1262-1267, April 1972. (Also in Palmore,
      Erdman (ed.), Normal Aging II, pp. 243-251, Durham, NC:
      Duke University Press, 1974. This was read at the 124th
      annual meeting of the American Psychiatric Association,
      Washington, D.C., May 3-7, 1971.)
      Sexual behavior data were gathered on 241 white women and
261 white men. The ages ranged from 45 to 69. Men reported
more interest and activity than women. Sex was found to be most
important to the majority of subjects even though activity and interest
had declined. 3 references

185 _____; _____; and Wang, Hsioh-Shan. "The Natural
      History of Sexual Behavior in a Biologically Advantaged
      Group of Aged Individuals," in Journal of Gerontology, Vol.
      24, 193-198, April 1969. (This was read at the Annual
      Meeting of the Gerontological Society, Denver, Colorado,
      October 31-November 2, 1968.)
      A group of elite subjects were examined over a ten-year
period. There was a high proportion of men who had a high sexual
interest. Sexual activity, however, declined slowly over time. The
proportion of women showing sexual interest was smaller than that
of the men with even less having continuous sexual activity. Over
time, however, the women showed no further interest or activity
decline. Findings from this group cannot be generalized to the rest
of the population. Lower sexual interest and activity in women may
be due to: 1) women in general may have lower levels of sexual
interest, 2) sexual declines may occur earlier for women, and 3)
the climacteric may be a negative effect on sexuality. More research is needed to explore these areas. 7 references

186 _____; _____; and _____. "Sexual Behavior in Aged
      Men and Women. I. Observations on 254 Community Volun-
      teers," in Archives of General Psychiatry, Vol. 19, 753-
      758, December 1968. (Also in Palmore, Erdman (ed.),
      Normal Aging, pp. 299-303, Durham, NC: Duke University
      Press, 1970.)
      For aging people who ceased having intercourse, men assigned
responsibility to themselves and the women blamed their spouses.
With regard to reported frequency of sexual intercourse and for reasons of cessation of intercourse, there was a very high level of
agreement between husbands and wives. 9 references

187 Pruyser, Paul W. "Aging: Downward, Upward, or Forward?"
      in Pastoral Psychology, Vol. 24, 102-118, Winter 1975. (Also
      in Hiltner, Seward (ed.). Toward a Theology of Aging, pp.
      110, 114, New York: Human Sciences Press, 1975.)
      Pruyser suggests "to love is to be lovable, to be loved is
to be loving, and to be lovable is both to love and be loved." In
age, he also suggests, sexual attitudes and activities can be more
relaxed, resulting in more enjoyment. 16 references

188   Puner, Morton.   "Will You Still Love Me?" in Human Be-
        havior, Vol. 3, No. 6, 42-48, June 1974.   (From the book
        To the Good Long Life: What We Know About Growing Old
        by Morton Puner, New York: Universe Books, 1974.)
        Presents some of the stereotypes of the aging and sexuality
especially with regard to jokes.   General facts about aging and
sexuality are presented for both men and women.   Sex as a clinical
problem is presented through several case studies.   Other topics of
discussion include menopause and remarriage in old age.

189   Reedy, Margaret Neiswender, and Birren, James E.   "How
        Do Lovers Grow Older Together?   Types of Lovers and Age,"
        in Gerontologist, Vol. 18, No. 5, Part 2, 115, November
        16-20, 1978.   (Paper presented at the National Gerontological
        Society Meeting, Dallas, Texas.   November 1978.)
        This research identified a typology of styles of loving in
satisfying heterosexual love relationships and examined the relationship between age and styles of loving.

190   Reiff, Theodore R.   "Use It or Lose It?" in Medical Aspects
        of Human Sexuality, Vol. 14, No. 3, 98, March 1980.
        Suggests that there is a psychological and physiological basis
for believing that sexual function should be continued in order for it
to remain in the later years.   However, more research is needed
on sexuality and aging.

191   Reuben, David.   "September Sex," Chapter 16 in his Every-
        thing You Always Wanted to Know About Sex ... But Were
        Afraid to Ask, pp. 308-334, New York: David McKay Co.,
        Inc., 1969.
        Questions are answered about sexuality and aging men and
women.   Some case studies are cited.   The language is meant for
the non-professional reader and Dr. Reuben injects humor into his
writing.

192   Roff, Lucinda Lee, and Klemmack, David L.   "Sexual Activity
        Among Older Persons.   A Comparative Analysis of Appro-
        priateness," in Research on Aging, Vol. 1, No. 3, 389-399,
        September 1979.
        Data for this study were gathered from a stratified, random
sample of 210 residents of a mid-sized Southern city.   Comparisons
were made between the appropriateness of a variety of sexual behaviors for older persons and individuals in general.   Sexual activity
among the aged was not perceived to be less appropriate than sexual
activity in the general population.   This result was contrary to the
researcher's expectations.   11 references

193   "Romance and the Aged," in Time, Vol. 101, No. 23, 48,
        June 4, 1973.
        This article asserts that many of the elderly are still looking
for sex and romance.   Elderly have paired off in "unmarriages of
convenience" for the purpose of companionship and sex.   If they
were to marry, this article asserts, they would receive less Social

Security income.   In Florida, informal relationships among the elderly are becoming quite acceptable.   The children of elderly parents
who become interested in the opposite sex are not always thrilled at
the idea.   This is because it is not widely known or accepted that
sexual desires can persist into the 80's and beyond.   Institutions
such as nursing homes have become more flexible in dealing with
sexual contact between married and unmarried residents.   Two interesting pictures are included in the article, pictures that are rare
to find.   One shows an elderly couple kissing on a park bench.   The
other shows an elderly couple holding hands in a shopping center.

194 Rossman, Isadore.   "Sexuality and Aging: An Internist's Per-
        spective, " in Solnick, Robert Lewis (ed.), Sexuality and
        Aging (revised), pp. 66-77, Los Angeles: University of
        Southern California, 1978.
        Discussion of sexual problems ensues in this chapter.   Sev-
eral studies are cited concerning incidence of impotence.   Male menopause is touched on.   Causes of impotence which are covered include
coronary artery disease, diabetes, alcoholism, hypothyroidism, hy-
popituitarism, and tobacco and other drugs.   Female issues are
covered in a small section and not in much detail.   10 references

195 _____.   "Sexuality and the Aging Process: An Internist's
        Perspective, " in Burnside, Irene Mortenson (ed.), Sexuality
        and Aging, pp. 18-25, Los Angeles: University of Southern
        California, 1975.
        Basically this chapter is the same as the one in Solnick's
book.

196 "Roundtable: Sex After 50, " in Medical Aspects of Human
        Sexuality, Vol. 2, No. 1, 41-43, 46-47, January 1968.
        This roundtable at the University of Pennsylvania School of
Medicine in Philadelphia is moderated by Harold I. Lief, M. D.,
with panel members S. Leon Israel, M. D. , Celso-Ramón García,
M. D. , and Charles W. Charny, M. D.   Common sexual problems of
women over 50 are discussed first.   Impotence and frigidity are
discussed with impotency of males being a larger problem than
frigidity in females for people over 50.   An "automatic" pattern of
intercourse can be established without the showing of affection and
preliminary loveplay.   Potency problems and premature ejaculation
are covered as well as estrogen lubrication of the vagina.   1 reference

197 Rowland, Kay Ford, and Haynes, Stephen N.   "A Sexual En-
        hancement Program for Elderly Couples, " in Journal of Sex
        and Marital Therapy, Vol. 4, No. 2, 91-113, Summer 1978.
        (D. A. , Vol. 38, No. 12, 6171 B, 1978.)
        The effects of a group sexual enhancement program for elderly
couples were examined by this study.   Ten married couples ranging
in age from 51 to 71 were placed in one of three sexual enhancement
groups based on differences in schedules.   Over the course of the
sexual enhancement program, significant increases in sexual satisfaction, frequency of certain sexual activities, and positive attitudes

about marital and life satisfaction were found to occur.   This study
was submitted in partial fulfillment of the requirements for a Ph. D.
degree at the University of South Carolina.   43 references

198   Rubin, Isadore.   "Common Sex Myths," in Sexology, Vol. 32,
          512-514, March 1966.
          Dr.   Rubin examines five common sex myths which are im-
portant to dispel and which he does in fact dispel.   They are: 1)
that high sexual activity in early years will not result in the sex
life ending early, 2) most child molesters are not over 65, 3) after
menopause a woman may not have less sex drive, 4) removal of the
prostate does not necessarily have to result in impotence, and 5)
under proper conditions and with medical advice it is possible for
heart patients to continue to have sexual activity.   No references

199   _____.   Sexual Life After Sixty.   New York: Basic Books,
          Inc., 1965.   (S. A., Vol. 13, B 8107, 1965.) (paperback,
          New York: New American Library, 1967.)
          Health problems related to sexuality are discussed including
heart disease, prostatic problems, hypertension and diabetes.

200   _____.   "Sex After Forty--and After Seventy," in Brecher,
          Ruth, and Brecher, Edward (eds.), An Analysis of Human
          Sexual Response, pp. 251-266, Boston: Little, Brown and
          Co., 1966.   (Also found in Huyck, Margaret Hellie, Growing
          Older--Things You Need to Know About Aging, pp. 52-68,
          Englewood Cliffs, NJ: Prentice-Hall, Inc., 1974.
          Summarizes the work of Masters and Johnson, the Kinsey in-
vestigators, Drs. Gustave Newman and Claude R. Nichols at Duke
University, urologists at the University of California School of Medicine at San Francisco, and by Dr. Joseph T. Freeman of Philadelphia.   Stresses the importance of regularity of sexual performance to maintain sexual capacity.   Problems of postmenopausal
years and maintaining male responsiveness are discussed.

201   _____.   "Sex Needs After 65," in Sexology, Vol. 30, 769-
          771, June 1964.
          Sex can be important to the well-being of older people.
Some people might welcome the ending of sex life while others may
still derive satisfaction from sexual activity.   No references

202   _____.   "Sex Over 65," in Beigel, Hugo G. (ed.), Advances in
          Sex Research, Vol. 1, 138-142, 1963.   (S. A., Vol. 12, No. 6,
          B2226, 1964.)
          The following citation and annotation report on the same study.

203   _____.   "Sex Over 65," in Sexology, Vol. 28, 622-625, April
          1962.
          This was a report which was delivered to the Society for the
Scientific Study of Sex and was sponsored by Sexology magazine.   A
committee of physicians headed by Dr. Harry Benjamin and Dr.
LeMon Clark sent a questionnaire to 6000 men over 65.   All were
highly successful in their careers or professions.   Of the total
6000 sent out, 832 replies were obtained (14 percent).   The vast

majority were potent and sexually active.   Fear of heart attack was
not a deterrent to coitus although a prostate condition was sometimes
a deterrent.   Some data on masturbation are included: 1) 66 of
279 married men with satisfying coitus engaged in masturbation,
2) 9 of 49 men reporting unsatisfying coitus engaged in masturbation, and 3) 25 of 105 impotent males engaged in masturbation.
People who work with elderly males need to consider their sexual
needs.

204 _____. Sexual Life in the Later Years. Study Guide No.
          12. New York: Human Sciences Press, 1970.
     Covers stereotypes, the research data, factors responsible
for declining male sex activity, sexual aging in women, the importance of regularity of sexual expression, myths and misconceptions,
common medical problems in the older years, impotence, sex needs
of the unmarried, and implications of our new knowledge.   5 items
in selected bibliography

205 Sanville, Jean, and Shor, Joel.   "Age Games in Play-Mating:
          Some Clinical Cues to Qualities of 'Intimacy' Between Lovers
          of Widely Disparate Ages, " in Clinical Social Work Journal,
          Vol. 3, No. 3, 187-200, Fall 1975.
     The author set forth the forms of "disturbance" in attempts
at intimacy by men and women of widely disparate ages.   These
lovers have hidden obstacles to identification, participation, and
communication in their play-mating relationships.   6 references

206 Sarrel, Philip M. , and Sarrel, Lorna.   Sex in Aging and
          Disease.   New York: Network for Continuing Medical Educa-
          tion, Videocassette No. 214, 1974.
     This videocassette is about 18 minutes long and presents
physiological changes which involve sexuality as well as studies
about cardio-vascular disease, diabetes, vaginitis, and gynecological
disease.   Physicians should be aware of the fact that any disease
condition affecting sensory perception and/or central nervous system
discharge, blood flow, vascular system or muscular tension will affect their sexuality.

207 Schaie, K. Warner, and Gribbin, Kathy.   "Adult Development
          and Aging, " in Annual Review of Psychology, Vol. 26, 65-
          96, 1975.
     Major methodological issues in adult development and aging
are covered as well as developments in the research literature.   Attitudes toward sexuality are considered.

208 Schlesinger, Benjamin, and Mullen, Richard Albert.   "Sexuality
          and the Aged: Taboos and Misconceptions Must Give Way
          to Reality, " in Schlesinger, Benjamin (ed.), Sexual Behaviour
          in Canada: Patterns and Problems, pp. 66-75, Toronto:
          University Press, 1977.
     Attitudes, misconceptions and myths that stereotype the eld-
erly person are presented.   Research findings on sexuality are then
discussed.   Sexual aging in the man and sexual aging in the woman

are presented and young male and female responses are contrasted
with old male and female responses.   The role of professionals
(doctors, nurses, attendants, orderlies, social workers, administrators, legislators) is to educate older people to the realities of sex
in the later years.   17 footnotes, 15 references

209   Schwartz, Arthur N. , and Mensh, Ivan N. (eds.)   <u>Professional</u>
        <u>Obligations and Approaches to the Aged.</u>   Springfield, IL:
        Charles C. Thomas, 1974.
        Older people need and should seek affection.   Many institu-
tions do not provide options to facilitate sexual behavior and/or
privacy for their residents.   Sexual adjustment of older people can
sometimes be a problem.   A case study of a man who suddenly
became impotent at retirement is discussed.   It is very important
for the older man and woman to have continuous sexual activity.
Widows have a difficult time because they do not remarry in the
numbers or as soon as divorcees do.   Sometimes they feel they
cannot find someone who is the equal of their mate.   In addition,
with the plurality of women, it is not always possible to even find
a mate.

210   Sedgwick, Rae.   "Myths in Human Sexuality: A Social-Psycho-
        logical Perspective, " in <u>Nursing Clinics of North America,</u>
        Vol. 10, No. 3, 539-550, September 1975.
        Presents a number of myths about sexuality and dispels them
through the use of case illustrations.   Several myths--including 1)
menopause is an affliction signifying the end of sex and 2) age and
sex are good indicators of a person's attitude toward sexuality--are
shown to be totally false based on the case illustrations.   Implications for nurses are given.   7 references, 4 suggested readings

211   Selye, Hans.   "Stress and Sex, " in Ellis, Albert, and Abar-
        banel, Albert (eds.), <u>Encyclopedia of Sexual Behavior,</u> pp.
        1010-1011, New York: Hawthorn Books, 1967.   (New York:
        Jason Aronson, Inc. , 1973 edition, pp. 75-81.)
        Stress can cause sexual derangements and stress can be a
result of sexual derangements.   4 references

212   <u>Sex and Aging: Topical Packet C.</u>   New York: SIECUS, n. d.
        This packet includes "Sexuality and Aging, " "The Sexuality
of Aging, " "The Now of the Kinsey Findings, " "Honk! If You Masturbate, " and study guides on Masturbation, Characteristics of Male
and Female Sexual Responses, Sexuality and the Life Cycle, and
Sexual Life in the Later Years.

213   Sex Information and Education Council of the U. S. (SIECUS).
        <u>Sex, Love and Intimacy--Whose Life Styles?</u>   Proceedings
        of the Second Annual SIECUS Symposium, New York, Novem-
        ber 5, 1971.
        These proceedings consist of five sections, the meat of which
are three papers preceded by an introduction and a program listing.
The first paper is entitled "Intimacy: Definitions and Distortions"
by Roy W. Menninger, M. D.   The second is entitled "Sex, Love

and Intimacy: New Interpretations--New Life Styles" by lsao Fuji-
moto, Ph. D.   The third has the most relevance to the topic of
aging and is entitled "First Isadore Rubin Memorial Lecture: Love,
Sex, Intimacy and Aging as a Life Style" by Mary S. Calderone.
Intimacy in aging is important as a meaningful facet of living, especially when so many other losses are occurring at the same time.

214 _____. Sexuality and Man.   New York: Charles Scribner's
        Sons, 1970.
        Contains a section on Sexuality and the Life Cycle.   Anno-
tated separately--see Kirkendall, Lester A. , and Rubin, Isadore.
Sexuality and the Life Cycle: A Broad Concept of Sexuality, SIECUS
Study Guide No. 8.   Also in McCary, James Leslie, and Copeland,
Donna R. (eds.), Modern Views of Human Sexual Behavior, pp. 5-
15, Chicago: Science Research Associates, Inc., 1976.   (paperback)
Specifically covers sexuality in adulthood, menopause and aging,
sexuality in the family life cycle, and parent-child relations.

215 _____. SIECUS Report, Vol. 2, No. 5, May 1974.   One
        of ten position statements adopted by the SIECUS Board of
        Directors.
        "Aging people are too often deprived of opportunities for
sexual companionship and expression, which they need despite un-
scientific beliefs to the contrary.   Society has an obligation to
create conditions conducive to the fulfillment of these needs. "

216 Sheehy, Gail.   Passages, pp. 304-320 (hardcover); pp. 440-
        464 (paperback); New York: E. P. Dutton (hardcover), 1974;
        New York: Bantam Books (paperback), 1976.
        Contains information on facing the facts of male and female
sexual life cycles, the diverging sexual life cycles, the ups and
downs of testosterone, mysteries of the climacteric, and sex and
menopause.

217 Solnick, Robert Lewis (ed.).   Sexuality and Aging (revised).
        Los Angeles: University of Southern California, 1978.
        (paperback)
        Originally published in 1975 with Irene Mortenson Burnside
as editor, this revised edition of the book contains some new chapters and deletes some chapters from the 1975 edition.   It is divided
into four sections: 1) the Broad Perspective, 2) Physiological, Psychological, and Sociological Issues, 3) Sexual Growth, 4) The Role
of Love in Late-Life Sex.   This book is an excellent resource for
the gerontologist or other professional interested in sexuality and
aging.

218 Spinazzola, Angelo J.   "Sexual Patterns in the Process of
        Aging, " in Health Education, Vol. 6, No. 4, 11-13, July/
        August 1975.
        The general facts about sexual desires and capacities existing
in old age are presented.   Psychological and physiological changes
occur in men and women which affect their sexuality.   Sympathy
and understanding should be afforded to older adults and not myths

and misconceptions about sexuality.   Maintenance of an active sex
life is the key to successful aging and successful living.

219   Stanford, Dennyse.   "All About Sex ... After Middle Age, " in
       American Journal of Nursing, Vol. 77, No. 4, 608-611,
       April 1977.
          Changes occur in sexual functioning throughout life but sex
lives can continue through old age.   The article is a general discussion of sexuality in the aging female, the aging male, and counseling of the elderly.   12 references

220   Steele, Harold C. , and Crow, Charles Brandon.   "A Close
       Look at Sex, " in their How to Deal with Aging and the Eld-
       erly, pp. 36-42, Huntsville, AL: Strode Publishers, Inc. ,
       1970.
          The possible effects of the menopause on sexuality in a
woman are covered.   Problems of male sexuality are also dealt
with.   A discussion of the effect of nutrition on sexuality is included.

221   Steffl, Bernita M. , and Kelly, James J.   "Teaching and Learn-
       ing About Sexuality and Aging, " in Educational Gerontology,
       Vol. 4, No. 4, 377-388, October-December 1979.
          Presents the authors' experiences in developing teaching and
learning content on sexuality and aging.   Includes course outline
suggestions, experiential learning for students and implications of
findings for gerontological educators.   9 references

222   Stephens, Joyce.   Loners, Losers and Lovers: Elderly
       Tenants in a Slum Hotel.   Seattle and London: University
       of Washington Press, 1976.   (Reviewed in Gerontologist,
       Vol. 17, No. 3, 279-280, 1977.)
          Tom Tissue of the Social Security Administration in Washing-
ton, D. C. , reviews this book in The Gerontologist.   As a graduate
student in sociology, Joyce Stephens used participant observation to
obtain data.   A symbolic interactionist perspective is taken in order
to explain the behavior which went on around her.   The social system of the slum hotel and all its participants are examined, and
sexual and romantic interludes are included.   The reader can enjoy
and understand the book without having to be a sociologist.

223   Stern, Edith M.   A Full Life After 65.   New York: Public
       Affairs Pamphlets No. 347A, 1976.
          Suggestions for the older person on how to have a full life
after 65 including remarriage for those who are widows or widowers.
Sex is suggested as being proper at any age.

224   Stokes, Walter R.   "Modern View of Masturbation, " in Sexol-
       ogy, Vol. 27, 586-590, April 1961.
          Solitary masturbation is not as satisfying as intercourse but
it has a positive place in a person's sex life.   Masturbation or
mutual masturbation can be a useful and pleasurable supplement
for intercourse.   No references

225 _____ . "Sexual Pleasure in the Late Years," in Professional Psychology, Vol. 2, No. 4, 361-362, Fall 1971.
(This paper is adapted from a paper presented at the meeting
of the National Council on Family Relations, Washington,
D. C., 1969.)
A general summary of current information and attitudes on
sexual pleasures in the late years. 2 references, 7-item bibliography

226 Sutterley, Doris Cook, and Donnelly, Gloria Ferrarro. Perspectives in Human Development: Nursing Throughout the
Life Cycle, pp. 145-151, Philadelphia: Lippincott, 1973.
A discussion on the sexual process in adulthood, the middle
years and the later years. Some basic problems of sexuality in the
later years are touched upon. Specific references to nursing at
this point in the life cycle are made.

227 Sviland, Mary Ann P. "The New Sex Education and the Aging,"
in Otto, Herbert Arthur (ed.), The New Sex Education: The
Sex Educator's Resource Book, Chapter 17, pp. 222-244,
Chicago: Follet Publishing Co., 1978. (The book is reviewed by Paul D. Bishop in SIECUS Report, Vol. 8, No. 2,
pp. 10-11, November 1979.)
Presents background material on sexuality among the aged including cultural stereotyping and myths about aging, research short-
comings on elderly sexuality, research findings on physical and environmental effects on elderly sexuality, and restrictive cultural and
physiological factors. The author also provides an approach and
program to sex education with the aging, and touches briefly on
retirement programs, nursing homes, and sex education. A very
helpful section about teaching materials and resources is included.
Listed in this section are references for the sex educator, suggested
audience readings, selected films, and selected slides. There are
63 notes and references listed and 33 additional resources.

228 Tarail, Mark. "Sex Over 65," in Sexology, Vol. 28, 440-445,
February 1962.
A questionnaire was used to gather responses from 832 professional men who ranged in age from 65 to 92. Sexual intercourse
as a continued activity was reported by 397 men. A main factor
which may have accounted for this continued activity was the marital
status of the respondent. Impotence was reported more after the
age of 65. Most subjects declaring impotence did not seek treatment for it.

229 Troll, Lillian E. Early and Middle Adulthood, pp. 25-29, 52,
58, 78, 87-88, Monterey, CA: Brooks/Cole, 1975.
A general discussion of sexual activity, fertility, menstruation and sex cycles, menopause, and sex and social-class differences. Sexual adjustment is briefly touched upon.

230 Vallentine, C. L. Sexperts, pp. 38-39, New York: Exposition
Press, 1959.

A very small section on sexuality and aging is included. The author suggests that most men are good bed partners later in life and that women seem to have the highest point of their sex drive from 30 to 35 years of age. Some women can be more active sexually after the menopause. Sex for both men and women can exist at almost any age. No references

231   van den Berghe, Pierre L.   Age and Sex in Human Societies: A Biosocial Perspective.   Belmont, CA: Wadsworth, 1973.
    Dr. van den Berghe's book consists of seven chapters. Age and sex in evolutionary perspective, among primates, and the human biology of age and sex comprise the first three chapters. Sex and age differentiation in human societies are the topics covered in the next two chapters. Chapter six covers the dynamics of age and sex conflicts. The final chapter covers effects of industrial technology on age and sex roles. At the end of the book is a glossary, bibliography and index. It is an interdisciplinary study of the impact of age and sex differentiation on society.

232   Vātsyāyana.   The Kama Sutra, p. 149.   Translated by Burton, R. F., and Arbuthnot, F. F.   Medallion edition.   New York: G. P. Putnam's Sons, 1963.
    Concerning men and their fear of intercourse with older women:

> As to coiton with old women, it acts like a fatal poison ... Do not rummage old women. ...   Beware of mounting old women ... [even] if they cover you with favours. ...   The coitus of old women is a venomous meal.

233   Verwoerdt, Adriaan.   "Normal Psychology of the Aging Process, Revisited; I: Discussion," in Journal of Geriatric Psychiatry, Vol. 9, No. 2, 211-219, 1976.
    A discussion of Martin A. Berezin's review of the literature on sexuality and old age in Journal of Geriatric Psychiatry, Vol. 9, No. 2, 189-209, 1976. Research and literature on senescent sexuality began appearing in the 1950's. It had not appeared earlier due to myths, taboos, and denial. Because of the increasing numbers of older people, the problems of old age living, including sex, have been focused on. Dr. Verwoerdt elaborates on 1) effects of aging on sex, 2) later life quality of sexual experience, 3) sexual problems in later life. Under sexual problems he suggests that patients in geriatric institutions who sexually act out do so because of psychological conflicts. No references

234   _____; Pfeiffer, Eric; and Wang, Hsioh-Shan.   "Sexual Behavior in Senescence.   Changes in Sexual Activity and Interest of Aging Men and Women," in Journal of Geriatric Psychiatry, Vol. 2, 163-180, 1969.
    Report on the sexual behavior of 254 volunteers aged 60 and up. This report is the first of a series. These subjects were interviewed at three-year intervals from 1955-1964. The interviews were conducted to determine the effects of marital status, sex, and age on frequency of sexual interest and activity. In this study,

sexual activity was sexual intercourse and sexual interest referred
to heterosexual activities.   Frequency and incidence of sexual intercourse and degree of sexual interest were focused on.   A gradual
decline in sexual activity and interest occurs with age but many
variables other than age are significant.   Men have higher levels of
sexual activity in all age groups than women.   In the 60's, frequency of coitus is about 50 percent.   This frequency drops to lower
than 20 percent in the 80's.   In women, sexual interest and sexual
activity appear to be related.   In men, however, there was discrep-
ancy between interest and activity which was consistent and significant.

235 _____; _____; and _____.   "Sexual Behavior in Se-
        nescence, II.   Patterns of Sexual Activity and Interest," in
        Geriatrics, Vol. 24, 137-154, February 1969.
        Individual patterns of change in sexual behavior were studied
from longitudinal data on 254 men and women from 60 to 94.   Age
and degree of sexual activity were related to other variables including health.   After age 75 sexual interest was higher than activity
with very little existence of intense interest.   Males have a greater
difference between sexual activity and interest and this difference increases with age.   Men have more sexual activity and interest than
women; however, marital status was less important with advanced
age.   Males have sustained activity and interest through the 60's
while females have lower interest in the late 60's.   Sexual activity
and interest for both men and women decreased through the 70's.

236 Wales, Jeffrey B.   "Sexuality in Middle and Old Age: A
        Critical Review of the Literature," in Case Western Reserve
        Journal of Sociology, Vol. 6, 82-105, May 1974.
        The author incorrectly states that a critical review of the
literature on this topic had not been published when in fact Martin A. Berezin (1969) had published one in the Journal of Geriatric
Psychiatry.   However, Wales does mention both sexuality in institutions for the aged and homosexuality and the aged, topics which
Berezin overlooked.   The review covers biological, social and subjective variables but does not contain an extensive bibliography.   27
references

237 Wasow, Mona.   Sexuality and Aging.   Madison, WI: 1120 Edge-
        hill Drive, 53705.   Dated 1976.   Illustrated pamphlet avail-
        able from author.
        An easy to read pamphlet designed for older adults.   Gen-
erally covers sexuality and aging and changes that occur in men
and women.   A short reference is made to sexuality in nursing
homes.   The final section is devoted to sexuality and health.   4
suggestions for further reading

238 _____, and Loeb, Martin B.   "The Aged," Chapter 4 in
        Gochros, Harvey L., and Gochros, Jean S. (eds.), The
        Sexually Oppressed, pp. 54-68, New York: Association
        Press, 1977.   (Review of the entire book by Flynn, Robert
        J. in Sexuality and Disability, Vol. 1, No. 1, 73-74, Spring
        1978.)

A general overview of sexuality and aging is presented in the beginning of the chapter.   This chapter is a most important one as far as sexuality in nursing homes is concerned.   It reports on the study done by these researchers in a nursing home, one of the few studies which exist.   This study was probably the first ever done on a formal basis anywhere.   Staff and residents were interviewed. Several salient points are made.   One, the staff didn't express a great deal of interest in providing for privacy of the residents and this is prerequisite in supporting sexual expression.   Secondly, the researchers see a great need for in-service training programs on sexuality in the aged.   Sex education classes would also be helpful for the residents.   Nursing home staff are not prepared to be supportive in ensuring privacy and promoting affection and sensuality among residents who may desire it as one of their last pleasures before death.

239   Wax, Judith.   "It's Like Your Own Home Here," in New York
        Times Magazine, 38-40, 87-88, 90, 92, 96, 98, 100, Sunday,
        November 21, 1976.
        The average age of residents in this experiment in communal living was 82.   The residence was located in a renovated townhouse complex in Evanston, Illinois, and was called the Weinfeld Group Living Residence.   Each resident's independence is insured by maintaining community and family ties.   The residents help each other cope.

240   _____.   "Sex and the Single Grandparent," in New Times,
        Vol. 5, No. 6, 42-47, September 19, 1975.
        A series of short scenarios of elderly couples who choose to live together and the reasons for the choice.   Reasons include the fact that it prevents depression and hopelessness, the loss of Social Security benefits if the couple married, and love and affection. Eric Pfeiffer and Masters and Johnson are referred to for data that sexual activity should continue into the later years.   Most older women need a sanctioned partner.   One interviewee claims orgasm is "...such a release from the tensions."   Some residents of a hotel for elderly experienced love for the first time; some who never even have sex!

241   Weg, Ruth B.   "Physiology and Sexuality in Aging," in Burn-
        side, Irene Mortenson (ed.), Sexuality and Aging, pp. 7-17,
        Los Angeles: University of Southern California, 1975.
        This is similar to the chapter in the Solnick book but not quite as detailed.   Mainly what is covered are the general physiological changes which occur with age.   20 references

242   _____.   "The Physiology of Sexuality in Aging," Chapter 5
        in Solnick, Robert Lewis (ed.), Sexuality and Aging (revised),
        pp. 48-65, Los Angeles: University of Southern California,
        1978.
        An important point which is stressed at the beginning of this chapter is that behavioral and environmental dimensions influence anatomical and physical aspects of sexual expression and vice versa.

The physiological changes in both male and female are discussed.
The consequences of illness and disease, namely disinterest, frustration, dysfunction, and impotence are discussed. Of special importance to sexuality and aging are drug abuse, coronary disease,
diabetes, osteoporosis, and surgery of the urogenital system. Some
suggestions made include: 1) hormone replacement therapy, 2) sexual therapy, 3) continuation of sexual expression throughout the life-
span, 4) five research goals, 5) alteration of attitudes toward aging,
6) encouraging the elderly to enjoy each other, 7) acceptance of differences in sexual expression, and 8) making sure the helping professions treat the aged as people. Older persons should not be
forced into sexual expression. 42 references

243 _____. "Sexuality in Middle Age: There Is No Time Limit, "
        in Dynamic Years, Vol. 12, No. 4, 20-22, July-August 1977.
        Denial of sexuality in the middle age (about 35 to 64) can
result in painful damage to the self concept. Changes occur in men
and women physiologically as they grow older but these do not have
to greatly affect sexuality if they are understood. Regular sexual
expression will ensure retention of sexual capability. Now the feeling is that sex is a sharing thing and not one sided in its initiation
or enjoyment. No references

244 Weinberg, Jack. "Sexual Expression in Late Life, " in Amer-
        ican Journal of Psychiatry, Vol. 126, No. 5, 713-716, No-
        vember 1969. (Reprinted in Steury, Steven, and Blank,
        Marie L. (eds.), Readings in Psychotherapy with Older Peo-
        ple, pp. 211-214, Rockville, MD: National Institute of Men-
        tal Health, 1977.)
        The need for contactual relationships in older people is em-
phasized. When lack of a partner or poor health interferes with
sexual activity adaptation to the environment can take many forms.
Two case reports are included. 8 references

245 _____. "Sexuality in Later Life, " in Medical Aspects of
        Human Sexuality, Vol. 5, No. 4, 216-227, April 1971.
        Sexual expression of an inappropriate nature can result when
all intimacy is denied the elderly. Sexuality should continue all
through life. 4 references

246 Weisberg, Martin. "Sexual Medicine: Sex and Aging, " in
        New Physician, Vol. 26, No. 10, 42, 1977.
        A general discussion on sexuality and aging admonishing the
physician to be open and frank in discussing sex with his or her patients. 3 references

247 West, Norman D. "Sex in Geriatrics: Myth or Miracle?"
        in Journal of the American Geriatrics Society, Vol. 23, No.
        12, 551-552, 1975. (P.A., Vol. 55, Abstract No. 07009,
        1976.)
        A brief discussion of the role of physical love and sex in the
aged states that the young are ignorant of the fact that sex continues
after age 50 and as a result many cruel jokes about sex and the eld-

erly have been perpetuated. Information gathered from twelve years
of work with geriatric residents in a rural nursing home might be
used to consider the sexual needs of the aged and supportive procedures which might be used to meet these needs. 6 references

248 Wikler, Revy, and Grey, Peg Savage. Sex and the Senior
       Citizen. New York: Frederick Fell, Inc., 1968. (Book re-
       view of this by Walter C. Alvarez, in Geriatrics, Vol. 24,
       No. 4, 71, 75, April 1969.)
       This book is printed in large print and intended for the lay
senior citizen. Problems of living as an older person are given
and sex is suggested as natural and healthy. Specifics about sexuality and the aging are not covered in detail.

249 Wilson, W. Cody. "The Distribution of Selected Sexual Atti-
       tudes and Behaviors Among the Adult Population of the United
       States," in Journal of Sex Research, Vol. 11, No. 1, 46-64,
       February 1975.
       This is a description of selected sexual attitudes and be-
haviors in the United States. Responses of 92 percent of a national
probability sample of 2,486 adults in the 48 contiguous states were
used. Differences in sexual attitudes and behaviors are related to
gender, age, and education. 8 references

250 Witkin, Ruth K., and Nissen, Robert J. (eds.). How to
       Live Better After 60. Port Washington, NY: Regency Press,
       1978. (Reviewed by Backman, Anne in SIECUS Report,
       Vol. 7, No. 6, 15, July 1979.)
       Contains a section on "How to Maintain Your Sex Life."
Maintains that sex can be one of the greatest pleasures of maturity.

251 Woodruff, Diana S., and Birren, James E. (eds.). Aging:
       Scientific Perspectives and Social Issues, pp. 242-243, New
       York: D. Van Nostrand Co., 1975.
       Basic sexual changes for both men and women are presented
with respect to aging. Sexual activity most often declines due to
unavailability of a partner and/or illness.

252 Woods, Nancy Fugate. Human Sexuality in Health and Illness,
       Chapter 3, pp. 45-56, St. Louis: C. V. Mosby, 1975.
       Considers biological, social, and psychological aspects of
the aging process and sexuality from young adulthood through the
later years. Factors which might interfere with sexual function
during these stages are discussed. 23 references

253 Yeaworth, Rosalee C., and Friedeman, Joyce Sutkamp.
       "Sexuality in Later Life," in Nursing Clinics of North Amer-
       ica, Vol. 10, No. 3, 565-586, September 1975.
       A general discussion of sexuality in later life in the follow-
ing sections: 1) biophysical changes with aging--male, female, hormonal changes, the effects of disease, disability, or surgery; 2)
cultural and social influences on sexuality; 3) aging and sexual behavior; and 4) implications for nurses and other helping profes-

sionals.   Older persons should be helped in trying to overcome their sexual problems.   Nurses can take an active role in sexual counseling of their patients.   30 references

SOCIAL AND PSYCHOLOGICAL ASPECTS
OF SEXUALITY AND AGING

254 Bergman, S. , and Amir, M. "Crime and Delinquency Among
the Aged in Israel, " in Geriatrics, Vol. 28, No. 1, 149-157,
January 1973.
This article on deviant behavior by 60-year-old people or
older examines the offenses, offenders, and reasons which have a
tendency to elicit such behavior. Problems of immigrants who are
aged when they come to Israel are emphasized, especially cultural
and social problems. Sexual offenses were committed by recidivists
and first offenders. The recidivists were sexually maladjusted at
an early age. The offenses prominent among this group were pedophilia, exhibitionism, and homosexuality. The deterioration of inhibitions through age was given for the first offenders' behavior. 1
reference

255 Butler, Robert N. , and Lewis, Myrna I. "Sexuality in Old
Age: Societal Attitudes Toward Sexuality in Old Age, " in
their Aging and Mental Health, pp. 99-105. St. Louis, MO:
C. V. Mosby, 1973.
This is primarily concerned with societal attitudes toward
sexuality in old age. Nursing homes are mentioned as adding to the
impression that the aging are sexless. Segregation of men and
women often occurs and conjugal visits are not allowed. Masturbation, the last resort of the elderly, is upsetting to nursing personnel who aren't sure how to deal with it. Research findings are
summarized (Kinsey, Masters and Johnson, and Duke longitudinal
studies) to show that sexual interest and activity exists in older
people. Physical characteristics of sex in old age in both older
men and older women are presented separately. The topic of sex
and chronic physical conditions receives some attention as do mental health treatment considerations. The importance of sex education for old people as well as masturbation to preserve sexual functioning is mentioned.

256 Cameron, Paul. "The Generation Gap: Beliefs About Sexuality
and Self-Reported Sexuality, " in Developmental Psychology,
Vol. 3, No. 2, 272, 1970.
Our opinions of the sexuality of generations seem to be
stereotypic. Middle-aged are thought to be cognitively superior
about sex. The young are thought to be the most virile. The old
are seen as asexual. 2 references

257 Comfort, Alex. Sex in Society. New York: Citadel Press;
     London: Duckworth, 1966.
     Covers the scope and purposes of sexual sociology, the bio-
logical background, the social background and its problems, monog-
amy and the pattern of sexual conduct (including extramarital relations), law and the pattern of sexuality (including law and deviation),
and remedies and methods. 69 references

258 Cooley, E. E. "Psychosocial Aspects of Sex and Aging," in
     Kelly, J. T., and Weir, J. H. (eds.), Perspectives on
     Human Sexuality. Minneapolis, MN: Craftsman Press, 1976.
     A discussion of the sexual and psychosocial aspects of aging
in contrast with the myths and research information presently available. Healthy older people can and should continue to have sexual
activity.

259 Davies, Leland J. "Attitudes Toward Old Age and Aging As
     Shown by Humor," in Gerontologist, Vol. 17, No. 3, 220-
     226, 1977.
     An analysis of jokes in jokebook anthologies was done. Nega-
tive attitudes as shown in humor were directed to aging, old age
and death. There was a great emphasis on negative attitudes toward
aging women. There was some attitude ambivalence displayed. Education might alleviate myths and emphasize positive aspects of old
age. 29 references

260 Dean, Stanley R. "Sin and Senior Citizens," in Journal of the
     American Geriatrics Society, Vol. 14, No. 9, 935-938, 1966.
     Because of a flaw in the Social Security Act, many elderly
couples were forced to live "in sin" or lose a large portion of their
Social Security benefits through marriage. 1 reference

261 Dressel, Paula L., and Avant, W. Ray. "Neogamy and Older
     Persons: An Examination of Alternatives for Intimacy in
     Later Years," in Alternative Lifestyles, Vol. 1, No. 1, 13-36,
     February 1978. (Abstract in Aged Care and Service Review,
     Vol. 1, No. 4, 14, 1978.)
     The article explores the converging demographic and social
factors regarding older persons as they relate to the need for and
the expression of intimate relationships. It attempts to bring together the literature on neogamy among older people and to provide
a conceptual framework for its understanding. The authors examine
the existence and implications of new forms of intimacy among older
people. Implications of these issues for research, counseling, and
public policy are finally presented. 53 references

262 Fry, William F., Jr. "Psychodynamics of Sexual Humor:
     Sex and the Elderly," in Medical Aspects of Human Sexuality,
     Vol. 10, No. 2, 140-141, 146-148, February 1976.
     Fifteen jokes about sex and the elderly are presented. Many
contradictions appear. On one hand, the aged are viewed as sexless; and on the other hand, they are viewed as oversexed lechers.
No references

263   Gebhard, Paul H.   "Normal and Criminal Sexual Behavior at
         Older Ages," in Beiträge zur Sexualforschung, Vol. 41, 83-
         87, 1967.
         Sexual aging is neuro-physiological deterioration which causes
25 percent of males in the sample to be impotent by age 65 and 50
percent to be impotent by 75.   The impotence is usually psychogenic
in origin.   One-half of married females were having married coitus
by age 65.   Only one-eighth of widowed and divorced women were
having coitus by age 60.   Many older women resorted to masturbation for sexual relief.
         It is usually males who are involved in criminal sexual behavior.
Most sex offenses are not committed by older men.   Regardless of
age, a healthy older person should continue to function sexually.   6
references

264   Gochros, Harvey L.   "The Sexually Oppressed," in Social
         Work, Vol. 17, No. 2, 16-23, 1972.   (Based on a paper
         presented at the NASW Eastern Regional Institute, Washing-
         ton, D. C., October 25, 1971.)
         Sections of this article include the sexual elite, the aged,
the homosexually oriented, the hospitalized mentally ill, and the
imprisoned.   The section on the aged is short but states that there
are some homes for the aged that provide privacy which encourages
romance and remarriage.   Social workers need to help the aged develop contacts through social clubs.   Sex education may be needed
for the aged.   Masturbation should be encouraged.

265   Golde, Peggy, and Kogan, Nathan.   "A Sentence Completion
         Procedure for Assessing Attitudes Toward Old People," in
         Journal of Gerontology, Vol. 14, 355-360, 1959.   (A pre-
         liminary version of this article was presented at the Novem-
         ber 1958 meeting of the Gerontological Society, Inc.)
         The hypothesis that attitudes about older people are different
from "people in general" was tested.   The instrument which was
developed was a sentence completion one.   The stem "most old people" was used in the experimental instrument.   The control form of
the instrument used "most people" as the stem.   Each form contained 25 sentences which were incomplete.
         Students (100) from ages 17 to 23 were given the forms.
Fifty were given the control form and fifty the experimental form.
The results showed there was a statistically significant difference
in the responses to items on both forms.   10 references

266   Grauer, H.   "Brief Guide to Office Counseling: Deviant Sexual
         Behavior Associated with Senility," in Medical Aspects of
         Human Sexuality, Vol. 12, No. 4, 127-128, April 1978.
         (Abstract in Excerpta Medica, Vol. 21, Section 20, No. 3586,
         1978.)
         Lists sexual problems sometimes seen in the aged including
delusions of infidelity, sexual promiscuity, exhibitionism, voyeurism,
and homosexuality, pedophilia, and public masturbation.   Treatments
are suggested.

267 Groth, A. Nicholas. "The Older Rape Victim and Her Assail-
ant," in Journal of Geriatric Psychiatry, Vol. 11, No. 2,
203-215, 1978. (Also entitled "Rape of the Elderly" and reprinted in Groth, A. Nicholas, and Birnbaum, H. Jean, Men
Who Rape: The Psychology of the Offender, pp. 164-174,
New York: Plenum Publishing Co., 1979.)
   Presents a review of the literature, the method of study,
findings and discussion. The findings included a section on the offenders, the victims, and the offense including location, relationships, and assault. Four cases are presented to illustrate the domi-
nant motive to be rage and not sexual desire in the assaults. The
author stressed that age is no defense against rape. 7 references

268 Hamilton, G. V. "Changes in Personality and Psychosexual
Phenomena with Age," Chapter 16, pp. 459-482, in Cowdry,
Edmund Vincent (ed.), Problems of Ageing, 1st edition.
Baltimore: Williams and Wilkins, 1939. (Second edition,
ibid., Chapter 30, pp. 810-831, 1942.)
   Four major turning points which are recognizable throughout
a total life span include a period in which the personality changes
from a matured to an aging structure. The author questions
whether the climacteric represents a decline in sexual potency and
desire in men and women. Psychological reactions to the conditioned
reduction in sexual potency can bring on these symptoms. Frustration can be a factor in the appearance of psychosexual regression.
18 references

269 Kahana, Boaz. "Social and Psychological Aspects of Sexual
Behavior Among the Aged," Chapter 7 in Hafez, E. S. E.
(ed.), Aging and Reproductive Physiology, pp. 89-95. Ann
Arbor: Ann Arbor Science, 1976.
   There are still taboos against sex in old age and sexuality
of this age group has not been studied enough. Methodological
problems of studying aging and sexuality are discussed. The findings of the three major research studies done to date are presented;
namely, 1) Kinsey studies, 2) Masters and Johnson studies, and 3)
the Duke University studies. Some mention is given to sexual attitudes of the aged in nursing homes. 10 references

270 Lawton, M. Powell. "Social Rehabilitation of the Aged:
Some Neglected Aspects," in Journal of the American Geriatrics Society, Vol. 16, No. 12, 1346-1363, December 1968.
(This was a paper presented at the Annual Meeting of the
Pennsylvania Association of Nonprofit Homes for the Aged,
May 1, 1968, in Pittsburgh, PA.)
   The philosophy of rehabilitation is covered. Goals set for
improvement should only be the next step higher in functioning and
this will improve the possibility of success. Certain fresh approaches are presented to such problems as placing the aging in a
home, especially the waiting and entry periods. Rehabilitation from
the stress brought on by change of residence is important. Staff
importance is covered from a number of viewpoints. Space, private

and social, as well as furnishings are also discussed.   23 references

271   Leviton, Dan.   "The Significance of Sexuality as a Deterrent
       to Suicide Among the Aged," in Omega: Journal of Death
       and Dying, Vol. 4, No. 2, 163-174, Summer 1973.   (Address
       presented before the Symposium on Aging, November 23,
       1971, Metropolitan Jewish Geriatric Center, New York City.)
       (P. A., Vol. 51, No. 05557, 1974.)
       No empirical research data were gathered via experimenta-
tion, but the author makes a very good point supported by literature
which already exists.   The main premise of the article is that desire for death is low when sexuality is strong.   The aged person
who is encouraged and able to have a satisfying sexual life will be
less inclined to suicide.   There is an important need for the health
professions to understand the relationship of sexuality with other aspects of therapy in treating the aged.   Dr. Leviton contends that
"nearly all forms and types of loss can be related to the dysfunc-
tioning of sexuality."   Leviton concludes that a revitalization of sexuality decreases hopelessness, depression and suicidal behavior.
Sexuality reminds us that we are living and that hope exists.   Five
recommendations are given: 1) aging people need to understand that
they are attractive and can have relationships with others; 2) physical
fitness must be emphasized, not only for health reasons, but also
as a means of social interaction; 3) encouragement for human relationships should be given and marriage at older age should be encouraged; 4) affectional-sexual relationships should be encouraged;
5) health personnel need to understand the therapeutic effects of sex
on the older individual.

272   Lockhart, William B. (ed.).   The Report of the Commission on
       Obscenity and Pornography.   Washington, D.C.:   U.S. Govern-
       ment Printing Office, September 1970.
       Adult participation data in so-called "pornographic" entertain-
ment (movies, adult bookstores, etc.) are presented.   Throughout the
book, pros and cons of "pornography" are discussed toward the end
of leaving the reader to wonder what pornography and obscenity actually are.

273   Mohr, Johann W.   "The Child Molester," in Sexology, Vol. 29,
       479-481, February 1963.
       The old age group (over 50) is the smallest group of sexual
molesters compared to adolescents and the mid-to-late thirties
groups.   Child molesters engage in sexual play that children usually
engage in themselves.   Activities include fondling, looking, showing,
touching, and sometimes masturbation.   Intercourse is rare except
in cases of other severe mental disorders.   Violence is also rare.
In most cases, the child and man know each other, may be related,
or the man may be a friend of family or a neighbor.   Most activity
takes place in the man's or child's home.   A child's sexual curi-
osity can contribute to incidents.   Child molesters need help in adjusting to stresses and strains of adult life.   No references

274 _____. "The Man Who Exposes Himself," in Sexology, Vol.
29, 238-240, November 1962.
    Exhibitionism should be carefully defined. The author de-
fines it as "the exposure of the male genital to an unsuspecting female in a public place, without any intention of further sexual contact." This clearly separates the exhibitionist from the rapist.
Danger spots for exhibitionists include the beginning of marriage and
pregnancy. Even though some exhibitionists expect the availability
of sex in marriage to eliminate the problem, this is not always
the case. Sometimes a good marriage can help, but often the exhibitionist chooses a wife whose own problems heighten the urge to
expose. Females who encounter exhibitionists need not experience
extreme fright or shock or fear sexual assault. No references

275 Nuttall, R. L., and Costa, R. L. "Drinking Patterns as Af-
    fected by Age and by Personality," in Gerontologist, Vol.
    15, No. 5, Part 2, 35, 1975. (A paper given at the 28th
    annual meeting of the Gerontological Society, Louisville, Ken-
    tucky, October 1975.)
    Younger men and men of any age of the anxious/extrovert
type were more likely to drink to lessen their own sexual inhibitions.
Age appropriate social norms and expectations as well as personality can affect drinking patterns.

276 Palmore, Erdman. "Attitudes Toward Aging As Shown by
    Humor," in Gerontologist, Vol. 11, 181-186, Part 1, Autumn
    1971.
    Societal attitudes toward aging were analyzed by examining
264 jokes about aging. Most of the jokes reflected a negative view
of aging. Women were viewed more negatively than men as reflected by the jokes about aging. 21 references

277 Petras, John W. Sexuality in Society, p. 65. Boston: Allyn
    and Bacon, 1973. (1975 (2nd edition) new title: The Social
    Meaning of Human Sexuality. 1978 edition entitled The So-
    cial Meaning of Human Sexuality. pp. 145-170.
    Contains in Chapter 5 two experience levels relevant to sex-
uality and aging, adulthood to old age and old age.

278 Reed, David M. "Sexual Behavior in the Separated, Divorced,
    and Widowed," in Sadock, Benjamin J.; Kaplan, Harold O.;
    and Freedman, Alfred M. (eds.), The Sexual Experience,
    pp. 249-255. Baltimore, MD: Williams and Wilkins, 1976.
    Sociological, physiological, and psychological factors of sex-
ual behavior in separated, divorced, and widowed are covered.
Different types of crises which are common to these groups of people include separation crisis, divorce crisis, and widowhood crisis.
Crisis characteristics are explained. 16 references

279 Richman, Joseph. "The Foolishness and Wisdom of Age: At-
    titudes Toward the Elderly As Reflected in Jokes," in Ger-
    ontologist, Vol. 17, No. 3, 210-219, 1977. (This paper
    was originally presented at the 28th Annual Scientific Meet-

ing of the Gerontological Society, Louisville, October 28,
1975.)
When jokes about the aged and jokes about children were
compared, negative attitudes toward the aged were found and positive attitudes toward the children were found.   Numbers of jokes
compared included 100 for the aged and 160 for the children.   Old
age jokes displayed ambivalence.   Decline and nearness to death
were displayed as well as affirmation and transcendence.   13 references

280   Rodstein, Manuel.   "Crime and the Aged: 2.   The Criminals, "
      in Journal of the American Medical Association, Vol. 234,
      No. 6, 639, 1975.
      A review of the characteristics of the aged criminal.   Only
5 percent of prisoners are over 45 years old.   Chronic brain syndrome (CBS) may be associated with a loss of inhibitions resulting
in illegal sexual behavior.   2 references

281   Rubin, Isadore.   "The 'Sexless Older Years'--A Socially
      Harmful Stereotype, " in Annals of the American Academy of
      Political and Social Sciences, Vol. 376, 86-95, March 1968.
      (Also in Sagarin, E. (ed.), Sex and the Contemporary Amer-
      ican Scene.   Philadelphia: The American Academy of Polit-
      ical and Social Science, 1968, pp. 86-95.)
      Sex can play an important role in later years, and there is
no specific time where sex should end.   Society needs to become
more tolerant and understanding of sexual expression in older persons.   51 references

282   Rummel, Roy LaMar.   "Implicit Moral Values and Interper-
      sonal Behavior As Related to College Aged Students and Eld-
      erly People. "   Unpublished doctoral dissertation, Ohio State
      University, 1972.   (D. A. , Vol. 33, 4532A, 1973.)
      The study focused on generation gap similarities and differ-
ences on basic moral values between college-aged students and re-
tired-aged elderly.   The elderly were most accurate in their attri-
butions to the college students on items like those dealing with the
current influence of the church.   The elderly misperceived the students on items relating to theoretical assumptions about personality
dynamics and effective personal adjustment.   There was no significance to sex differences for the total group.

283   Silfen, Peter; Ben David, Sarah; Kliger, Dina; Eshel, Rachel;
      Heichel, Hayah; and Lehman, Dina.   "The Adaptation of the
      Older Prisoner in Israel, " in International Journal of Offender
      Therapy (etc.) (London), Vol. 21, No. 1, 57-65, 1977.
      Fifteen Israeli prisoners over 50 years of age were inter-
viewed by the use of an extensive structured interview and also by
a psychiatrist.   The psychiatrist was to determine sexual activity
among other things.   For the older prisoner whose inner resources
are weak, the prison represents a supportive rather than demanding
framework.   3 references

284 Snyder, Eldon E., and Spreitzer, Elmer. "Attitudes of the
     Aged Toward Nontraditional Sexual Behavior," in Archives
     of Sexual Behavior, Vol. 5, No. 3, 249-254, 1976.
        A United States national probability sample was used as a
data source. Two age cohorts were separated, respondents over
65 and respondents under 65, and group comparisons were made.
A correlation of attitudes toward nontraditional sexual behavior was
made with age. The nontraditional behaviors toward which attitudes
were measured were homosexuality, premarital sexual relations,
and extramarital sexual relations. The conservative sexual attitudes
were held by older respondents. Predictors of sexual attitudes for
both age groups were background variables of sex, social status,
church attendance, marital status, and parenthood. There exist
many individual differences among the aged. More changes throughout
a greater range was predicted for the future. Author abstract
modified; 20 references

285 Watkins, R. A.; Correy, J. F.; Wise, D. A.; and Perkin,
     G. J. "Social and Psychological Changes After Sterilization:
     A Reevaluation Study on 425 Women," in Medical Journal of
     Australia, Vol. 2, No. 7, 251-254, 1976.
        A questionnaire designed to assess social and psychological
changes after tubal sterilization was responded to by 425 women.
Dissatisfaction with operation outcome had no relationship to patients'
history of emotional instability, religious affiliation, parity or age
at time of operation. A number of the sample reported positive
emotional and sexual adjustment with a small percentage reporting
negative social and psychological changes. 6 references

286 Whiskin, Frederick E. "The Geriatric Sex Offender," in
     Geriatrics, Vol. 22, 168-172, October 1967. (Reprinted in
     Medical Aspects of Human Sexuality, Vol. 4, No. 4, 125-
     129, April 1970.)
        The elderly sex offender is usually a benign and impotent
person. Three reasons why the older sex offender is maligned are:
1) the age, 2) the offense relates to sex, 3) the offense is an abnormal one which relates to sex. Two case histories are presented.
A short discussion on managing the sex offender completes the article. 9 references

287 Wilson, Joseph G. "Signs of Sexual Aberration in Old Men,"
     in Journal of the American Geriatrics Society, Vol. 4, 1105-
     1107, November 1956.
        There are two types of old sexually aberrant men: harmless
ones and dangerous ones. There is appropriate treatment for each
type. Sexual aberrance is more of a public nuisance than a crime
since sexual aberrance in elderly men is suspected more than it actually exists. Signs which identify sexually dangerous or potentially
dangerous senile men need to be studied. 3 references

SEXUALITY AND THE AGING FEMALE

288 Ballard, Lester A., Jr. "Gynecologic Surgery in the Aged," in Geriatrics, Vol. 24, No. 4, 172-178, April 1969.
    Physiological fitness for pelvic operative procedures cannot be determined solely from chronological age. Biological age and chronological age need to be evaluated. Evaluations should be conservative and operations performed only when they don't endanger the patient's life. 8 references

289 Brand, Patrick C., and van Keep, Pieter A. (eds.). Breast Cancer: Psycho-Social Aspects of Early Detection and Treatment. Baltimore: University Park Press, 1978.
    Includes experiences of women who have had a mastectomy and their relationship with professionals; couples and mastectomy, adjustment to mastectomy, psychiatric problems after mastectomy, delay in seeking medical advice for breast symptoms, some considerations for reconstruction of the breast, psychological problems related to the conservative treatment of breast cancer, psychological reactions of breast cancer patients to radiotherapy, factors affecting participation in cancer screening programs, and discussion of participants and non-participants in a mammography mass screening.

290 Branson, Helen K. "Sex Drive After Forty," in Sexology, Vol. 37, 67-69, March 1071.
    In the middle years, women no longer have to worry about pregnancy. At this time, they may realize their full potential for sexual expression. No references

291 Brooks, Leslie. "Erotic Transference in a 73-Year-Old Female," in Geriatric Focus, Vol. 6, No. 18, 1-3, 5-6, December 1, 1967. (A report given at a symposium on "Sex and the Aged Person" sponsored by the Boston Society for Gerontologic Psychiatry.)
    Sex drives and wishes are ageless; however, so are the defensive and adaptive mechanisms mobilized by the psyche to cope with them. A case history is presented to illustrate erotic transference in a 73-year-old female and how the doctor dealt with it.

292 Brown, Jerri J., and Hart, Darrell H. "Correlates of Females' Sexual Fantasies," in Perceptual and Motor Skills, Vol. 45, 819-825, 1977.
    University women (N=102) students between 19 and 45 years of age were studied. Data were obtained on female sexual fantasy

with relation to personality, background, and attitudinal factors to
the amount of sexual fantasies.   Instruments used included the Sixteen Personality Factor Questionnaire, the Attitude Toward Women
Scale, and the Female Sexual Fantasy Questionnaire.   Data for
analysis were provided by background variables of religion, marital
status, sexual experience, and age.   Findings were that 99 percent
of the women at least occasionally fantasize about sex and that frequency of sexual fantasy was related to liberal attitudes toward
women, anxiety, independence, sexual experience, and age.   Author
abstract modified.   17 references

293   Burdick, Daniel.   "Rehabilitation of the Breast Cancer Patient,"
      in Cancer, Vol. 36 (2, supplement), 645-648, 1975.   (This
      paper was presented at the American Cancer Society--Na-
      tional Cancer Institute National Conference on Advances in
      Cancer Management, Part I: Treatment and Rehabilitation,
      New York, N. Y., November 25-27, 1974.)
      Rehabilitation programs for breast cancer patients must con-
sider the sociopsychological, functional, vocational, and physical
needs of the patient.   Careful attention should be given to details in
the preoperative period during the operation, during the immediate
postoperative period, and in the long-term follow-up.   All members
of the medical team should work together to provide support to be
given with encouragement and hope.   3 references

294   Butler, Robert N.   "Answers to Questions: Sexual Frustration
      of Older Women," in Medical Aspects of Human Sexuality,
      Vol. 8, No. 12, 50-51, December 1974.
      An answer to a question about sexual frustration of older
women.   Many older women are sexually frustrated due to the early
death of men compared to women, social mores, loss of sexual interest by husband, or physical disability of husband.   However, now
a sense of a right to sexual satisfaction with age has come about
due to an increased sexual permissiveness in society.

295   Calderone, Mary Steichen.   "Sexual/Emotional Aspects," in
      Trager, Natalie P. (ed.), No Longer Young: The Older
      Woman in America, pp. 111-115, Part IV, The Institute of
      Gerontology of the University of Michigan and Wayne State
      University, 1975.   (Proceedings of the 26th Annual Confer-
      ence on Aging sponsored by the Institute of Gerontology in
      Ann Arbor in 1973.)
      Written by the well-known world-wide expert on human sexu-
ality, this chapter projects what sexuality will be like for women in
the 1990's.   It is an optimistic view.   3 references

296   Christenson, Cornelia V., and Gagnon, John H.   "Sexual
      Behavior in a Group of Older Women," in Journal of Geron-
      tology, Vol. 20, No. 3, 351-356, July 1965.   (This article,
      in a revised form, was presented at the annual meeting of
      the American Psychological Association, Los Angeles, CA,
      September 1964.)
      Interviews were conducted with white females (N= 241), who

were 50 years or older and who had been married.   Sexual activity
after 50 was affected by the aging process, but variation existed as
a result of marital status and type of sexual activity.   Marital coitus and masturbation were of lower frequency in women who had
frequent church attendance.   If the female desired to have orgasm
after the marriage ended, this desire was a strong factor in the decision to continue coitus.   Women had a higher orgasm capacity
with men of the same age than with men younger or older.   4 references

297   Christenson, Cornelia V. , and Johnson, Alan Blaine.   "Sexual
      Patterns in a Group of Older Never-Married Women, " in
      Journal of Geriatric Psychiatry, Vol. 1, No. 1, 80-98, 1973.
        A sample of 71 single (never-married) white women was
studied.   They were all 50 years old or older.   There was a wide
range of individual differences.   One-third of the women had little
development of sexual interests so that aging effects on these aspects
could not be studied.   Two-thirds of the women displayed varying
levels and types of sexual activity on which aging effects began at
around 55.   Never-married women have lower sexual activity than
formerly married women, but aging seems to affect the patterns of
each group about the same.   11 references

298   _____ , and _____ .   "Sexual Patterns in a Group of Older
      Single Women. " Paper presented at the Midwest Psychological
      Association Meeting, Chicago, Illinois, May 6, 1966, 4 pp.
        This report is very similar to an earlier one (Christenson
and Gagnon, Journal of Gerontology, Vol. 20, 351-356, 1965), and
was based on a similar sample or 241 "never married" women.
One-third of the women showed very little erotic responsiveness development.   The remaining two-thirds experienced low levels of
sexual behavior similar to women of the same age who formerly
married.   Aging effects on sexuality are clear by the middle of the
50's. No references

299   Cocke, W. M.   "Reconstruction of the Breast Following Radi-
      cal Mastectomy, " in Journal of the Tennessee Medical Asso-
      ciation, Vol. 68, No. 1, 15-16, January 1975.   (This was
      presented at the 159th Semi-Annual Meeting of the Middle
      Tennessee Medical Association, Nashville, Tennessee, May
      16, 1974.)
        The basic patterns or combinations of deformity following
mastectomy include: 1) infraclavicular depression, 2) axillary de-
formity, 3) loss of soft tissue over the anterior chest wall, and 4)
loss of nipple and areolar complex.   No exact guidelines exist for
women who are suitable candidates for reconstruction although the
author states that advanced age with nodal metastasis would rule
out reconstruction.   Psychological management of the patients is a
problem and several pre-operative consultations are suggested.   A
table is presented matching surgical problem with technique.   No
references

300   Cooper, Ralph L. , and Linncila, Markku. "Sexual Behavior
      in Aged, Noncycling Female Rats, " in Physiology and Be-
      havior, Vol. 18, No. 4, 573-576, 1977.
          The sexual behavior in old (19-month-old), noncycling female
rats was studied to determine if they show a decrease in sexual behavior and whether the decrease is related to the ovarian state of
the female.   Aged female rats are still able to show a lordosis
response despite disruptions of regular ovarian cyclicity.   18 references

301   Crile, George, Jr.   What Every Woman Should Know About
      the Breast Cancer Controversy.   New York: Pocket Books,
      1974.
          Provides an alternative to radical mastectomy.   Covers
topics including causes of cancer of the breast, history of the treatment of breast cancer, advantages and disadvantages of various
treatments, radiation in the treatment of breast cancer, and estrogen and breast cancer.

302   Datan, Nancy, and Rodeheaver, Dean.   "Dirty Old Women:
      The Emergence of the Sensuous Grandmother. "   Paper pre-
      sented at the Annual Convention of the American Psychologi-
      cal Association, San Francisco, California, August 26-30,
      1977.   ED 150 467.   (This abstract is also found in Educa-
      tional Gerontology, Vol. 4, No. 1, 93, 1979, under "Learn-
      ing Resources, " edited by Allen B. Moore and Joan Walter.)
          Focuses on the injustices in the socialization of women's
sexuality.   The developmental injustices are traced to a historical
concern with female sexuality, particularly the reproductive cycle.
The sexual expression in the older woman can be shaped by processes of socialization.   The authors suggest future trends which
might lead to the emergence of sensuous grandmothers.

303   Delaney, Janice; Lupton, Mary Jane; and Toth, Emily.   The
      Curse: A Cultural History of Menstruation.   New York: E.
      P. Dutton and Co. , 1977.
          A book covering physiology and psychology, myths and the-
ories, taboos, and literary references on menstruation.   The authors are very cautious concerning the use of estrogen to deal with
menopause.

304   Drellich, Marvin G.   "Sex After Hysterectomy, " in Medical
      Aspects of Human Sexuality, Vol. 1, No. 3, 62-64, Novem-
      ber 1967.
          Hysterectomy, with or without ovariectomy, need not result
in any change in sexual desire or activity.   Disturbances which occur are usually psychological effects of surgery on the genitals.   1
reference

305   Durbin, Mary Sylvan.   "Geriatric Gynecology, " in Nursing
      Clinics of North America, Vol. 3, No. 2, 257-258, June
      1968.
          Gynecologic diseases discussed include senile vaginitis,

vulvitis, perineal pruritus, uterine prolapse, and cystitis. Nursing care should focus on three principles: 1) the patient's assets should be emphasized; 2) the total patient needs to be considered, i.e., body, mind, feelings, faith, etc.; 3) the patient should be encouraged to help herself. 5 references

306   Ervin, Clinton V., Jr. "Psychologic Adjustment to Mastectomy," in Medical Aspects of Human Sexuality, Vol. 7, No. 2, 42-46, 48, 51, 53, 57, 61, 65, February 1973.
      Emotional support from the husband enables a woman to recover better from mastectomy and crises which may accompany it. No references. Commentary by J. Herbert Dietz, Jr., M.D., and Bromley S. Freeman, M.D.

307   Eschen, Caryn, and Huyck, Margaret Hellie. "Women's Experiences with Hysterectomy," in Gerontologist, Vol. 15, No. 5, Part 2, 57, 1975. (A paper given at the 28th annual meeting of the Gerontological Society, Louisville, Kentucky, October 1975.)
      Women who had experienced total hysterectomy (cervix and uterus removed, ovaries intact) were studied. A non-clinical group of 25 premenopausal, middle-class women, aged 25 through 50 was used. Attitudes toward hysterectomy, body image, and sexuality were assessed by checklists. No evidence was found of distorted body image or sexual maladjustment due to the hysterectomy. Negative images found in professional literature need modification.

308   Eskin, Bernard A. "Sex and the Gynecologic Patient," in Oaks, Wilbur W.; Melchiode, Gerald A.; and Ficher, Ilda (eds.), Sex and the Life Cycle, pp. 199-212. New York: Grune and Stratton, 1976. (A paper presented at the 35th Hahnemann Symposium, Philadelphia, PA.)
      Problems covered include contraception/sterility, increased sexual satisfaction and relief from dysfunctional hormonal pattern for the mature adult. The premenopausal patient's problems include self-examination in terms of sexual competence and potential, discomfort from increasing hormone deficiency, and prevention of premature aging. The problems of menopausal patients include sexual gratification, therapy for menopausal symptomatology, and developing self-confidence to diminish aging process effects. The role of the gynecologist in helping the patient handle these problems is described. 14 references

309   Fisher, Seymour. The Female Orgasm, pp. 25-26. New York: Basic Books, Inc., 1973.
      Includes a short section on the effects of age on a woman's sexual responsiveness.

310   Fuchs, Estelle. The Second Season: Life, Love, and Sex-- Women in the Middle Years. Garden City, NY: Doubleday, 1977.
      Concerns facts about social, cultural, and physical aspects of women in the middle years. Topics covered include sex and at-

tractiveness, roles of women, menopause, health and drugs, and divorce and widowhood.   A chapter on men and the middle years is included.

311   Glik, I., and Soferman, N.   "Gynecological Survey of Hos-
        pitalized Elderly Women," in Journal of the American Geri-
        atrics Society, Vol. 19, No. 1, 61-67, January 1971.
        A survey of 235 older women from ages 60 to over 80 showed
that the reasons for admission were: 1) postmenopausal bleeding
(117 women or 50 percent); 2) genital prolapse (78 women or 33
percent); and 3) genital tumors (40 women or 17 percent).   The patients were admitted to the Obstetrics and Gynecology Department
of a Municipal Governmental Hospital in Tel Aviv, Israel.   The patient's age in most cases was no contraindication for surgery.   If
appropriate procedures were taken, the postoperative course was no
different than in younger women.   8 references

312   Gorney, Sondra, and Cox, Claire.   "What Every Woman Over
        Forty Should Know About Sex," Chapter 3 in their How
        Women Can Achieve Fulfillment After Forty, pp. 43-69.
        New York: The Dial Press, 1973.
        Takes the position that sex over forty can be better than sex
in youth.   A number of prominent researchers are quoted.   An explanation of menopause is presented and male sexual problems are
briefly touched upon.

313   Hale-Harbaugh, Julia; Norman, Ann Duecy; Bogle, Jane; and
        Shaul, Susan.   Within Reach: Providing Family Planning
        Services to Physically Disabled Women.   Everett, WA:
        Planned Parenthood of Snohomish County, Inc., 1977.   (Re-
        view of this by Fithian, Marilyn A. in Journal of Sex Re-
        search, Vol. 14, No. 3, 213-214, August 1978.)
        Contains a section on female sexuality, reproduction function
and special consideration for contraceptive methods.   Counselors
and physicians could use this as a reference book for counseling
handicapped patients.   26-item bibliography

314   Hall, M.-Françoise, and Reinke, William A.   "Factors Influ-
        encing Contraception Continuation Rates: The Oral and the
        Intrauterine Methods," in Demography, Vol. 6, No. 3, 335-
        346, August 1969.
        The relative duration of use of oral and intrauterine contra-
ception among 12,000 women in Baltimore, Maryland.   The women
were from lower socioeconomic groups.   Records of the women,
who received their contraception through the Baltimore public services, were analyzed.   The woman's age was found to be one of the
factors influencing the probability of continuing contraception.   It
was concluded that intrinsic characteristics of each method of contraception might lead to a clinical impression favoring the oral
method.   This is true even when statistical evidence might favor
the intrauterine method.   12 references

315   Harris, Janet.   The Prime of Ms. America: The American
      Woman at Forty.   New York: G. P. Putnam's Sons, 1975.
      (Also a Signet paperback.)
         A feminist book covering the topics of role conflict, relation-
ships between mothers and daughters, active vs. passive sexuality,
marriage, work, leisure years, age barriers, and general middle-
aged renewal.   About 60 references, listed by chapter.

316   Hendricks, Shelton E.; Lehman, James R.; and Oswalt, Gay-
      lon L.   "Effects of Copulation on Reproductive Function in
      Aged Female Rats," in Physiology and Behavior, Vol. 23,
      No. 2, 267-272, August 1979.
         Old female rats in PVE (persistent vaginal estrus) were ex-
posed to different degrees of copulatory stimulation.   Observations
suggested that age-related changes in the reproductive capacity of
female rats may be due to changes in the sensitivity of ovulatory
and progestational mechanisms to hormonal and sensory influences.
21 references

317   Hite, Shere.   The Hite Report: A Nationwide Study of Female
      Sexuality, pp. 507-524.   New York: Dell Publishing Co.,
      Inc., 1976 (paperback).   New York: Macmillan Publishing
      Co., Inc., pp. 349-362 (hardcover).   London: Collier Mac-
      millan Publishers.
         Contains a section on "Older Women."   Discusses how age
may affect female sexuality.   Many women felt that sexual pleasure
had increased with age and some felt that sex was not that important to them any more.   Some of the older women were interested
in sex but had difficulty finding partners they liked.   Some older
women had lovers and some had begun to have sexual relations with
other women.   Some women enjoyed sex with younger men, but quite
a few were disappointed and bitter about their sexual experiences.
A number of women were finding new sexual experiences.

318   Hollender, Marc H.   "Hysterectomy and Feelings of Feminity,"
      in Medical Aspects of Human Sexuality, Vol. 3, No. 7, 6-
      15, July 1969.
         Hysterectomy can sometimes be experienced by a woman as
an assault on her feeling of femininity.   12 references

319   Horn, Robert E.   "Psychosexual Problems of the Middle
      Years," in Clinical Obstetrics and Gynecology, Vol. 13,
      746-755, 1970.
         Dr. Horn discusses marriage and parenthood in the middle
years and then touches upon the middle years and menopause.   Regarding the middle years and menopause, he talks about four aspects of this time: 1) there is organic decline, 2) the children
leave, 3) the parents die, and 4) menopause begins.   The psycho-
pathology of the middle years is presented through three case studies: 1) the melancholic-psychotically depressed patient, 2) the
euphoric-hypomanic patient, and 3) the suspicious-paranoid psychotic
patient.   Management of middle age is discussed in terms of psych-
tropic drugs and estrogen replacement.   13 references

320 Huyck, Margaret Hellie. "Sex and the Older Women," in
       Troll, Lillian E.; Israel, Joan; and Israel, Kenneth (eds.),
       Looking Ahead: A Woman's Guide to the Problems and Joys
       of Growing Older, pp. 43-58. Englewood Cliffs, NJ: Pren-
       tice-Hall, Inc., 1977.
         Very little research has been done on sexuality among older
women.   Reasons for this are partly because of age and partly because of gender.   Women differ from each other in many ways that
affect their sexuality.   General statements about women's sexuality
are usually not as reliable as those about men's.   There may be a
reciprocal link between sexual activity and health.   Altered patterns
of sexual activity in later years can be due to the significance of
the differences in the meanings of sexuality between women and men,
differences over historical periods, and incentives for sexual behavior.   29 references

321 Hyman, Herbert, and Barmack, Joseph E. "Sexual Behavior
       in the Human Female," in Psychological Bulletin, Vol. 51,
       No. 4, 418-432, 1954.
         This consists of two parts.   Part I consists of a discussion
and criticism of the psychological data of the Kinsey study on female sexuality.   Part II consists of a discussion of the biological
data from the Kinsey study.   Part I, 4 references; Part II, no
references

322 Kent, Saul. "Coping with Sexual Identity Crises After Mastec-
       tomy," in Geriatrics, Vol. 30, No. 10, 145-146, October
       1975.
         A woman may experience anxiety and depression after a
mastectomy and this in turn may cause her to question her value
as a sex partner.   No references

323 Kimsey, Larry R. "Sexual Expressions of Widows," (answer
       to question) in Medical Aspects of Human Sexuality, Vol. 9,
       No. 9, p. 157, September 1975.
         Although Dr. Kimsey states there aren't a great deal, if
any, figures on masturbation in widows, they probably turn to this
as a sexual release.

324 Kinsey, Alfred C., and Gebhard, Paul H. Sexual Behavior in
       the Human Female. Philadelphia: W. B. Saunders Co.,
       1953.
         No one chapter is devoted to sexuality and aging, but the
topic is interwoven throughout the book.

325 Kobosa-Munro, Lyn. "Sexuality in the Aging Woman," in
       Health and Social Work, Vol. 2, No. 4, 70-88, November
       1977.
         Menopause need not put an end to sexual activity in the aging
woman.   Families, therapists, and even the women themselves may
ignore the sexual aspect of older women.   Social workers should be
aware of the sexuality of aging women and acknowledge the continuing need for intimacy into old age.   32 notes and references

326 Koomen, W., and De Niet, R.   "Determinants of Sexual Satis-
     faction and Frequency of Sexual Intercourse of the Married
     Dutch Female," in Sociologia Neerlandica, Vol. 9, No. 1,
     10-23, 1973.
        This article is a secondary analysis of compiled material
on "Sex in Nederland" (Sexuality in the Netherlands--1969).   Data
on 635 women who stated that they were married or had previously
been married were analyzed.   Age categories formed include 21-24
years of age (9 percent), 25-34 (25 percent), 35-49 (39 percent),
50-64 (27 percent).   A young-old categorization was also set up:
21-34 (34 percent) and 35-64 (66 percent).   Sexual satisfaction and
age in the four groups showed a curvilinear relationship.   For the
older nonreligious women, there was more sexual satisfaction with
more elementary education.   The researchers found a negative relation of age to frequency of sexual intercourse.   15 references

327 Kushner, Rose.   Breast Cancer: A Personal History and an
     Investigative Report.   New York and London: Harcourt Brace
     Jovanovich, 1975.   (New York: Signet Books, 1977. paperback)
        Written as a guide for women and not designed for profes-
sionals.   It could be useful to professionals as a counseling tool.
Covers myths, early detection, surgery (freedom of choice), after
surgery (physical and psychological), chemotherapy, radiotherapy,
immunotherapy, and an excellent extensive bibliography.

328 Lief, Harold I.   "What's New in Sex Research?: Sexual Con-
     cerns of Mastectomy Patients," in Medical Aspects of Human
     Sexuality, Vol. 12, No. 1, 57-58, January 1978.
        From his personal questioning and from some recent research
by others, Dr. Lief concluded: 1) sexual concerns after mastectomy are kept secret by patients, 2) most physicians don't deal with
these concerns, and 3) the initiative for discussion must lie with
the physician as most women would not bring it up.   No references

329 McKeithen, W. Shands, Jr.   "Major Gynecologic Surgery in
     Elderly Females 65 Years of Age and Older," in American
     Journal of Obstetrics and Gynecology, Vol. 123, No. 1, 59-
     65, 1975.   (This was presented at the Thirty-Seventh Annual
     Meeting of the South Atlantic Association of Obstetricians
     and Gynecologists, Hot Springs, Virginia, February 2-5,
     1975.)
        Women aged 65 and over who had major gynecologic surgery
from 1970 to 1973 were reviewed.   There were 185 women and they
were operated on in a 350-bed community hospital.   A private staff
physician performed the operation on his/her private patient.   Vaginal operations (112), abdominal operations (73), and cancer surgery (42) were performed.   Two deaths occurred and there were 9
postoperative complications.   Major gynecologic surgery presents
no great problem for the older women if performed in a modern
hospital.   Discussion follows by Dr. Ralph A. Tillman and Dr. J.
Richard Sosnowski (pp. 63-65).   8 references

330 McMahon, Judith Wantland. "Sex, Guilt, Reported Heterosex-
     ual Behavior, and Attitudes Toward Premarital Permissive-
     ness Among Women." Unpublished doctoral dissertation,
     Washington University, St. Louis, 1972. (D. A. , Vol. 33,
     3953B, 1973.)
     Some indications were cited in support of the proposal that
sexual experience may be a more important factor than marital
status among young women as a correlate of guilt feelings and sexual attitudes. Young women today have more liberal attitudes and
less guilt about sex than twenty years ago.

331 Mannes, Marya. "Of Time and the Woman," in Psychosomat-
     ics, Vol. 9, No. 4, Two Sections, Section 2, 8-11, July-
     August 1968.
     The author states that the "single greatest factor in aging is
rigidity," that is, resistance to change and growth. She contends
that the hardest thing a woman has to bear in later life is the end
of desirability as a woman even though her capacity does not
change. Also, the psychosomatic effects of sexual rejection or the
loss of love can include symptoms of a wide range of ailments.

332 Masters, William H. , and Johnson, Virginia E. "The Aging
     Female," Chapter 15 in Human Sexual Response, pp. 223-
     247. Boston: Little, Brown and Co. , 1966.
     Consists of two main sections: 1) anatomy and physiology
and 2) clinical considerations. Included in the first section are extragenital reactions of the breasts, sex flush, myotonia, urethra
and urinary bladder, and the rectum. The external genitalia (cli-
toris, the major labia and the minor labia as well as the Bartholin's
glands) are covered. The reproductive viscera including the vagina,
the cervix, and the uterus are discussed with respect to aging. Section two includes clinical experience related to the sexual problems
of the aging woman.

333 Masters, William H. , and Johnson, Virginia E. "Sexual In-
     adequacy in the Aging Female," Chapter 13 in their Human
     Sexual Inadequacy, pp. 335-350. Boston: Little, Brown and
     Co. , 1970.
     The chapter begins with a discussion of natural variations in
the female sexual cycle which develop with the aging process.
Steroid replacement in the postmenopausal woman is covered and
is accompanied by case histories.

334 Merriam, Eve. "A Conversation Against Death," in Ms. , Vol.
     1, 80-83, September 1972. (A poem.)
     As women grow older, they want many of the same things
they had when they were young. Basically, that is what this poem
focuses on.

335 Murray, Linda. "Reconstructive Surgery: New Confidence for
     Some Patients," in Forum: The International Journal of
     Human Relations, Vol. 7, No. 8, 40-41, May 1978.
     Covers the areas of what reconstructive surgery after mas-

tectomy will and won't do for sex, what it looks like, when reconstruction takes place, how it is done, the drawbacks of reconstructive surgery, and where to find out more about it.

336 _____ . "Sex After a Mastectomy," in Forum: The Inter-
      national Journal of Human Relations, Vol. 7, No. 8, 35-39,
      May 1978.
      Loss of the breast does not have to interfere with a woman's
sex life.   Suggests ways a couple can deal with resuming sex after
a mastectomy.

337 Nadelson, Carol. "On the Psychology of the Aging Woman.
      Discussion: Mid-Life Marital Issues: Renewal or Regres-
      sion?" in Journal fo Geriatric Psychiatry, Vol. 12, No. 1,
      57-70, 1979.
      Covers engagement in a relationship, marriage and intra-
psychic process, and conflict in marriage.   19 references

338 Notman, Malkah T. , and Nadelson, Carol C.   The Woman Pa-
      tient: Medical and Psychological Interfaces.   Vol. 1. Sexual
      and Reproductive Aspects of Women's Health Care.   New
      York: Plenum Press, 1978.
      Twenty-five chapters comprise this volume concerning women.
Its focus is twofold.   First, it focuses on reproduction.   Second, it
focuses on sexuality.   Emphasis is placed on practical approaches
to women's health care in each topic area.   Topics include reproduction, fertility, contraception, abortion, gynecology, hysterectomies, mastectomies, breast disorders, problems in sexual functioning, rape and menopause.   Most of the writers are women with
distinguished credentials.   This is an important reference book for
anyone interested in sexual and reproductive aspects of women's
health care.

339 Panayiotis, Georghiou; Ellenbogen, Adrian; and Grunstein,
      Stephan.   "Major Gynecologic Surgical Procedures in the
      Aged," in Journal of the American Geriatrics Society, Vol.
      26, No. 10, 459-462, October 1978.
      A review was made of major gynecologic operations in 160
women over the age of 65 and the results were compared with results in 120 younger women from 40-55 years of age.   The majority
of complaints from the older women were about genital prolapse.
Daily discomfort and anxiety were the results of this condition.
Most of the operations on the older women were vaginal; and in
most cases of uterine prolapse, vaginal hysterectomy was the pre-
ferred procedure.   Spinal anesthesia was used; there were very few
postoperative complications.   If care is taken during the medical
evaluation, choice of anesthesia, and performance of the operation
the older patient can usually tolerate major gynecologic surgery.
9 references (author abstract modified)

340 Paulshock, Bernadine Z.   "What Every Woman Should Know
      About Hysterectomy," in Today's Health, Vol. 54, No. 2,
      23-26, February 1976.

Reasons for hysterectomies and myths about them are discussed. Three specific cases are discussed. Written for nonmedical reading. No references

341 Payne, Barbara, and Whittington, Frank. "Older Women: An Examination of Popular Stereotypes and Research Evidence," in Social Problems, Vol. 23, No. 4, 488-504, 1976.
The stereotype that an older woman is sexually uninterested and sexually inactive is shown by the authors to be dependent on a woman's access to a capable sex partner and on her sexual satisfaction history. 73 references

342 Peterson, James Alfred, and Briley, Michael P. "To Sleep Alone Or ...," Chapter 10, pp. 168-183, in Widows and Widowhood. New York: Association Press, 1977.
Covers remarriage, the single person, communal living, therapy groups, cross-age sexual relationships, and retirement communities. Several personal accounts present typical problems of widows. In order for a widow to remarry or find a new boyfriend she has to exert quite a bit of effort. Especially helpful to her in this respect would be to join a social, service, or religious organization.

343 Philipp, Elliot. "The Sexual Aspects of Ageing; The Ageing Female," in British Journal of Sexual Medicine, Vol. 2, No. 3, 28, 30, 32, June 1975.
Covers atrophic vaginitis and related problems as well as treatment for them. Intended primarily for physicians. No references

344 Reuben, David. Any Woman Can! Love and Sexual Fulfillment for the Single, Widowed, Divorced ... and Married. New York: D. McKay Co., 1971.
An easy to read, question-and-answer style. Covers problems about sex, picking a man, getting married, alternatives to marriage, and secrets of male sexuality. Perhaps the most relevant chapter is 13 entitled "Widows Have Special Problems." Menopause is briefly discussed under "More Myths of Female Sexuality."

345 Robinson, Jean M. "Community Services for Elderly Women," in Clinical Obstetrics and Gynecology, Vol. 20, No. 1, 209-213, March 1977.
Topics of discussion include aged women in the United States, implications of longer life expectancy, community services (including financial resources, senior citizen centers, volunteer programs, supportive services in the home, educational resources, and outreach and informational services), and summary. 12 references

346 Seskin, Jane, and Ziegler, Bette. Older Women: Younger Men. Garden City, NY: Anchor Press/Doubleday, 1979. (Review of this by Edward M. Brecher in The Journal of Sex Research, Vol. 16, No. 1, 88-89, February 1980.)
Prior literature is reviewed and data are presented as well

as quotations from a number of authorities. Data were collected
from men and women who responded to the following advertisement:
"Are you now or have you ever played a part in an older-woman/
younger-man relationship? If so, we would like to talk with you
for a serious book. Confidentiality guaranteed. " Patients or clients
in similar relationships might benefit by reading this book.

347   Shanor, Karen Nesbitt.   The Fantasy Files: A Study of the
       Sexual Fantasies of Contemporary Women. New York: The
       Dial Press, 1977.
       Results of a questionnaire survey on sexual fantasies are
presented here.   Fantasies were described as they occurred in
three different situations: during daydreaming, masturbation, and
sexual relations. Cf particular interest here are sections on age
and sexual fantasies and menopause and fantasy.   The questionnaire
which was used by the researcher is included in the appendix.

348   Shaul, Susan; Bogle, Jane; Hale-Harbaugh, Julia; and Norman,
       Ann Duecy.   Toward Intimacy: Family Planning and Sexuality
       Concerns of Physically Disabled Women.   New York: Human
       Sciences Press, 1978.   (Review of this by Fithian, Marilyn
       A. in Journal of Sex Research, Vol. 14, No. 3, 213, Aug-
       ust 1978.)
       This publication helps dispel some of the myths about the
sexuality of the handicapped.   The authors are handicapped persons
themselves and have included suggestions to facilitate sexuality in
people who have bowel or bladder problems.   Nurses or health
care professionals would find this a terse, handy guide for interaction with handicapped or nonhandicapped patients.   4 references

349   Silverman, Eugene M. , and Silverman, Alida G.   "Brief Com-
       munication: Presence of Spermatozoa in Cervicovaginal
       Smears from Young and Old Women, " in Experimental Aging
       Research, Vol. 5, No. 2, 155-159, 1979.
       Routine Pap smears from 1, 239 women aged 16 to 92 were
examined for spermatozoa.   The highest percentage, 25 percent,
was found in the 20-24 age group.   In the 70-79 age group, 2
percent of the smears showed the prevalence of spermatozoa; the
oldest woman with spermatozoa in her smear was 76 years old.
The persistence of spermatozoa in the lower genital tracts of women
was evaluated from smears prepared from 697 women.   These
women volunteered time of last coitus, douching practices, and
birth-control methods.   Sperm could be found in the smears up to
ten days after coitus.   Coital activity can continue until late in a
woman's life.   1 reference

350   _____ , and _____ .   "Sexual Activity in Women in the
       Later Years of Life: Coital Frequency as Measured by the
       Incidence of Spermatozoa in Pap Smears, " in Gerontologist,
       Vol. 15, No. 5, Part 2, 36, 1975. (This was a paper given
       at the 28th annual meeting of the Gerontological Society,
       Louisville, Kentucky, October 1975.)
       To study the sexual activity of the older woman, routine Pap

smears from 1, 239 women were examined for spermatozoa. The women ranged in age from 16 to 92, and the incidence of spermatozoa was determined for each age group. The greatest percentage of spermatozoa was found in the 20- to 24-year-old age group. A gradual decline occurs until age 50 when the decline is abrupt. The oldest woman with spermatozoa in her Pap smear was 76.

351 Sontag, Susan. "The Double Standard of Aging," in Saturday Review, Vol. 55, 29-38, September 23, 1972. This is reprinted in Trager, Natalie P. (ed.), No Longer Young: The Clder Woman in America, pp. 31-39, Ann Arbor, MI: University of Michigan--Wayne State University, 1975. (Proceedings of the 26th Annual Conference on Aging sponsored by the Institute of Gerontology in Ann Arbor in 1973.)
   Presents a protest against the double standard of aging in our society which looks at aging as being enhancing to a man but anathema to a woman. The losses and problems of women are magnified by this added burden. Women lose their eligibility for sex much earlier than men do. A woman who has not been taken in marriage by the time she reaches an older age is pitied.

352 Sorg, David A., and Sorg, Margaret B. "Sexual Satisfaction in Maturing Women," in Medical Aspects of Human Sexuality, Vol. 9, No. 2, 62, 64, 67-68, 70-71, 75, 78-79, February 1975.
   Experience with sex after a few years of regular coital contacts will increase a woman's potential for orgasm. If, after this time, she doesn't have an orgasm, her chances of having one decrease significantly. 9 references (author abstract modified). Commentary follows by Frederick Lemere, M. D.; Victor Kassel, M. D.; W. J. Jones, M. D.; Leah C. Schaefer, M. D.; and Eleanor B. Rodgerson, M. D.

353 Tavris, Carol. "The Sexual Lives of Women Over 60," in Ms., Vol. 6, 62-65, July 1977.
   If a person has sex for a long time and enjoys it, they can continue to enjoy it by the use of masturbation or with a partner. Several letters from older women explaining their enjoyment of sex at an older age are excerpted. Experts cited include Isadore Rubin, John Cuber, Masters and Johnson, Robert N. Butler, Myrna I. Lewis, Susan Sontag, Simone de Beauvoir, and Lydia Bragger. These experts suggest that there are many problems for those who would like to have an enjoyable sex life in old age. Lesbians also have concerns and problems similar to those of heterosexual women.

354 Trager, Natalie P. (ed.). No Longer Young: The Clder Woman in America. Ann Arbor: University of Michigan--Wayne State University Institute of Gerontology, 1975. (Proceedings of the 26th Annual Conference on Aging sponsored by the Institute of Gerontology in Ann Arbor in 1973.)
   Contains two papers which are annotated separately in this bibliography. Cne, "The Double Standard of Aging" by Susan Sontag and the other entitled "Sexual/Emotional Aspects" by Mary Steichen Calderone.

355 Troll, Lillian E.; Israel, Joan; and Israel, Kenneth (eds.).
     Looking Ahead: A Woman's Guide to the Problems and Joys
     of Growing Older. Englewood Cliffs, NJ: Prentice-Hall,
     Inc., 1977.
     Three chapters are relevant to the topic of sexuality and
aging, Chapter 3, "More Than Wrinkles," by Ruth B. Weg; Chapter
4, "Sex and the Older Woman," by Margaret Hellie Huyck; and
Chapter 18, "Sexuality, Power, and Freedom Among 'Older' Women,"
by Constantina Safilios-Rothschild. Each one is annotated separately
in this bibliography.

356 Turkel, Witold V.; Stone, Martin L.; and Napp, E. Edward.
     "A Geriatric Gynecological Survey," in Journal of the Amer-
     ican Geriatrics Society, Vol. 17, No. 2, 191-197, February
     1969.
     A greater number of geriatric gynecological problems are
appearing because of the increased life expectancy of American females. The Bird S. Coler Hospital cares for about 800 female patients (whose average age is 71.5 years). Most of the patients are
admitted for chronic disabling disorders. The gynecological care
covers two phases: 1) a routine screening examination and 2) consulting services. A medical clearance and gynecological examination are required of candidates for surgery. Patients were screened
and 3.5 percent received clearance for surgery. Surgery was successful in 57 percent of the cases. This survey was compared to
one done ten years earlier. Comparisons are made. 10 references
(authors' abstract modified)

357 Waxenberg, Sheldon E. "Psychotherapeutic and Dynamic Impli-
     cations of Recent Research on Female Sexual Functioning,"
     in Goldman, George David, and Milman, Donald S. (eds.),
     Modern Woman: Her Psychology and Sexuality, pp. 3-24.
     Springfield, IL: Charles C. Thomas, 1969.
     Presents the effects of adrenalectomy on female sexuality.
The author suggests that male and female sexual hormones are not
sex specific and androgens promote and sustain libido in both males
and females. Changes in sexual behavior in relation to vaginal
smears are given. Female sexuality is a combination of genital-
erotic drives and diffusely affectionate needs. Money's theory of
eroticism in humans is discussed. Research into the female sexual
response cycle by John Money at Johns Hopkins and Masters and
Johnson is summarized. Emphasis is placed on the fact that sexual
capacity and performance need not cease in the menopausal years.
Discussion follows by Gordon F. Derner. 36 references

358 Weg, Ruth B. "More Than Wrinkles," in Troll, Lillian E.;
     Israel, Joan; and Israel, Kenneth (eds.), Looking Ahead:
     A Woman's Guide to the Problems and Joys of Growing
     Older, pp. 22-42. Englewood Cliffs, NJ: Prentice-Hall,
     Inc., 1977.
     Because of its nontechnical nature, this chapter provides a
general overview of the physiology of the female human which can

easily be understood.   The impact of food and exercise is covered.
Factors detrimental to the female body which are covered include
periodontal disease, cigarette smoking, hypertension, stress, osteoporosis, and arthritis.   Reproduction decline in the later years is
covered with interest and capacity for sex as well as the climacteric.
Sexual dysfunction, estrogen therapy, and sexual therapy are briefly
covered.   48 references

359   "What You Should Know About the Controversy Over Breast
          Surgery," in Good Housekeeping, Vol. 178, No. 4, 177-179,
          April 1974.
          A general discussion of the differences between radical sur-
gery and conservative surgery.   Cpinions are presented from the
American Cancer Society (ACS), the National Cancer Institute (NCI),
and experts at New York City's Memorial Sloan-Kettering Cancer
Center who cannot accept the claims made for partial mastectomy.
No references

360   Woods, Nancy Fugate.   "Psychologic Aspects of Breast Can-
          cer: Review of the Literature," in Journal of Obstetric,
          Gynecologic and Neonatal Nursing, Vol. 4, No. 5, 15-22,
          September-October 1975.
          This eight-page article is a review of nursing and medical
literature on the psychological aspects of breast cancer.   Topics
covered include antecedent psychological factors affecting breast
cancer, women's attitudes toward it, the hospital experience, rehabilitation, and professional intervention.   A discussion follows
of the psychological effects of breast cancer and breast cancer
therapies.   Future research suggestions are presented.   Some 33
references are listed.

361   _____, and Earp, Jo Anne L.   "Women with Cured Breast
          Cancer: A Study of Mastectomy Patients in North Carolina,"
          in Nursing Research, Vol. 27, No. 5, 279-285, September-
          October 1978.
          This was a study of 49 postmastectomy patients in North
Carolina four years after surgery.   The women did not feel they
had been adequately prepared for the postoperative experiences.
These women had persisting physical complications, didn't know of
Reach to Recovery (a supportive organization), and only examined
their remaining breast occasionally.   Sexual adjustment was related
to the quality and importance of the marital-sexual relationship.
20 references

362 Bolton, William. "That's a Good Question--Male Change of
    Life?" in Today's Health, Vol. 44, No. 2, 13, February
    1966.
        Change of life in men has never received formal recognition
by the medical profession. Some gonadal changes occur, but they
do not have a parallel relationship with the female change. Men
may have psychological reactions, however, to decreased sexual
activity. Circulation changes may result from the psychological reactions.

363 Bowskill, Derek, and Linacre, Anthea. The Male Menopause.
    Los Angeles: Brooke House Publishers, 1977.
        A general presentation given in three parts: 1) the meno-
pause syndrome, 2) the phenomena, and 3) the remedy.

364 Browning, William J. "Male Climacteric and Impotence:
    Value of Gonadal Stimulation," in International Record of
    Medicine, Vol. 173, 690-694, November 1960.
        Because men live longer now, there exists a need for geri-
atric therapy for older men. Gradual decline of gonadal endocrine
secretion can lead to the male climacteric. Loss of potency, libido,
and nervous and circulatory problems are seen in the clinic. Chorionic gonadotropin (fortified) produces a high level of gonadal stimulation and can be used to treat the male climacteric. Anginal and
other symptoms of male senility can be treated in the same way.
22 references

365 Butler, Robert N. "Answers to Questions: Sexuality of Aging
    Men," in Medical Aspects of Human Sexuality, Vol. 9, No.
    8, 77-78, August 1975.
        An answer to a question about impotence suggesting that im-
potence need not be a result of aging in men. Causes of impotence
in aging men include tranquilizers, anti-hypertensives, and chronic
alcoholism.

366 Cilento, Raphael. Sex Forever: The Key to Male Sexual
    Longevity. Chicago: Playboy Press, 1977.
        A guide for men interested in keeping and developing their
sexual abilities.

367 Daut, R. V. So You're Going to Have a Prostatectomy.
    Norwich, NY: Eaton Laboratories, 1974.

This is a manual which can be given to men who are undergoing a prostatectomy to instruct them about basic anatomy of the male pelvis, what the operation is all about in layman's terms, and what to do after the operation. A pronouncing glossary is provided at the end of the manual. No references

368 Edwards, Allan E., and Husted, June R. "Penile Sensitivity, Age, and Sexual Behavior," in Journal of Clinical Psychology, Vol. 32, No. 3, 697-700, July 1976.
    Eighteen men, from 19 years of age to 58 years of age, kept a log of sexual behavior for four weeks. These men then had vibrotactile thresholds measured on the toe, finger, flaccid and erect penis. Data were adjusted for three psychological variables, level of General Sensation Seeking, Defensiveness, and Social Introversion. Sensory threshold at penis was correlated negative .57 with the number of sex acts (coitus) and .49 with age. Age-related decrease in penile sensitivity may explain the decline of sexual activity with age. 10 references

369 Felstein, Ivor. "The Sexual Aspects of Ageing; The Ageing Male," in British Journal of Sexual Medicine, Vol. 2, No. 3, 23-28, June 1975.
    There is no real evidence that Vitamin E can be an anti-impotence agent or aphrodisiac for the aging male. Impotence can result from diabetes mellitus in the male. This state, however, can be biochemically controlled. Levodopa therapy can restore libido and the ability to express sexual needs. Ginseng (the Panax herbal root) has been claimed to improve both the cerebral and sexual functioning in aging men and women. At no time does sexual interest or activity have to end for the aging male. Physical illness can limit sexual activity as well as marital and psychological difficulties. Administration of replacement hormones may improve potency or restore libido. The oral preparation of testosterone, fluoxymesterone, is recommended. No references

370 Ferber, Andrew S.; Tietze, Christopher; and Lewit, Sarah. "Men with Vasectomies: A Study of Medical, Sexual, and Psychosocial Changes," in Psychosomatic Medicine, Vol. 29, No. 4, 354-366, 1967.
    Questionnaires were filled out by 73 men who had undergone vasectomies. Summary tables of these responses are given. Topics covered by the questions included outcome of the operation, motivational factors, the operation per se, and personal characteristics. Outcome analysis covered physical health both preoperatively and postoperatively, factors of psychosocial adjustment, such as marital, community, and job relationships, as well as concern with children. In addition, satisfaction with the outcome of the operation and social behavior with respect to the operation were analyzed. The respondent also evaluated his wife's attitude, condition, and behavior for most of the questions. There is discussion of postoperative sperm tests and the medical aspects of the vasectomy. 14 references; 11 bibliography citations (author's abstract modified)

371   Finkle, Alex Louis. "Emotional Quality and Physical Quantity
      of Sexual Activity in Aging Males," in Journal of Geriatric
      Psychiatry, Vol. 6, No. 1, 70-79, 1973.
      A man can retain sexual activity into old age, but men with
low sex drives will rarely have a vigorous sex life in later years.
A willing, cooperative partner is the most important factor in continuing sexual activity into advancing years. Many factors such as
socioeconomic, religious, and sexual experience will influence the
search for and activity with a sexual partner. Most impotence is
psychogenic in origin and can be treated best by encouragement by
the physician. Individual psychotherapy, encounter sessions led by
physicians, or a Masters and Johnson therapeutic format can be
used to treat impotence caused by complex emotional problems. 27
references (author summary modified)

372   _____. "Psychosexual Problems of Aging Males: Urolo-
      gists' Viewpoint," in Urology, Vol. 13, No. 1, 39-44, Janu-
      ary 1979.
      Most sexual impotence is psychogenic in origin. Most pa-
tients will respond to simple encouragement and support and may
not need sophisticated psychology. The physician should identify
key points in the patient's medical history in order to diagnose
psychogenic impotency. The author describes the diagnostic approach. According to the author, most patients resumed sexual
intercourse within three visits. 29 references

373   _____. "Sex After Prostatectomy," in Medical Aspects of
      Human Sexuality, Vol. 2, No. 3, 40-41, March 1968.
      A general article on the topic suggesting that most patients
can retain potency after prostatectomy. 11 references

374   _____. "Sexual Psychodynamics of Aging: Urologic Per-
      spectives," in Journal of the American Geriatrics Society,
      Vol. 25, No. 9, 393-395, September 1977. (This was pre-
      sented at the 34th Annual Meeting of the American Geriatrics
      Society, Fairmont Hotel, San Francisco, CA, April 13-14,
      1977.)
      The urologist must be able to recognize the many factors
which influence sexual function of males. The urologist must also
know the difference between psychogenic and organic causes of impotence. Emotional support and attentive listening can be used at
weekly sessions to treat impotence in short amount of time. Different patients may require different approaches. 32 references
(author abstract modified)

375   _____, and Finkle, Paul S. "How Counseling May Solve
      Sexual Problems of Aging Men," in Geriatrics, Vol. 32, No.
      11, 84-89, November 1977. (Adapted from a presentation at
      the annual meeting of the Western Section, American Urologi-
      cal Association, San Francisco, March 1977.)
      Most aging persons have active sexual interests. What is
needed is a socially sanctioned situation and a willing partner. When
patients come to physicians with impotence problems, the physicians

should listen intently with a nonjudgmental attitude.   Androgens have
produced some good results in treating impotence; however, they
may also provoke prostatic cancer.   Some investigators refer patients with impotence to urologists because they don't believe in
administering male hormones.   Since most sexual problems of aging
men are psychogenic, it is important for the urologist to distinguish
them from organic problems.   Encouragement and supportive attitude can help rebuild self-esteem which will help restore potency
even if organic disease is present.   34 references

376 _____, and Moyers, Thomas G.   "Sexual Potency in Aging
        Males: IV.   Status of Private Patients Before and After
        Prostatectomy, " in Journal of Urology, Vol. 84, No. 1,
        152-157, July 1960.   (Abstract in Journal of the American
        Geriatrics Society, Vol. 9, 80, January 1961.)
        A number of types of prostatectomies were performed on 101
private urological patients.   After the operation only 50 percent were
sexually potent.   Potency was retained by 70 percent of the men,
independent of the operative route which was taken.   Reasons for
psychogenic impotence are presented.   It must be emphasized that
the physician's attitude toward the patient can greatly influence potency.   18 references (author summary modified)

377 Fisher, Charles.   "Dreaming and Sexuality, " in Loewenstein,
        Rudolph; Newman, Lottie M. ; Schur, Max; and Solnit, Al-
        bert J. (eds.), Psychoanalysis--A General Psychology, pp.
        537-569.   New York: International Universities Press, 1966.
        (This paper is a modified version of the Abraham A. Brill
        Memorial Lecture given before the New York Psychoanalytic
        Society on November 23, 1965.)
        Presents some new experimental findings which have implica-
tions for the problem of somatic sources of instinctual drives.   In
addition, the physiological, neuro-physiological, and biochemical
correlates of drive activation are related to dreaming.   Includes a
section on the erection cycle in men over 70.   6 footnotes; 30-item
bibliography

378 _____; Gross, Joseph; and Zuch, Joseph.   "Cycle of Penile
        Erection Synchronous with Dreaming (REM) Sleep, " in Ar-
        chives of General Psychiatry, Vol. 12, 29-45, January 1965.
        (A portion of this paper was read before the New York Psy-
        choanalytic Society, March 17, 1964.)
        A nocturnal cycle of penile erections occurs in males.   The
episodes of erection occur during rapid eye movement periods
(REMP).   Seventeen men were studied for 27 nights.   In 95 percent
of 86 REMPs, full or partial erection was observed.   There is a
long discussion of the relationship of the extensive REMP erections
to dream content and dreaming and the influence of psychological
and/or physiological factors.   35 references

379 Frank, Stanley.   The Sexually Active Man Past Forty.   New
        York: Macmillan Co. , 1968.
        Contains chapters on making a living vs. making a life, the

climacteric, the great taboo, impotence, female sexuality, the arts of love, and mutual seduction.   164 citations in the bibliography

380   Freeman, Joseph T.   "Sexual Capacities in the Aging Male,"
      in Geriatrics, Vol. 16, No. 1, 37-43, January 1961.
         Although sexual activity and interests decline with age, the
aging male has sexual desires and can express them through sexual
activity.   This activity varies widely depending on the individual,
the convenience, and the combined experience of both partners.   11
references

381   Giambra, Leonard M.   "Daydreaming from Late Adolescence
      to Old Age: A Replication," in Gerontologist, Vol. 15, No.
      5, Part 2, 71, 1975.   (A paper given at the 28th annual
      meeting of the Gerontological Society, Louisville, Kentucky,
      October 1975.)
         Retrospective information on daydreaming and related mental
activity was obtained on a replication sample of men.   The sample
consisted of 200 males aged 17 through 91 years of age.   At every
age, problem-solving daydreams were predominant; but sexual daydreams predominated in the youngest males.

382   _____, and Martin, Clyde E.   "Sexual Daydreams and
      Quantitative Aspects of Sexual Activity: Some Relations for
      Males Across Adulthood," in Archives of Sexual Behavior,
      Vol. 6, No. 6, 497-505, November 1977.
         Frequency and intensity of sexual daydreams decreases with
increasing age.   Sexual daydreams have disappeared after age 65.
12 references

383   Goldzieher, Max, and Goldzieher, Joseph W.   "The Male
      Climacteric and the Post-Climacteric States," in Geriatrics,
      Vol. 8, 1-10, 1953.
         The evidence of a male climacteric seems to be the satis-
factory response to testosterone.   Progressive hormonal deficiency
in middle-aged and elderly males is presented.   The metabolism
and circulation of testosterone is decreased and there may be, sec-
ondarily, sexual effects.   Urinary ketosteroids are low in the male
during climacteric.   This level goes even lower in the post-climac-
teric.   14 references

384   Heller, Carl G., and Myers, Gordon B.   "Male Climacteric:
      Its Symptomatology, Diagnosis and Treatment; Use of Thera-
      peutic Test with Testosterone Propionate (Androgen) and
      Testicular Biopsies in Delineating Male Climacteric from
      Psychoneurosis and Psychogenic Impotence," in Journal of
      the American Medical Association, Vol. 126, No. 8, 472-
      477, October 21, 1944.   (This was read in part at the annual
      meeting of the American Society for Clinical Investigation,
      Atlantic City, N.J., May 10, 1942.)
         An elevation in gonadotropic hormone excretion helped these
researchers study the male climacteric in 23 men.   The amount of
gonadotropic hormone found was quantitatively similar to that found

in castrates.   Eight cases were given biopsies and testicular atrophy
and degeneration was found.   Twenty cases responded to androgen
therapy.   Gonadotropic assays can help determine psychogenic impotence from the climacteric.   The assay, if high in the hormone,
indicates male climacteric; and a low assay indicates psychogenic
impotence.   Intramuscular injections of testosterone and testosterone
pellet implantation obtained satisfactory results.   Methyltestosterone
administered orally or sublingually did not yield satisfactory results.
Male climacteric affects a very small amount of older men.   13
references

385   Hsu, Cheng-Jen, and Chen, Pao-Hwei.   "Sexual Activities in
       Older Males: I.   Observation on the Patients of Department
       of Internal Medicine, N. T. U. H. , " in Journal of the Formosa
       Medical Association, Vol. 64, No. 3, 129-133, March 28,
       1965.
       A personal interview was used to record the sexual activity
of 127 men who were over 60 years of age.   Older men have a
gradual decline in sexual activity and strength of sexual drive.   Rea-
sonably good health and healthy partners are what is needed in order
to continue sexual activity into old age.   6 references

386   Hursch, Carolyn J. ; Karacan, Ismet; and Williams, Robert L.
       "Some Characteristics of Nocturnal Penile Tumescence in
       Early Middle-Aged Males, " in Comprehensive Psychiatry,
       Vol. 13, No. 6, 539-548, November/December 1972.
       Characteristics of nocturnal penile tumescence (NPT) are
described for a group of males aged 30-39 years.   Neural activity
which is generally present during REM sleep is not always a condition for nocturnal penile tumescence.   Penile tumescence may
have more than one function for the human male.   More research
is needed to determine what functions these episodes of nocturnal
penile tumescence serve.   25 references (author's summary modified)

387   Irwin, Theodore.   Male "Menopause": Crisis in the Middle
       Years.   New York: Public Affairs Pamphlet No. 526, 1975.
       There is still much debate on whether a male menopause
exists.   The psychosocial stages of manhood are presented as well
as the physical, psychological and social pressures which bring on
the male mid-life crisis.   Sexual trouble may occur at this time.
Guidelines for coping with the "climacteric" syndrome are listed.

388   Jackson, Don D.   "Forbidden Ground: Book Review of Human
       Sexual Response, " in Medical Opinion and Review, Vol. 2,
       No. 1, 32-33, October 1966.
       Suggests that physicians cannot accurately advise postcoronary
patients on whether or not intercourse is permissible because very
little relevant information is available on the subject.   Reports that
myths about sexuality are dispelled by the book, i. e. , that male
genital size is not related to sexual adequacy and age does not necessarily render a man impotent.

389 Janczewski, Zygmunt; Bablok, Leszek; and Czaplicki, Maciej.
     "Premature Male Climacteric, " in Polish Endocrinology, Vol.
     18, No. 1-2, 33-39, 1967.
         Twenty-four of fifty-eight male patients with sexual disturb-
ances exhibited a severe form of premature male climacteric.   The
patients ranged in age from 40-50.   A decrease in testicular endocrine and spermiogenetic activity was seen in these 24 patients with
sexual disturbances upon examination in the laboratory.   12 references

390 Kahn, Edwin.   "The Sleep and Cther Characteristics of the
     Aged. "   Ann Arbor, MI: University Microfilms, 1968.
     (D. A. , Vol. 29, 2221-B, 1968.)   Unpublished doctoral disser-
     tation, Yeshiva University, 1968.
         The subjects for study were 21 paid, healthy men, aged 71
to 96 years.   Studies were done on each from four to six nights
each.   Every night, sleep EEG recordings were made; and on half
of the nights, penile erection was measured with a mercury strain
gauge.   The function of rapid eye movement (REM) sleep is unclear.
In healthy males, the amount of REM sleep appears to be related
to the physical condition of the male.

391 _____, and Fisher, Charles.   "REM Sleep and Sexuality in
     the Aged, " in Journal of Geriatric Psychiatry, Vol. 2, No.
     2, 181-191, Spring 1969.   (This was presented at the Seventh
     Annual Scientific Meeting of the Boston Society for Geron-
     tologic Psychiatry, September 23, 1967.)
         Male subjects (N=18), ranging in age from 71 to 96 years,
were studied for two or three nights.   In order to measure penile
erection, a mercury strain gauge was used.   Full or moderate
erections were achieved in 45 percent of REM periods, and slight
or no erection was achieved in 55 percent of the REM periods.
Reduced erections were not found in all of the older males.   Erections similar to young males were found in five of the twelve males
aged 71 to 80.   The three oldest males, aged 87, 95 and 96, had
some REM erection; but it was one-third of full circumference.
Based on the dreams of several subjects, it is apparent that sexual
interest persists into very old age.   Discussion follows (pp. 181-191)
by Dr. Marcel Heiman, Dr. Elias Savitsky, Dr. Alvin I. Goldfarb,
Dr. Sidney Levin, and Dr. David Blau.   36 references

392 _____, and _____.   "Dream Recall and Erections in the
     Healthy Aged, " in Psychophysiology, Vol. 4, No. 3, 393-394,
     January 1968.
         A study of 13 healthy male subjects from 70 to 87 years of
age was made.   Two to eleven REM period awakenings (78 total)
were made during 20 subject-nights.   Dream recall existed in 32
instances or 41 percent of the time.   Young adult recall was previously reported by the same researchers to be 87 percent.   In
another study, REM sleep erections in the aged were measured.
Three of the oldest subjects (87, 95 and 96 years of age) were
measured for eight measurement nights.   Only the 95-year-old had
no erection.

393 _____, and _____. "The Sleep Characteristics of the
    Normal Aged Male," in Journal of Nervous and Mental Dis-
    ease, Vol. 148, No. 5, 477-494, 1969.
    This research was based in part on a section of a disserta-
tion which was submitted by Dr. Edwin Kahn to the Department of
Psychology of Yeshiva University for the degree of Doctor of Philosophy. The normal elderly male was studied. Sixteen volunteers
from 71 to 95 years of age slept in the laboratory at least two or three
base line nights each. Increased sleep disturbance was found between
the ages of 71 and 95 years. REM sleep did not appear markedly
reduced until late old age. The latency period from the beginning
of sleep to the first REM period in the elderly seemed shortened.
There were more frequent interruptions of REM periods by stretches
of stage 2 sleep in the older volunteers. 62 references

394 _____, and _____. "Some Correlates of Rapid Eye
    Movement Sleep in the Normal Aged Male," in Journal of
    Nervous and Mental Diseases, Vol. 148, No. 5, 495-505,
    1969.
    This research sought to study the effects of cognitive and
drive functioning on amounts of REM sleep in the aged. Sixteen
normal male subjects served as sources of sleep data. The men
ranged in age from 71 to 95 years. Findings indicate a general
physiological decline with age. This decline affects the amount of
REM sleep, erection, and cognition as well as other aspects of
functioning. These declines are most likely due to deterioration of
the central nervous system. 53 references

395 Kales, Joyce D., and Kales, Anthony. "Aging and Sleep," in
    Goldman, Ralph, and Rockstein, Morris (eds.), The Physi-
    ology and Pathology of Human Aging, pp. 187-202. New
    York: Academic Press, Inc., 1975.
    Contains a small section on sexuality in the aging. Speci-
fically, the section discusses the relation between male penile erections and rapid eye movement (REM) sleep as a way of determining
frequency and amount of nocturnal erection or of assessing sexual
capacity. 28 references

396 Karacan, Ismet. "The Developmental Aspects and the Effect
    of Certain Clinical Conditions upon Penile Erection During
    Sleep," in Excerpta Medica International Congress Series
    No. 150, pp. 2356-2359, Proceedings of the Fourth World
    Congress of Psychiatry, Madrid, September 5-11, 1966.
    Studies of monkeys and humans have shown that each group
had special kinds of erections. Questions raised included 1) Is
sleep erection somehow related to psychosexual development? 2) Is
the sleep erection cycle a manifestation of sexual drives? 3) Are
any adaptive functions fulfilled by the erection cycle? The author
stresses the importance of developing a theory to explain the function of REM sleep and erection cycle. The erection cycle is re-
sistant to change. 10 references

397 _____; Goodenough, D. R.; Shapiro, A.; and Starker,
    Steven. "Erection Cycle During Sleep in Relation to Dream

Anxiety," in Archives of General Psychiatry, Vol. 15, 183-
189, August 1966. (This study is basically an abstraction
from a dissertation submitted by Dr. Karacan as partial fulfillment of the requirements for the degree of Doctor of Medical Science, May 1965, State University of New York, Down-
state Medical Center, Department of Psychiatry, Brooklyn,
NY.)
Erection cycles during sleep as well as the relationship between rapid eye movement (REM) sleep erection to report of REM
anxiety. Adult male volunteers ($\underline{N}$=16) slept in the laboratory once
a week for six nights. The volunteers were paid and slept during
their normal sleep period. Measurements which were recorded included eye movements, electroencephalograms, and measurements
of penile erection cycles through the sleep period. Erections accompanied 80 percent of REM periods. During each REM period,
subjects were awakened to report on dream anxiety. REM sleep
did not accompany 19 erections (three types). REM awakening reports on the dreams with high anxiety had an irregular or no erection ($\underline{p}$<0. 01). 34 references (author's summary modified)

398 _____ ; Hursch, Carolyn J.; and Williams, Robert L. "Some
       Characteristics of Nocturnal Penile Tumescence in Elderly
       Males," in Journal of Gerontology, Vol. 27, No. 1, 39-45,
       1972.
       The characteristics of nocturnal penile tumescence are de-
scribed in detail for eleven older males aged 60 to 69 years.
Neural activity which occurs during REM sleep is not a necessary
condition for nocturnal penile tumescence to occur. Tumescence is
likely to serve more than one function for an organism. 17 references

399 _____ ; Salis, Patricia J.; Thornby, John I.; and Williams,
       Robert L. "The Ontogeny of Nocturnal Penile Tumescence,"
       in Waking and Sleeping, Vol. 1, 27-44, 1976.
       A brief review of the history of research on nocturnal penile
tumescence. Also presented are the efforts to develop a valid and
reliable transducer to monitor nocturnal penile tumescence (NPT).
NPT data from boys and men aged 3 to 79 were used to discuss
ontogenetic trends. NPT occurs in all healthy males and is greatly
affected by age. The authors, based on the data presented, suggest
a relationship between NPT, sexual capacity and function, and psy-
cho-sexual development. More knowledge of NPT may help researchers study and treat impotent men. 46 references

400 _____ ; Williams, Robert L.; Thornby, John I.; and Salis,
       Patricia J. "Sleep-related Penile Tumescence as a Function
       of Age," in American Journal of Psychiatry, Vol. 132, No.
       9, 932-937, 1975. (A revised version of a paper which was
       presented at the 127th annual meeting of the American Psy-
       chiatric Association, Detroit, Michigan, May 6-10, 1974.)
       A study of nocturnal penile tumescence (NPT) was conducted
on 125 healthy males aged 3 to 79. EEG recordings were used to
provide normative data. The researchers sought to determine how
general NPT is, the range of its characteristics, and the extent to

which it is related to man's sexual function. NPT occurs regularly
in healthy males and is affected by age. NPT is related to psychosexual development and needs more research. It can be a useful
way of distinguishing organic impotence from psychogenic impotence.
28 references

401 Kinsey, Alfred C.; Pomeroy, Wardell B.; and Martin, Clyde
     E. "Age and Sexual Outlet," Chapter 7 in their Sexual Be-
     havior in the Human Male, pp. 218-262. Philadelphia: W.
     B. Saunders Co., 1948.
     Graphs and statistics are used to show the effects of aging
on male sexuality. Discussion on masturbation, petting to climax,
impotence, homosexual activity, and marital intercourse is related
to the aging male.

402 Larsson, Knut. "Age Differences in the Diurnal Periodicity
     of Male Sexual Behavior," in Gerontologia, Vol. 2, No. 2,
     64-72, 1958.
     Two groups of male rats were studied to determine if there
existed a diurnal change of sexual activity. A group of 38 rats
ranged in age from 5-7 months and another group ranged in age
from 14-16 months. Performance during the active phase showed
no difference. During the passive phase, 48.8 percent of older
animals failed to ejaculate; while only 10.8 percent of young rats
failed to ejaculate. This difference was attributed to central nervous system changes with age. These changes make more intense
the inhibitory stimuli whether unconditioned or conditioned. Highest
sexual activity exists during darkness. The summary is given in
English, German, and French. 16 references (author's summary
modified)

403 _____. "Sexual Activity in Senile Male Rats," in Journal
     of Gerontology, Vol. 13, No. 2, 136-139, April 1958.
     The effects of age on 16 male rats were studied at age 10
months and later at age 22 months. Number of ejaculations and
copulations per hour went down. The number of intromissions before ejaculation also went down. Refractory periods, however, increased. No relationship of any significance was found between
sexual activity and respiratory disease in senile rats. 10 references (author's summary modified)

404 _____, and Essberg, Leif. "Effect of Age on the Sexual
     Behaviour of the Male Rat," in Gerontologia, Vol. 6, 133-
     143, 1962.
     Four different age groups, 103-114, 125-164, 450-510, and
573-651 days, were used to study mating behavior in male rats.
The rats were mated until they were exhausted (a specified cri-
terion). Older rats were most resistent to exhaustion and had more
ejaculations than the younger ones. Intromissions before ejaculation
were highest in the younger rats and went down with age. Response
latencies went down to the age group of 450-510 days but were prolonged in the oldest group. Young rats copulated with maximum
speed. Rats in the two oldest groups responded by minimal re-

sponse latencies in the presence of effects from one or two series
of copulations. Old age may have a heightened threshold for copu-
lation response. Summary is in English, German, and French. 2
references (author's summary modified)

405   Laury, Gabriel V. "Sex in Men over Forty," in Medical As-
        pects of Human Sexuality, Vol. 14, No. 2, 65-68, 71,
        February 1980.
        A middle-aged man can bring many assets to a sexual rela-
tionship. Several case studies are presented. The role of the
physician in dealing with the sexually dysfunctional middle-age man
is covered. Commentary follows by Kathleen M. Mogul, M. D. ,
Larry M. Davis, M. D. , Stanley H. Cath, M. D. , and Susan G.
Krinsky, Ed. D.

406   McCary, James Leslie. "Sexual Advantages of Middle-Aged
        Men," in Medical Aspects of Human Sexuality, Vol. 7, No.
        12, 138-160, December 1973.
        Accurate information about sexual potentials as well as
healthy attitudes can help a middle-aged man cope with the physical
changes which are the result of aging. 11 references. Commentaries by Melvin Prosen, M. D. , and Silas B. Coley, Jr. , M. D.

407   McGavack, Thomas Hodge. "The Male Climacterium," in
        Journal of the American Geriatrics Society, Vol. 3, No. 9,
        639-655, September 1955. (This was presented at the Grad-
        uate Symposium on Geriatric Medicine given by the American
        Geriatrics Society in New York City, November 12 and 13,
        1954.)
        The male climacteric (presumed present when no single sign,
laboratory finding, or pathognomonic symptom is found) can be
treated by the careful and appropriate use of androgens. 40 references

408   Madorsky, Martin; Drylie, David M. ; Finlayson, Birdwell, "Ef-
        fect of Benign Prostatic Hypertrophy on Sexual Behavior," in
        Medical Aspects of Human Sexuality, Vol. 10, No. 2, 8-11, 15-
        16, 21-22, February 1976.
        The evaluation of potency after surgery is more difficult because
of decreased libido in older men. It is not clear whether there is a
cause-and-effect relationship between benign prostatic hyperplasia and
decreased sexual activity. In the article is included a short discussion
of sexual behavior in elderly men as well as sections on symptoms of
benign prostatic hyperplasia, types of corrective surgery, sexual impotence, sexual behavior after surgery, physiology of erections, treatment of impotence, and penile prostheses. 26 references

409   Masters, William H. , and Johnson, Virginia E. "The Aging
        Male," Chapter 16 in Human Sexual Response, pp. 248-270.
        Boston: Little, Brown and Co. , 1966.
        Consists of two main sections: 1) anatomy and physiology
and 2) clinical considerations. Included in the first section are
extragenital reactions of the breasts, the sex flush, myotonia, and

the rectum.   The external genitalia including the penis, the scrotum,
and the testes are covered.   Ejaculation is also covered.   Section
two includes clinical considerations.   Factors in male sexual involu-
tion include the following: 1) monotony in sexual relationship, 2)
male concern with economic pursuit, 3) mental or physical fatigue,
4) overindulgence in food and drink, 5) physical and mental infirmi-
ties, and 6) fear of failure.

410 _____, and _____.   "Sexual Inadequacy in the Aging Male, "
      Chapter 12 in their, Human Sexual Inadequacy, pp. 316-334.
      Boston: Little, Brown and Co. , 1970.
      Begins by discussing a number of specific physiological
changes with age in the male cycle of sexual response.   Continues
with the effects of aging on male ejaculatory demand, male sex-
steroid replacement and erectile response in the aging male (including sexual dysfunction in the aging male along with composite
case studies).   Finally, statistical considerations of the aging male
and female populations are presented.

411 Merriam, Sharan Ballard.   "Coping with Male Mid-Life: A
      Systematic Analysis Using Literature as a Data Source, "
      Unpublished doctoral dissertation from Rutgers University,
      1978.   (A shorter version of this was presented at the Adult
      Education Research Conference, San Antonio, Texas, April 7,
      1978.)   (D. A. , Vol. 39, No. 5, 2690 A, 1979.)
      Middle-aged men desire to remain youthful and attempt ego
rejuvenation through two ways: 1) the mentor relationship and 2)
through sexual activity.   Sexual activity is a hedge on aging.

412 Norcross, K.   "The Male Climacteric. "   Paper presented at
      Good Hope Hospital Post-Graduate Medical Centre, Sutton
      Goldfield, April 1973.
      A discussion of the male climacteric under three headings:
1) a great reduction of testosterone (an androgen) production in the
older man, 2) a gradual reduction in sexual vigor over a period of
years, and 3) secondary matters which occur in response to 1 and
2.   The use of testosterone replacement for aging males does not
have much clinical support.   6 references besides books quoted

413 Nyström, Anton.   "Impotence in Young and Sexual Vigor in
      Old Men, " in Journal of Sexology and Psychoanalysis, Vol. 1,
      No. 2, 173-179, March 1923.   (Translated for Zeitschrift f.
      Sexualwissenschaft, October 1922.)
      A very old and somewhat amusing article.   It is amusing be-
cause of some of the false statements about sexuality which are made.
The author claims that excess sexual activity can lead to impotence
but then goes on to discuss older men having intercourse two or
three times every day and who live to a ripe old age.   The author
states that old men can possess strong sexual powers, can love
passionately and can father children.   Sexual desire can be an indi-
cator of a man's health.   A number of men who continued to have
sex into old age are named.   No references

414   Pearlman, Carl K.   "Frequency of Intercourse in Males at Dif-
        ferent Ages," in Medical Aspects of Human Sexuality, Vol. 6,
        No. 11, 92-113, November 1972.
              Based on a study of 2,801 patients "normal frequency" of sex-
        ual intercourse may be quite different depending on age and marital
        status.   The sex life of a person is an important part of the overall
        adjustment to old age.   9 references

415   Pearson, Manuel M.   "Middle-Aged Male Crises," in Medical
        Aspects of Human Sexuality, Vol. 2, No. 8, 6-7, 10-13, Aug-
        ust 1968.
              What is usually thought to be middle-aged male crisis can
        actually be an atypical depression brought about by declining sexual
        and physical powers.   Proper therapy can be instituted and a good
        prognosis can be offered.   Several treatment modalities might be
        used including anti-depressant drugs, electroshock therapy, psycho-
        therapy, or combinations of them.   15 references

416   Pease, Ruth A.   "Female Professional Students and Sexuality
        in the Aging Male," in Gerontologist, Vol. 14, 153-157, April
        1974.
              Elderly male patients may make covert or overt sexual ad-
        vances to female professional students.   Three examples involving
        nursing students are presented.   Stereotypic thinking of the young
        about sexual needs of old men is discussed.   There is a review of
        the literature on aging male sexuality.   Certain helping teaching strat-
        egies are outlined.   There are suggestions made for curriculum to be
        used in professional schools such as social work, nursing, psychol-
        ogy, and medicine.   8 references

417   "REM Sleep and the Libido in Elderly Males," in Geriatric Fo-
        cus, Vol. 7, No. 1, 1-3, January 1968.
              Report of a study conducted at the Sleep Laboratory of the
        Mount Sinai Hospital in New York by Dr. Charles Fisher.   The study
        was reported by Edwin Kahn at a symposium entitled "Sex and the
        Aged Person" sponsored by the Boston Society for Gerontologic Psy-
        chiatry.   Twenty-one paid volunteers from ages 71-96 participated in
        the study.   The mean age of the participants was 80.5 years.   It was
        found that there exists a high incidence of sexual activity other than
        intercourse which led to orgasm in the aged.   Other results included:
        1) a declination of REM tumescence with age, 2) a statistical correla-
        tion between age and proportion of full erection, 3) there is great in-
        dividual variation in erection of some subjects past the age of 70, 4)
        erection doesn't cease entirely after 85 though it may diminish a bit.
        Sexual wishes and complexes of early life can continue into old age.

418   Research Group of Gerontology.   "Preliminary Report of the Ger-
        ontological Sexological Research Group."   Unpublished paper.
        Copenhagen, Denmark, October 1975.
              A study done at the University of Copenhagen on nine age
        groups of men.   It is a preliminary report with very little discussion
        of the results.   The 25-item (plus optional short essay) questionnaire
        is included.   All the age groups reported some sexual activity.   Of

the oldest group, age 91-95 (94 men), 3 percent have coitus, 23 percent still masturbating, 31 percent still having morning erection, and
35 percent still having sexual interest regardless of potency.   No
references

419   Ruebsaat, Helmut J., and Hull, Raymond.   The Male Climac-
        teric.   New York: Hawthorn Books, 1975.
        An easy-to-read book divided into three parts: 1) effects of
the climacteric including symptoms, sex and family life, and the man
in society; 2) causes of the climacteric including physical, psychological, and social causes; and 3) practical advice to men in the climacteric.   A glossary of terms is included.

420   _____, and _____.   "Psychological Causes of the Male
        Climacteric," in Geriatrics, Vol. 30, No. 9, 166-170, 175,
        1975.
        A reprinting of Chapter 5 of Ruebsaat and Hull's book, The
Male Climacteric.   The most distressing symptoms of the male climacteric are impotence and/or a serious decline of potency.

421   Saxe, Louis P., and Gerson, Noel.   Sex and the Mature Man.
        New York: Pocket Books, 1964.
        Written for the layman, the book covers sex problems in the
middle years including impotence, depression, alcoholism and related
emotional problems.   In addition, there are chapters on the physical
aging process, mental adjustment to aging, and planning for an active
retirement.

422   Solnick, Robert Lewis.   "Alteration of Human Male Erectile Re-
        sponsiveness and Sexual Behavior," Unpublished doctoral dis-
        sertation from University of Southern California, 1977. (D.A.,
        Vol. 38, 5045-B, 1977.)
        It was found that following a period of fantasy training and
practice, level of sex activity and erectile response of middle-age
males was increased.   This increase lasted for two weeks after termination of practice.   It was not clear from the study whether biofeedback would improve response rate in a group over another without biofeedback.   The male's sexual response goes through a critical
period during the middle-age years.   Fantasy and biofeedback might
help in retaining a desired response.

423   _____.   "Sexual Responsiveness, Age, and Change: Facts
        and Potential," in his Sexuality and Aging (revised), pp. 33-
        47.   Los Angeles: University of Southern California, 1978.
        Change in the human reproductive system with age is discussed.
However, much that is positive can come out of this change.   Much
of what is discussed is the result of data and findings from the author's dissertation done under the chairmanship of James E. Birren
and another similar study.   Most of the discussion is on change in
males including male erectile response, modification of erectile response rate change, and accelerating change in the middle years.
There needs to be more experiencing of sex for the older individual
as his/her potential for growth is great.   14 references

424 _____, and Birren, James E. "Age and Male Erectile Re-
        sponsiveness," in Archives of Sexual Behavior, Vol. 6, No. 1,
        1-9, 1977.
        Research was done to determine the difference of penile cir-
cumference increase per unit time between young males and normal
older males. Both groups of males (10 in each) viewed the same
erotic movie. Correlations were computed on penile shaft temperature increase and penile circumference increase. The erection rate
for the younger group was 5.8 times faster than the group of ten aged
males. The correlation coefficient was found to be 0.75. It was
based on the percent approach to 98.6° F (oral temperature) and penile
circumference percentage increase. 18 references

425 Spence, A. W. "The Male Climacteric: Is It an Entity?" in
        British Medical Journal, Vol. 1, 1353-1355, June 12, 1954.
        Dr. Spence presents reasons for the male climacteric as a
clinical entity: 1) androgen therapy improves similar symptoms in
eunuchoids and post-pubertal castrates, 2) there is a low 17-keto-
steroid secretion, 3) there is a lack of testosterone anabolic action,
4) gonadotrophin excretion in urine is increased showing testicular
insufficiency but not necessarily androgen insufficiency, 5) structural
changes may show up in testicular histology, 6) androgen therapy improves symptoms, 7) arguments against male climacteric could be
made against female climacteric. 13 references

426 Stokes, Walter R. "Sexual Function in the Aging Male," in
        Geriatrics, Vol. 6, No. 5, 304-308, September-October 1951.
        (This was read before a meeting of the American Association
        of Marriage Counselors, New York City. It also appears in
        De Martino, Manfred F. (ed.), Sexual Behavior and Person-
        ality Characteristics, pp. 376-383. New York: Citadel Press,
        1963.)
        Male potency is often lost early in life and in order to im-
prove this condition, we must understand how culture affects sexual
physiology. Psychotherapy for the impotent male is not very successful because it only aids him to accept and adjust to the problem. We
need more information in this area to provide better treatment. 3
references

427 Strickler, Martin. "Crisis Intervention and the Climacteric
        Man," in Social Casework, Vol. 56, 85-89, February 1975.
        (P.A., Vol. 54, Abstract No. 06042, 1975.)
        Three case illustrations are presented to show how crisis-
oriented techniques might be used to help the climacteric man deal
with this trying time in life. 3 references

428 Walker, Kenneth. "The Critical Age in Men," in Sexology,
        Vol. 30, No. 1, 705-707, May 1964.
        The question addressed by this article is whether men pass
through a climacteric or critical age resembling that which occurs
in women. The signs and symptoms of the climacteric in a man's
life are similar to those in a woman. The most dangerous psychological change that occurs in a man at this time is a sudden increase

in sexuality.   Onset of the male climacteric can be different in different countries and in different races.   The author feels that the
male climacteric usually begins during the early fifties.

429 Zinberg, Norman Earl.   "Normal Psychology of the Aging Process, Revisited--I: Social Learning and Self-Image in Aging, "
in Journal of Geriatric Psychiatry, Vol. 9, No. 2, 131-150,
1976.
Two case histories are presented.   One concerns depression
in a 64-year-old man who had sexual decline as a secondary symptom.
When introduced to sexual mores and attitudes of his grandchildren's
generation as well as finding cohorts with freer attitudes about sex,
his depression improved and his sexual anxieties were relieved.   Premature job retirement and sexual abstinence can diminish ego autonomy.   41 references

SEXUAL COUNSELING AND AGING

430   American Association of Sex Educators, Counselors and Thera-
       pists. The National Register of Certified Sex Educators, Cer-
       tified Sex Therapists. Washington, D.C.: AASECT, 1978.
       For therapists, the guide gives the method of treatment used
and the groups treated by each including the aged.

431   Berry, Jane. "Counseling Older Women: A Perspective," in
       Personnel and Guidance Journal, Vol. 55, No. 3, 130-131,
       1976.
       A presentation of problem areas of older women. Counselors
can be effective by helping women understand and cope with these
areas, among them being sexual needs.

432   Butler, Robert N. "Brief Guide to Office Counseling: Sexual
       Advice to the Aging Male," in Medical Aspects of Human Sex-
       uality, Vol. 9, No. 9, 155-156, September 1975.
       Dr. Butler presents 14 items to be considered when a man
troubled by potency seeks his help. No references

433   _____, and Lewis, Myrna I. "The Second Language of Sex,"
       in Solnick, Robert Lewis (ed.), Sexuality and Aging (revised
       edition), pp. 176-183. Los Angeles: University of Southern
       California, 1978. (From Butler, Robert N., and Lewis,
       Myrna I., Sex after Sixty, pp. 136-145. New York: Harper
       and Row, Inc., 1976.)
       Sex and love mean different things to different people. When
personality reaches its final stage of growth, love and sex have the
potential to be better than they ever were.

434   Finkle, Alex Louis. "Genitourinary Disorders of Old Age: Ther-
       apeutic Considerations Including Counseling for Sexual Dysfunc-
       tion," in Journal of the American Geriatrics Society, Vol. 26,
       No. 10, 453-458, October 1978.
       Aging and hormonal alterations due to aging cause physical
changes in genitourinary tissues. The greatest influence on continuing sexual function during aging is emotional. The emotional aspect
is directly related to the psychologic history of patient. The professional who is interested in such a patient should be willing to listen
to his or her problems and by doing so may be able to identify a
psychogenic basis for a sexual problem. Psychogenic impotence is
the most common form of the problem. An aging person is more
interested in the totality of sexual meaning than technique or perform-

ance. Beneficial results can be obtained if the patient is given supportive reassurance. 21 references (author abstract modified)

435 Finkle, Alex Louis, and Thompson, Richard. "Urologic Coun-
     seling in Male Sexual Impotence," in Geriatrics, Vol. 27, 67-
     72, December 1972.
     The physician can act as an auditor-counselor to help the im-
potent male regain potency. Treatment of 84 impotent men resulted
in 60 percent regaining sexual potency. Treatment was primarily
emotional support. 8 references

436 Finkle, Paul S., and Finkle, Alex Louis. "Urologic Counseling
     Can Overcome Male Sexual Impotence," in Geriatrics, Vol. 30,
     No. 5, 119-124, 129, May 1975.
     Sixty-two psychogenically impotent men were treated on an out-
patient basis. The patients were encouraged to reinstate self-esteem.
Fifty-eight men achieved restoration of sexual function. The authors
urge the use of more urologic counseling in the treatment of impotence. 36 references

437 Frisher, Karen Leah (ed.). Sex Counseling by Telephone. Cam-
     bridge, MA: Schenkman Publishing Co., 1976.
     Some questions about aging and sexuality are included in this
book on how to do sexual counseling by telephone. How to set up a
training program, the sessions of the program, sample questions (including those on menopause and menstruation) are presented. Referral sources including books and organizations round out the book.
Thayer Cory was the original author of the book. She is Director
of Training at Community Sex Information of Boston.

438 Gaitz, Charles M. "Brief Guide to Office Counseling: Sexual
     Activity During Menopause," in Medical Aspects of Human Sex-
     uality, Vol. 8, No. 12, 67-68, December 1974.
     Presents facts about menopause and sex for a physician to use
when counseling patients about sex. Because many myths have been
associated with menopause, more problems are anticipated by women
than actually come about. As women age they can still enjoy pleasure in sexual relations. The kind of adjustment a married woman
experiences during menopause will depend on the interaction which
takes place between the wife and the husband. Women who enjoy sex
in earlier years tend to enjoy sex in their later years also. Several
implications for the physician are presented.

439 Glover, Benjamin H. "Sex Counseling of the Elderly," in Hos-
     pital Practice, Vol. 12, No. 6, 101-104, 106, 109, 111-113,
     June 1977.
     A casual exchange with emphasis on practicality concerning
sex-related problems that a physician might find when treating the
elderly male, the elderly female, the elderly couple, and the elderly patient with coronary or other disease. Several graphs and illustrations are provided along with a question-and-answer quiz for
physicians on sex in the aging. 6 selected readings are suggested

440   Johnson, Warren R.   Sex Education and Counseling of Special
      Groups: The Mentally and Physically Handicapped and the
      Elderly.   Springfield, IL: Charles C. Thomas, 1975.   (Book
      review of this by Schiavi, Raul C., in Journal of Sex and Mar-
      ital Therapy, Vol. 2, No. 2, 144-146, Summer 1976.)
        The author uses his many years of experience with the prob-
lems of the aging, especially sexually related problems.   Sex problems which are discussed include masturbation, nudity, sex play, in-
cest, child molestation, and homosexuality.   Sex with intercourse is
recommended.   Controversial subjects which are discussed include
marriage, paid sexual companions, and parenthood by special group
members.

441   Labrum, Anthony H.   "Brief Guide to Office Counseling: Meno-
      pausal Symptoms: Distinguishing Psychogenic From Psysio-
      logic," in Medical Aspects of Human Sexuality, Vol. 14, No.
      2, 75-76, February 1980.
        A section on prevention includes detecting possible trouble
areas, planning for the future, marital conflict and health maintenance, and warning signs.   Annual physicals should include evaluation
of a woman's knowledge about the menopause.   Suggestions are given
for therapy for the hot flush, vaginal dryness and dyspareunia, depression, changes in mental functioning, and a summarization that the
menopausal woman needs a concerned and sympathetic person who is
willing to take a holistic approach to care.   No references

442   Lyons, Albert S., and Brockmeier, Marlene.   "Brief Guide to
      Office Counseling: Sex After Ileostomy and Colostomy," in
      Medical Aspects of Human Sexuality, Vol. 9, No. 1, 107-108,
      January 1975.
        A presentation of topics for counseling including: 1) technical
information, 2) sexual activity, 3) emotional status, 4) medical investigation, 5) adjustment to the stoma, 6) relations with sexual partner,
7) mechanics of sexual activity, 8) sources of information available
to the patient, and 9) referral to psychiatrist.

443   Mace, David R.   "The Sexual Revolution: Its Impact on Pas-
      toral Care and Counseling," in Journal of Pastoral Care, Vol.
      25, No. 4, 220-232, December 1971.
        A small section on sexuality in the later years is included in
this article.   An abandonment of sex life in the later years may lead
to high incidences of alienation and deterioration.   14 references in
all with 1 reference related to sexuality and aging

444   Marsh, Stewart.   "Beating the Middle Age Blues," in Practical
      Psychology for Physicians, Vol. 3, No. 1, 29-31, 35, 36, 1976.
        A dread of menopause and a decline in sexual capability may
lead to depression.   Males may need reassurance about their sexual
potency and females may require counseling about menopause.

445   Muckleroy, Robert N.   "Sex Counseling After Stroke," in Med-
      ical Aspects of Human Sexuality, Vol. 11, No. 12, 115-116,

December 1977. (Abstract in Excerpta Medica, Vol. 21 [Section 20], No. 2129, 1978.)
Covers problems that may arise in poststroke patients including: 1) fear of further damage, 2) paralysis, 3) difficulty in communication, 4) personality or mental changes, and 5) impotency. 2 references

446   Peak, Boyd D. "Should We Do Marriage Counseling for the Aged?" in Journal of the Kansas Medical Society, Vol. 66, 279-282, 1965.
Marriage counselors have neglected the older couple in counseling them about problems of old age. Stresses and tensions of old age can best be handled if a trained professional can provide awareness of the reasons for the problems. 9 references

447   Pitt, Brice. "Sexual Behaviour in the Elderly," in Crown, Sidney (ed.), Psychosexual Problems: Psychotherapy, Counselling and Behaviour Modification, pp. 297-303. London: Academic Press, 1976.
A short review of literature on sexuality and aging begins this chapter. Following this, clinical disorders contributing to the decline of sexual activity are presented. They are depression, mania and hypomania, and sexual misbehavior. Counseling the aged about sexuality requires tact and humility. 10 references

448   Preven, David W. "Brief Guide to Office Counseling: Sexual Problems of the Widowed," in Medical Aspects of Human Sexuality, Vol. 9, No. 2, 135-136, February 1975.
A short guide with two major sections: 1) sex and the grief process, and 2) two complications of the grief process. The two complications in the latter section are haste in forming a new relationship and procrastination in forming a new relationship. No references

449   Raskind, Murray A., and Preston, Caroline E. "Brief Guide to Office Counseling: Sexual Counseling of the Elderly," in Medical Aspects of Human Sexuality, Vol. 9, 153-154, May 1975.
This short guide is an overview of important topics for a physician to consider when doing sexual counseling with an elderly person. They include specific sexual problems in the elderly male, specific gynecologic problems in the elderly female, and general psychiatric problems in the elderly. A careful review of the patient's medications, especially antihypertensives and tranquilizers. Fears that sexual activity will precipitate or aggravate serious illness are usually exaggerated.

450   Sander, Faye. "Aspects of Sexual Counseling with the Aged," in Social Casework, Vol. 57, No. 8, 504-510, October 1976. (P.A., Vol. 59, Abstract No. 01696, 1978.)
Research findings on aging and sexuality were woven into casework services in a nonresidential community setting. Important con-

siderations include: 1) sexual activity and potency is not as high in later years but desire persists; 2) fear of failure and lack of or incorrect information about sexuality in old age may lead to impotency in the male; 3) women may be capable of a greater sexual response in later years than men, but the availability of partners becomes a problem; 4) distortions occur in patterns of sexual behavior which are complicated by the aging process; 5) there is a tendency for the elderly to replace love objects more readily due to their accumulation of losses. We must take a close look at our biases against aging people expressing themselves sexually. 13 references

451 Scalzi, Cynthia, and Dracup, Kathy. "Sexual Counseling of Coronary Patients," in Heart and Lung, Vol. 7, No. 5, 840-845, September-October 1978.
   Very little research has been done on sexual activity after a coronary event, and what data have been reported have been on male patients only. When counseling the myocardial infarction (MI) patient, the health-care professional must know 1) the physical status of the patient, 2) the physiological effects of sex, and 3) the psychological effects of a MI. A table is presented with assessment procedures, rationale, and instructions. A multidisciplinary approach to rehabilitation following a MI is suggested with both the patient and his/her spouse is suggested. 14 references

452 Schiller, Patricia. Creative Approach to Sex Education and Counseling. (2nd edition), Washington, DC: AASECT, n.d.
   This booklet describes the philosophy, curriculum, and process of group-centered approach to sex education and sex counseling. It presents model programs for all levels.

453 Schumacher, Sallie S., and Lloyd, Charles. Geriatric Sexuality As Viewed by a Research Team. Cassette No. D 15, produced by AASECT based on the program of the Annual Meeting of the National Sex Institute.
   This is a 30-minute cassette tape by Schumacher, a psychologist, and Dr. Charles Lloyd, an endocrinologist. Reviews some information on sexuality and aging and discusses the importance of this information for therapeutic treatment of the aged. Aging and sex are both new areas of scientific study but both are surrounded by emotional and attitudinal factors which cloud objectivity. Reports on Wasow and Loeb's study of sexuality in nursing homes.

454 Shearer, Marguerite R., and Shearer, Marshall L. "Sexuality and Sexual Counseling in the Elderly," in Clinical Obstetrics and Gynecology, Vol. 20, No. 1, 197-208, March 1977.
   A general article dealing with arousal, physiologic changes with age (male and female), continuity of sexual functioning, masturbation, organic and "silent" conditions affecting sexual functioning, lack of sexual interest and a short conclusions paragraph. Three cases are presented to provide a background for discussion.

455 Sviland, Mary Ann P. "Helping Elderly Couples Attain Sexual

Liberation and Growth, " in SIECUS Report, Vol. 4, No. 6, 3-4, July 1976.
The article concerns itself with a sex therapy program which could take place in a medical hospital or private practice setting. The steps into which the program can be broken down are interrelated. The first step is initial assessment. Ensuing steps include working through obstructive marital dynamics, granting permission to be sexual, increasing physical attractiveness, sex education tools, increasing eroticism and fantasy life, selected sexual exercises and pleasure communication, technique changes to minimize effects of aging in the male, and sexual growth. No references

456 _____. "Helping Elderly Couples Become Sexually Liberated: Psychosocial Issues, " in Counseling Psychologist, Vol. 5, No. 1, 67-72, 1975.
A discussion of society's negative social attitudes toward the aging and sexuality begins this article. Research findings on physical and circumstantial effects on elderly sexuality follows. Restricting physiological and cultural factors interact to restrict aging sexuality. Specific treatment approaches and considerations for effective sex therapy are discussed. 20 references

457 _____. "A Program of Sexual Liberation and Growth in the Elderly, " in Solnick, Robert Lewis (ed.), Sexuality and Aging (revised), pp. 96-114. Los Angeles: University of Southern California, 1978.
Basically the same message that the author has presented in a similar article in SIECUS Report, July 1976, this article is more detailed by reviewing some literature containing information on the cultural stereotyping and myths on aging sexuality, current knowledge of sexual behavior in the elderly, and restrictive cultural and physiological factors limiting elderly sexuality. The steps are the same as those presented in SIECUS Report but more detailed explanation is provided. 35 references

458 Taylor, Robert. Welcome to the Middle Years: A Doctor's Guide. Washington, DC: Acropolis Books, 1976.
Counseling tips are provided on menopause, problems of frigidity and potency, marriage and remarriage.

459 Vemireddi, Nanda Kumar. "Sexual Counseling for Chronically Disabled Patients, " in Geriatrics, Vol. 33, No. 7, 65-69, July 1978.
Sexual counseling may be needed for the patient who is chronically disabled. A coronary patient should be able to have intercourse two or three months after myocardial infarction if no complications are present. Patients with spinal cord injury can also enjoy sex. The attitudes of the physician or other health professional can influence the attitudes of the disabled patient. 16 references

460 Viamontes, Jorge A. "Brief Guide to Office Counseling: Alcohol Abuse and Sexual Dysfunction, " in Medical Aspects of Human Sexuality, Vol. 8, No. 11, 185-186, November 1974.

The article begins by giving a bit of background information on problems which may result from alcohol abuse, specifically marital and sexual ones. An eight-step counseling procedure is presented. No references

461   Wright, Robert Roy. Sex Education, Counseling and Therapy
       for the Aging. Washington, DC: American Association of
       Sex Educators, Counselors and Therapists (AASECT), 1979.
       Presents characteristics of the aging population, sexuality and the aging process (the aging female and male), and sex counseling and therapy with the aging. General health concerns such as heart problems, arthritis, diabetes, strokes, Parkinson's Disease, drugs, and relationships including self-image, body image, and gender role identity are included under sex counseling and therapy for the aging. Also included in this section are sensate focus and male and female sexual dysfunctioning. A conclusion sums up the booklet. 8 items in readings and bibliography

462   _____. Sex Education, Counseling and Therapy for the Phys-
       ically Handicapped. Washington, DC: American Association
       of Sex Educators, Counselors and Therapists (AASECT), 1979.
       Covers sex education, counseling and therapy for the physically handicapped including the following handicaps: 1) spinal cord injury, 2) cerebral palsy, 3) ostomies, 4) mastectomy, 5) diabetes, 6) cardiovascular disabilities, 7) the blind/deaf, and 8) multiple sclerosis. A conclusion sums up the booklet. 29 items in bibliography and readings

463   Zussman, Leon, and Zussman, Shirley. "Counseling the Meno-
       pausal Couple," in Practical Psychology for Physicians, Vol.
       3, No. 2, 36-40; 42-43, 1976.
       Sexual complications of aging are described. Guidelines for effective counseling are offered. Information should be given to the patient regarding menopausal sexuality. The general practitioner should provide sex counseling himself/herself instead of sending the couple to sex therapists.

SEXUALITY AND AGING IN NURSING HOMES

464 Bengston, Vern L. "Questions and Answers: Sex in Nursing
     Homes, " in Medical Aspects of Human Sexuality, Vol. 9, No.
     5, 21, 24, May 1975.
         This question is posed: "Is 'sex activity' between elderly
people in nursing homes tolerated or permitted anywhere in the United
States?" Dr. Bengston states that he knows of no nursing homes in
the United States where sexual activity between elderly individuals is
tolerated, although he suspects there may be. Several reasons for
administrators to be hesitant in admitting toleration include: 1) Ad-
jacent generations have difficulty accepting sexuality in each other.
2) Many nursing homes have affiliations with religious organizations.
According to Bengston, "... religious values of many denominations
do not include tolerance for open sexuality among individuals at any
age. " 3) Cultural values concerning aging haven't supported old age
as a time of sexuality; it is reserved only for the young.
         Widowhood is a most difficult time because it usually ends all
sexual activity for women due to prohibition by societal mores of sexual activity outside of marriage.

465 Blackwell, David L., and Hunt, Sara Stockard. "Staff Attitudes
     Toward Sexual Expression of the Aged, " in Gerontologist, Vol.
     18, No. 5, Part 2, 50. November 16-20, 1978. Paper pre-
     sented in Texas at the 1978 meeting of the Gerontological So-
     ciety.
         Reports on a pilot study to determine the attitudes of nursing
home employees toward the sexual expressions of older patients.
Eight private nursing homes in Southern Louisiana were given a 31-
item questionnaire. Results suggested that: 1) amount of formal education is inversely correlated with the degree of adherence to a
double standard for approved sexual expression; 2) decreasing age is
positively correlated with an increasing acceptance of intercourse before marriage; and 3) blacks are more accepting of intercourse before marriage than whites. Training programs will use this information to develop environmental modifications.

466 Chernick, Beryl, and Chernick, Avinoam. Sex in the Seventies.
     London, Ontario: Sound Feelings, Ltd., n. d.
         This is an 89-minute cassette with diagrams. The nursing
home physician discusses the fact that sexual feelings don't die as
we get old. The physician's discussion is with the residents of a
nursing home who are experiencing personal and sexual problems.

The physician suggests alternate ways of handling the situation to the staff.

467   Downey, Gregg W.   "The Next Patient Right: Sex in the Nursing
        Home," in Modern Healthcare, Vol. 1, 56-59, June 1974.
        (Also in Australas Nurses Journal, Vol. 3, 4, and November
        1974.)
            A Toronto Conference entitled "Sexuality in the Aging Individual"
provided the information for this article.   Restrictions and attitudes
among patients in nursing homes must be changed.   Emphases are
placed on sexual capacity throughout the life span, changes in the
physiology of sexuality (especially in the male), and the most important factors needed for sexual activity, which include good health, interested partner, and interesting partner.   The aged need to be educated about the facts of aging and sexuality so that myths can be dispelled.

468   _____ .   "Sexuality in a Health Care Setting," in Modern Health-
        care, Vol. 5, 20-27, May 1976.
            Mr. Downey begins the article with a series of vignettes of
sexual incidents between patients and staff in healthcare facilities.
A great number of administrators now realize that they must come
to grips with rational ways of dealing with sexuality in their institutions.   A series of prominent sex experts are interviewed and quoted
extensively.   They include William Masters, Virginia Johnson, Mary
Calderone, Richard Chilgren, Lonny Myers, Karen Fontaine, Joseph
Giovannoni, and Marianne Zalar.   William Masters says there is
marked increase in the subject.   Fontaine stresses the point that
medical and nursing schools don't stress sex education enough.   Patients often wonder what effects operations or treatments will have
on their sex lives, how health will affect sex, and how sex will affect their health.   It is especially crucial for people having prostatectomies and hysterectomies.   Four areas of controversy presently
exist in health-care settings: 1) masturbation, 2) homosexuality, 3)
oralgenital sexuality, 4) professional-patient sexual interaction.   What
is stressed throughout the article by all those interviewed is the need
for inservice training by health professionals on this topic.

469   Dunn, A. P.   "Liberating the Aged.   III. ," in Nursing Times,
        Vol. 71, 1086-1087, July 10, 1975.
            The aged in nursing homes need to receive better treatment
especially with respect to their sexuality.   Older people have sexual
needs which need to be satisfied.

470   Federal Register.   Skilled Nursing Facilities.   Washington, DC:
        Department of Health, Education and Welfare, 39 (193), Part
        2, October 3, 1974.
            "... A married patient in a long term care facility shall be
assured privacy for visits by his or her spouse, and married inpa-
tients may share a room unless medically contraindicated and so documented by the attending physician in the medical record.... [I]f a
patient is found to be medically incapable of understanding these rights
and responsibilities devolve to the patient's sponsor....   The patient

may associate and communicate privately with persons of his choice
... unless medically contraindicated (as documented by his physician
in the medical records). "

471   Hanebuth, Lorna S.; Ehrhart, Mary K.; and Peltzer, John T.
        Nursing Assistants and the Long-Term Health Care Facility,
        pp. 202-215. Hagerstown, MD: Harper and Row, 1977.
        Chapter 10 is entitled "Sexuality Needs" and covers such top-
ics as conditions that threaten sexuality needs in both male and female, collecting data about the patient's sexuality including breast examination and Pap smear. Other discussion is given on therapeutic
tasks and emotional support.   No references

472   Kaas, Merrie Jean.   "Sexual Expression of the Elderly in Nurs-
        ing Homes," in Gerontologist, Vol. 18, No. 4, 372-378, Aug-
        ust 1978.
        Attitudes toward sexual expression of the elderly by 85 nurs-
ing home residents were compared with 207 nursing home staff people.
The instrument used was a 32-item questionnaire.   The instrument
was administered independently to nursing staff and verbally to the
residents, and it related to attitudes toward various types of sexual
expression.   Residents did not feel sexually attractive and felt that
lack of privacy curtailed any sexual expression.   The staff responded
less conservatively than the residents.   Ways of promoting sexual
identity are presented.   15 references

473   Kassel, Victor.   "Sex in Nursing Homes," in Medical Aspects
        of Human Sexuality, Vol. 10, No. 3, 126, 129-131, March
        1976.
        People living in nursing homes experience erotic feelings and
seek expression of these feelings.   Nursing home personnel usually
react negatively to the exhibition of sexual intimacy.   Some disturbed
behavior which is demonstrated by nursing home residents may be the
result of unresolved sexual needs.   Orgasm can be therapeutic in the
sense that it relieves anxiety.   Masturbation, usually the only sexual
outlet for the nursing home resident, usually elicits disgust from
nursing home personnel.   This activity is detected in the home because of an almost complete lack of privacy.   The use of L-dopa for
parkinsonism often increases sexual interest also, a fact which both-
ers many nursing home administrators.
        Hand restraints, which are available in nursing homes, are
often used to prevent residents from fondling their genitalia.   Administrators of nursing homes have many outmoded ideas about sexuality
and the aged.   4 references

474   Krizinofski, Marian T.   "Human Sexuality and Nursing Practice,"
        in Nursing Clinics of North America, Vol. 8, No. 4, 673-681,
        December 1973.
        An introduction to the advent of the consideration of a patient's
sexuality in comprehensive nursing care.   It is essential for nurses
to assess their attitudes toward sexuality and develop communication
skills so intimate concerns and sexual problems can be discussed.
The nurse's challenge in the nursing home is to create a fully human

environment by including sexuality in comprehensive care.   21 references; 29 additional bibliographical listings

475 Kuhn, Margaret E.   "Sexual Myths Surrounding the Aging," in
     Oaks, Wilbur W.; Melchiode, Gerald A.; and Ficher, Ilda
     (eds.), Sex and the Life Cycle (The Thirty-Fifth Hahnemann
     Symposium), pp. 117-124. New York: Grune and Stratton,
     Inc., 1976.
        Myth number five is that "old people should be separated by
sex in institutions to avoid problems for the staff and criticism by
families and the community." The rules and regulations which call
for segregation by sex to different wings have been discussed by Margaret E. Kuhn with directors of nursing homes and staff.   They say
that this policy is for the sake of the staff, to prevent complaints
from adult children, and criticism from members of the board.   She
quotes Dr. Harold Lief three changes which are coming about: 1)
in attitude and behavior of youth--open friendship and open marriage,
2) in attitude and behavior of women, 3) in sexual attitude and behavior of aged.

476 LaTorre, Ronald A., and Kear, Karen.   "Attitudes Toward Sex
     in the Aged," in Archives of Sexual Behavior, Vol. 6, No. 3,
     203-213, 1977. (An abstract of this in Aged Care and Service
     Review, Vol. 1, No. 1, 19, 1978.)
        Forty staff members of a nursing home for the aged and eighty
university students rated their reactions to three stories: 1) a neu-
tral (decision-making) story, 2) a coital story, 3) and a masturbatory
story.   The age and gender of the main character were varied for
each story.   An absence of negative attitudes toward sex in the elderly
was indicated by the results.   Sex in the aged, however, was perceived as less credible than sex in young people.   Students had less
negative attitudes toward the sex stories than did nursing home staff
members with gender of the rater having little effect.   Masturbation
was rated more favorable for the female character than male character.   Coitus was rated higher in favorableness for the male character than for the female character.   18 references

477 Leiberman, Morton A., and Lakin, Martin.   "On Becoming an
     Institutionalized Aged Person," in Williams, Richard H.; Tib-
     bits, Clark; and Donahue, Wilma (eds.), Processes of Aging,
     Vol. I, 475-503. New York: Atherton Press, 1963.
        Libido of the aged is still active, but normal channels of ex-
pression are denied for institutionalized aged people.   However, heterosexual relationships is an area where potential growth and future
existed and the only one where purely conservational aspects of institutionalization did not predominate.   13 references

478 Loeb, Martin B.   "Sex in Nursing Homes," in Medical Aspects
     of Human Sexuality, Vol. 13, No. 5, 135, May 1979.
        Old people in nursing homes often form attachments and desire
sexual relations.   Sexuality can mean a variety of sensual, pleasurable
activities, not just sexual intercourse.   Nursing home staff members
often interfere with sexual activity although more "modern" homes are
becoming more tolerant of it.   No references

479 McKinley, Hedi, and Drew, Belle. "The Nursing Home: Death
     of Sexual Expression," in Health and Social Work, Vol. 2,
     No. 3, 180-187, August 1977.
        Nursing home staff have a great deal of difficulty accepting
sexuality among their patients. The attitudes of social workers,
physicians, nurses, and the general public are not aware of research
on sexuality and the aged, that it exists and that it may contribute to
the well-being of the patient. Education is needed in two areas. First,
the residents need sex education, especially with regard to sex in the
elderly. Second, sex education is needed for the health professionals
working in the institution. Sexual histories should be taken concur-
rently with social histories. The effects of drugs on the sexuality of
the residents should be known by the staff, and more communication
between staff and patients on sexual problems needs to be encouraged.
7 footnotes

480 Miller, Dulcy B. "Sexual Practices and Administrative Policies
     in Long Term Care Institutions," in Solnick, Robert Lewis
     (ed.), Sexuality and Aging (revised), pp. 163-175. Los An-
     geles: University of Southern California, 1978. (Same as
     Vol. 3, No. 3, 30-40, Summer 1975, of the Journal of Long-
     Term Care Administration.)
        The author begins by stating the patients' rights in nursing
homes as set forth in the Federal Register (1974), ". . . the patient
may associate and communicate privately with persons of his choice
. . . unless medically contraindicated (as documented by his physician
in the medical records)." She presents the literature on sex and the
aged and states that literature on sex in long-term care institutions
is almost nonexistent and highly subjective. The nature of the patient
population in nursing homes as well as the physical environment are
talked about briefly. She suggests what the philosophy and program
goals of the nursing home should be. Three lists are provided: 1)
individuals and groups who may be interested and/or affected by sex
in the institution, 2) a range of possible partners in the institutional
setting, and 3) a range of possible institutional sexual activities. Administrative implications and areas of consideration sum up this chapter. Sex in nursing homes provides motivation for residents to care
for themselves and to be alert and attractive. 10 references

481 Paradowski, William. "Socialization Patterns and Sexual Prob-
     lems of the Institutionalized Chronically Ill and Physically Dis-
     abled," in Archives of Physical Medicine and Rehabilitation,
     Vol. 58, No. 2, 53-59, February 1977.
        Social and sexual adjustment of 155 long-term physically dis-
abled patients was assessed by a post hoc survey. A dyadic relationship was found in 35 percent of the patients, with the majority of the
relationships occurring between unmarried patients at the hospital.
There was no social attachment in the remaining 65 percent. Sexual
outlet in one form or another was achieved by both socially attached
and socially unattached. Opportunity for sexual activity is important
to the physically disabled. 6 references

482 Pfeiffer, Eric. "Successful Aging: The Possible Dream--Suc-

cessful Nursing Homes: The Not Impossible Dream," in Journal of Long Term Care Administration, Vol. 3, No. 3, 16-21, Summer 1975. (This speech was originally given at the American College of Nursing Home Administrators Ninth Annual Convocation in San Francisco, November 2, 1974.)

Dr. Pfeiffer begins this paper by stating his prejudice about the aging: he likes them. As a psychiatrist, he dispels the myth that the elderly do not respond to psychiatric treatment as Freud once suggested. He gives examples of people whom he feels represent successfully aging individuals. In order to adapt to old age, one must first make a decision to adapt. Successfully aging persons continue training in three major areas of human functioning: 1) physical activity, 2) risk-taking involving emotional and intellectual challenges, 3) vigorous social intervention. Characteristics of successful nursing homes include: 1) pre-admission visiting and "comparison shopping," 2) the existence of a very active social life within the facility, 3) extensive contact with the community. The best way of improving the quality of care for the elderly in nursing homes is to improve the knowledge and skills of those in charge of caring for them.

483 "Rose by Any Other Name," Hempstead, NY: Adelphi University Center on Aging, 1979. (Review of this in SIECUS Report, Vol. 8, No. 3, 10, January 1980.)

This film is by Judith Keller, a nurse and film maker. The film focuses on an older person's need for affection and love as well as dignity. Rose Gordon, a 79-year-old woman living in a long-term care facility, was found in bed with a man. Her "indecent" behavior is poorly received by the nursing home administration. The problem is resolved when awareness is realized of the need for privacy in order to have freedom for sexual expression. This film can provide the foundation for frank discussions on sexuality and aging.

484 Stilwell, Edna M. "Sexual Feelings, Intimacy, and Touch as Factors in Long-Term Care," Chapter 47 in Reichel, William (ed.), Clinical Aspects of Aging, pp. 495-497. Baltimore, MD: Williams and Wilkins Co., 1978.

The total care of the elderly patient in a long-term care facility would ideally involve consideration of sexual feelings, intimacy, and touch. This short article gets right to the point by stating that health professionals need to be aware of these aspects of care and that they have their own attitudes regarding sexuality, intimacy, and touch. Married couples should not be separated in a nursing facility. Privacy should be given, and staff must be supportive not judgmental. A great need exists for sex education for all individuals who work with the elderly.

More research needs to be done on the importance of touch in medicine and nursing and the therapeutic effects of the laying on of hands. What might seem to be trivial to a health-care professional might be the only domain which is not listed under the loss column of an elderly person's life of accumulated losses.

485 Wasow, Mona. "Sexuality in Homes for the Aged," in Concern in Care of the Aging, Vol. 3, No. 6, 20-21, 1977.

Three salient issues are made in this short article: 1) in-service training programs must be developed for nursing home staff and administrators on sexuality and aging, 2) privacy must be provided in the homes, 3) more research is needed in the area of nursing home residents and sexuality. 4 references

486 _____, and Loeb, Martin B. "Sexuality in Nursing Homes," in Burnside, Irene Mortenson (ed.), Sexuality and Aging, pp. 35-41. Los Angeles: University of Southern California, 1975.
See annotation of the same topic by the same authors in Solnick's Sexuality and Aging. The chapters are identical.

487 _____, and _____. "Sexuality in Nursing Homes," in Journal of the American Geriatrics Society, Vol. 27, No. 2, 73-79, February 1979.
Very little has been written on sexuality in nursing homes. Some nursing home populations in Wisconsin were studied to examine sexual activity. There was some resistance but 27 men and 36 women finally agreed to be interviewed. A recently designed questionnaire was used and this was followed by a relaxed conversational period. The interviewees believed that sexual activity was appropriate for other elderly people in homes but because of lack of opportunity, they were not involved. However, they said that they had sexual feelings and thoughts. There was great reluctance among the medical and behavioral personnel to discuss the subject. It was suggested that some provision should be made for those residents in the nursing home who desire appropriate sexual activity. 23 references

488 _____, and _____. "Sexuality in Nursing Homes," in Solnick, Robert Lewis (ed.), Sexuality and Aging (revised), pp. 154-162. Los Angeles: University of Southern California, 1978.
Seven students at the University of Wisconsin-Madison School of Social Work worked on this project on sexuality in nursing homes under the supervision of Professors Wasow and Loeb. It is one of the first studies ever done in this setting on sexuality. One shortcoming of the study is that the interviewers were all young. Twenty-seven males, 35 females, and 17 staff members were interviewed. Only one staff member was male. Residents of the nursing homes definitely had sexual thoughts and sometimes displayed acting-out behaviors. Staff are often upset and confused about how to deal with this. Aging and sexuality has been very neglected as an area of study. Education and more research may help change that in the future. No references

489 White, Charles B. "Sexuality and Aging: The Institutionalized Aged," in Allied Health and Behavioral Sciences, Vol. 2, No. 2, 139-150, 1979.
The author suggests that the study of sexuality can be thought of as the "systematic destruction of a mythology." He also presents a summary of the research on sexuality in the aged with results in tabular form. Beneficial aspects of sexual activity are presented as well as suggestions for educational intervention. The author stresses

the importance of the need for environmental support in order to prevent sexual decline in old age.   The study of sexual behavior in the
aged should be undertaken in the context in which it occurs.   Behaviors can be dependent on the person-environment interaction and health
professionals can be an integral part of the environment.   37 references

490 _____. "Sexuality in Nursing Homes." Paper presented at
       the University of Georgia, Athens, Georgia, February 1978.
       A real lack of research on sexuality and aging reflects ageist
social science.   This research was encouraged by the Wasow Loeb
study in Wisconsin.   The author and three undergraduates interviewed
residents of a nursing home concerning sexuality in the home.   The
research was approached with two sides in mind: the institutional-
environment side and the sexual side.   The environment or institution
was considered the independent variable and sexual behavior was considered a dependent variable.   Although sexual behavior is usually
covert, it is perceived by the "institution" as unimportant.   Administrators and/or staff are usually never comfortable with any aspect
of sexuality in their residents.   The authors contends "the dynamic
interface of the person and the environment is important and neglected
data in the study of aging sexuality."   Effort should be made to understand sexual behavior in aged in the context in which it occurs. White
prefers to look at the person times environment (p x e) interaction.
The equation presented to help in understanding the broader aspects
of sexuality is B = F(p x e), behavior is a function of the person
times the environment.

491 _____. "Sexuality in the Institutionalized Aged: Methodolog-
       ical Issues." Paper prepared for National Institute of Mental
       Health Conference on Methodological Issues in Sex Research.
       Washington, DC, November 17-19, 1977.
       Environment is consistently hostile toward the aged and sex-
uality.   Socialization continues to suppress and put down such behavior.   The lack of support for sexual activity in the aged leads to:
1) self-fulfilling prophecy which is environmentally induced, 2) pre-
diction of decrements of activity due to breakdown of biological systems, 3) a weak biological system made weaker for lack of environmental support.   An interesting source of data is the person times
environment (p x e) interaction.   Contextualism should be used in the
study of sexuality and the aged.   Interpretation of age-related changes
in sexuality is not clear.   Questions posed included: what is the relationship between change in hormonal levels and context and frequency
of sex? between frequency of outlet and genital sensitivity? between
privacy vs. frequency of outlet? Nursing home staff have a very
great deal of control over the residents.   White suggests that sexual
problems of nursing home residents are primarily a result of the
nature of institutions and their impact on residents.   How do nursing
homes do what they do? Why do they do what they do?

492 _____. "Sexuality in the Institutionalized Elderly." Alfred
       University, 1975. Unpublished paper presented at the New
       York State Public Health Association Annual Meeting.   Buffalo,
       NY, June 17, 1975.

Suggests that there are many myths about sexuality and aging which arouse guilt and repression in the elderly.   Studies are quoted to suggest that age need not end sexual activity.   Sexuality for the institutionalized elderly is rarely, if ever, considered.   The author could find only one other study besides his own which examined sexual attitudes and behavior of institutionalized elderly.   That study, done by Wasow and Loeb in 1975, examined a sample of Wisconsin nursing home residents.   This paper reports on the author's research which represented a modification of the Wisconsin study in the sense that he used a modified version of their questionnaire in an attempt to assess staff attitudes about sexuality in the institutionalized elderly. Residents were also questioned.   The resident and staff questionnaires are included as are the compiled results of the questionnaires.   13 references

HOMOSEXUALITY AND AGING

493   Calleja, M. A.   "Homosexual Behavior in Older Men," in Sex-
      ology, Vol. 42, 46-48, August 1967.
      Interviews with 1,737 men whose average age was 64 revealed
the occurrence of homosexuality in a number of the men.   The interviews were conducted mostly in Spain but also in other countries in
Europe and the Americas.   More than half were agricultural workers
although there were also professional, clerical and skilled manual
workers.   All were white and enjoyed good physical and mental health.
Some were widowers, a few had remained bachelors all their lives
and 89 percent were married.   The reports given by the men indicated that 38.8 percent or 674 had experienced a homosexual act at
some time in their lives; 31.8 percent or 553 had experienced a homosexual act with varied frequency; 23.3 percent or 404 had experienced
a homosexual act with high frequency, some very intense; and 6.1
percent or 106 had varied homosexual activity after 60 years of age.
The 6.1 percent had, for most of their adult lives, been married and
entirely heterosexual.   These men over sixty seemed to prefer a mature man as a companion for their sexual practices, close to their own
age or slightly lower.   They were repulsed by the effeminate and passive homosexual.   According to the men, the reason they were led
into sexual acts with other men was the need for affection, of which
the men felt deprived or which they felt they were not getting to a
sufficient degree within their own families.

494   Campaign for Homosexual Equality.   Report on the Aging Homo-
      sexual.   London: London West End Group of the Campaign for
      Homosexual Equality, May 1974.   (Report of this paper was
      made in "Newsline" edited by Patrice Horn, in Psychology To-
      day, Vol. 8, No. 5, 35, October 1974.)
      More personal and statistical information on elderly homosex-
uals needs to be gathered.   Creation of special groups for the elderly
homosexual was not recommended as it was thought that this might
cut them from the mainstream of activities.   It is important to encourage the young to become interested in the elderly.   Problems of
older homosexuals differ in kind but not degree from problems of heterosexuals.   The problems of the elderly homosexual must require
different solutions.   The problem of our attitude toward the elderly
homosexual needs to be considered.

495   Francher, J. Scott, and Henkin, Janet.   "The Menopausal Queen:
      Adjustment to Aging and the Male Homosexual," in American
      Journal of Orthopsychiatry, Vol. 43, No. 4, 670-674, July
      1973.

The authors suggest homosexuality is functional in adjusting to the aging process. This view is in opposition to the popular mythology view. "Life crises" are experienced by homosexuals earlier in their lives so that later life role losses have less traumatic effects. 10 references

496 Kelly, James Joseph, III. "The Aging Male Homosexual," Chapter 11 in Gochros, Harvey L. , and Gochros, Jean S. (eds.), The Sexually Oppressed, pp. 160-169. New York: Association Press, 1977.
Covers stereotypes of aging male homosexuals, problems faced by older gays, adaptation to stigma, and social change and the problem of stigma. 18 references and recommended readings

497 Kelly, Jim [James Joseph, III]. "The Aging Male Homosexual: Myth and Reality," in Gerontologist, Vol. 17, No. 4, Part 2, 328-332, 1977 (Also reported in Gerontologist, Vol. 15, No. 5, 72, 1975.) (This was presented at the 18th Annual Scientific Meeting of the Gerontological Society, Louisville, Kentucky, October 1975.)
A study of 241 homosexual men ranging in age from 16 to 79 was made in the Los Angeles metropolitan area. Characteristics of these men were compared to popular myths about characteristics of homosexual men. According to the results of the study, very little evidence suggests that being homosexual causes problems in old age. Stigma in society may cause problems for aging homosexuals. 20 references (author's abstract modified)

498 _____. "Brothers and Brothers: The Gay Man's Adaptation to Aging." Dissertation at Brandeis University, Waltham, MA, 1974. (University Microfilm Order No. 75-24, 234; D.A. , Vol. 36, No. 5, 3130A, 1975.)
A comparison of specific popular myths of older gay men with actual respondent characteristics. It analyzed the attitudes of gay men, across their life span, toward aging.

499 Kimmel, Douglas C. "Life-History Interviews of Aging Gay Men," in International Journal of Aging and Human Development, Vol. 10, No. 3, 239-248, 1979-80. (Revised from a paper presented at the Gerontological Society Meetings, New York City, October 14, 1976.)
Fourteen gay men were interviewed about their life history and experiences as aging gay men. Their ages ranged from 55 to 81. The stereotype of the lonely, isolated old gay man was contradicted. 6 references

500 Laner, Mary Riege. "Growing Older Female: Heterosexual and Homosexual," in Journal of Homosexuality, Vol. 4, No. 3, 267-275, Spring 1979.
"Personal" ads of heterosexual and homosexual women were analyzed for age-related content. Theoretical notions about differences and similarities between nonlesbian and lesbian aging were used to derive hypotheses which were tested by the study. There was found

110 Sexuality and Aging

to be no over-representation of older advertisers of either sexual orientation. An over-representation was hypothesized for both sexual
orientations. Lesbians did not seek young partners. "Accelerated
aging" among heterosexual women was indicated by the age differences
between groups. There may be some advantages of lesbian over nonlesbian women in the experience of aging. 23 references

501 _____. "Growing Older Male: Heterosexual and Homosexual,"
in Gerontologist, Vol. 18, No. 5, 496-501, 1978. (Paper
originally prepared for presentation at a meeting of Society
for the Scientific Study of Sex, Inc., Santa Barbara, CA, June
1978.)
"Personal" ads of hetero- and homosexual men were analyzed
for age-related information. No support was found for the contention
that homosexuals have age acceleration or that they pursue young
mates. This was true for both hetero- and homosexual males. 20
references (author abstract modified)

502 _____. "Media Mating II: 'Personal' Advertisements of Lesbian Women," in Journal of Homosexuality, Vol. 4, No. 1,
41-61, Fall 1978.
This study was based on a design adapted from previous content analyses of "personal" advertisements of heterosexual men and
women and of homosexual men. Advertisements for lesbian partners
were studied. Findings of other studies of lesbianism as well as pre-
dictions derived from exchange theory served as background for the
study. The hypotheses proved true in that lesbians' advertisements
deemphasized the negative and emphasized positive characteristics.
The advertisements tended toward an androgynous style. 55 references

503 _____. "Permanent Partner Priorities: Gay and Straight,"
in Journal of Homosexuality, Vol. 3, No. 1, 21-39, Fall 1977.
This study was based on a previous research design with heterosexuals. Its focus was to assess permanent partner priorities of
gay and straight women and men. In addition, the perceptions of
those priorities by each gender and sexual orientation were assessed.
Homosexuals and heterosexuals had a tendency to misperceive the
priorities of their own and the other groups studied. The mispercep-
tion was explained as possibly being the result of varying societal
pressures experienced by homosexual and heterosexual women and
men. 29 references

504 _____, and Kamel, G. W. Levi. "Media Mating I: News-
paper 'Personals' Ads of Homosexual Men," in Journal of
Homosexuality, Vol. 3, No. 2, 149-162, Winter 1977.
This study is an analysis of 359 ads placed by male homosexuals. Hypotheses were made following exchange theory. Hypotheses
were: 1) self would be favorably presented, 2) the ads would be more
frank and specific about relationship goals than heterosexual ads, and
3) the male homosexual subculture would reveal a "virilization." These
hypotheses were strongly supported. 16 references (author abstract
modified)

505 Minnigerode, Frederick A., III. "Age Status Labelling in Homo-
     sexual Men," in Journal of Homosexuality, Vol. 1, No. 3,
     273-276, 1976.
        Ninety-five homosexual men were asked to make a classifica-
tion of themselves in categories of young, middle-aged, or old. The
men were between the ages of 25 and 68. The majority of the men
in their 20's and 30's described themselves as young. Most 40-year-
old men and all men over 50 described themselves as middle-aged.
The myth of acceleration of aging in homosexual men was not supported by any data. An anticipation of such changes might suggest
that these men have poorer psychological and/or physical health than
those men who do not anticipate the change. 5 references

506 _____, and Adelman, Marcy R. "Elderly Homosexual Women
     and Men: Report on a Pilot Study," in Family Coordinator,
     Vol. 27, No. 4, 451-456, October 1978. (This paper, in an earl-
     ier form, was originally presented at the meeting of the Geron-
     tological Society, New York City, October 14, 1976.)
        Eleven homosexual men and women, from 60-77 years old are
interviewed for four to five hours. The interviews were tape-recorded.
Parts of interviews which had to do with problems and adaptations of
aging heterosexual and homosexual men and women were examined.
Areas of examination included work, retirement, leisure time; physical health and change; social behavior; psychological function; life
course personal perspectives; and sexuality. 21 references

507 Schaffer, Ralph S. "Will You Still Need Me When I'm 64?" in
     Jay, Karla, and Young, Allen (eds.), Out of the Closets:
     Voices of Gay Liberation, pp. 278-279. New York: Douglas,
     1972.
        In rather earthy language, this short article condemns youth-
ism, the unconscious belief that older people are inferior, as oppress-
ing older gays. The author condemns gay liberation for ignoring the
older homosexual. No references

508 Weinberg, Martin S. "The Aging Male Homosexual," in Medical
     Aspects of Human Sexuality, Vol. 3, No. 12, 66-72, December
     1969.
        Aging homosexuals are happier and have improved adjustment
as they age. No references

509 _____. "The Male Homosexual: Age-Related Variations in
     Social and Psychological Characteristics," in Social Problems,
     Vol. 17, No. 4, 527-537, Spring 1970. (This is a revision of
     a paper delivered at the 125th annual meeting of the American
     Psychiatric Association, May 8, 1969, Miami Beach, Florida.)
        The folk view of the male homosexual and age suggests that
he has less sociosexual contact with other homosexuals because of the
shortage of young homosexuals. Another aspect of the folk view of
the male homosexual and age is that the older homosexual, as a result of the sociosexual situation, is lower in psychological well-being.
This paper presents data which support the social folk description.
The psychological folk description is not supported. 6 references

510 _____, and Williams, Colin J. Male Homosexuals: Their
     Problems and Adaptations. New York: Oxford University
     Press, 1974.
          Older homosexuals are most likely to be living alone, have
     homosexual sex less frequently than younger homosexuals, and tend
     to be less involved in the homosexual world. This is due to the sum
     of changes (psychological, social, and sexual) that accompanies aging
     in homosexuals. In some ways, older homosexuals are better off
     than younger homosexuals. Many stereotypes exist concerning the
     aging homosexual. Topics for needed research include the psycholog-
     ical and social character of the older homosexual's life, salience of
     sex for the older homosexual, and the kinds of supportive systems
     used by older homosexuals. Two tables are included, namely, social
     characteristics by age and psychological characteristics by age. Data
     from three countries (United States, Netherlands, and Denmark) are
     included. 7 footnotes

FERTILITY, REPRODUCTION, AND AGING

511 Berent, Jerzy. "Fertility Decline in East European Russia," in Population Studies, Vol. 24, No. 1, 35-58, 1970.
   Demographic, economic and social factors are examined to explain the dramatic declines in fertility levels which have occurred in Eastern Europe during the last 15 years. The impact of changes in age and sex structure and in nuptiality of the populations was considered. Genuine changes in attitudes toward family size have caused the decline. 37 references

512 Bishop, Marcus W. H. "Ageing and Reproduction in the Male," in Journal of Reproduction and Fertility, Supplement 12, 65-87, 1970.
   Aging in male mammals is discussed including decline in sexual activity, differential viability and its effects on sex ratio, degeneration of the testis and drop in hormone production, changes in spermatozoa and spermatogenic cells, and the acquisition and transmission of genetic load. Aging changes in accessory reproductive glands or support systems of the body are not discussed. 126 references (author abstract modified)

513 Cannings, C., and Cannings, M. R. "Mongolism, Delayed Fertilization and Human Sexual Behaviour," in Nature, Vol. 218, No. 5140, 481, May 4, 1968. (Letter answer to article by James German.)
   In this answer to a letter written by James German and published in Nature (Vol. 217, pp. 516-518, February 10, 1968) and annotated separately in this bibliography, suggests that the hypothesis set forth by Mr. German is too simple and that additional factors may have a greater influence on the incidence of mongolism with age. That is, delayed fertilization itself does not sufficiently answer the question of mongolism with increased maternal age. 3 references

514 Caughley, Graeme. "Offspring Sex Ratio and Age of Parents," in Journal of Reproduction and Fertility, Vol. 25, 145-147, 1971.
   Evidence that sex ratio of offspring demands on parental age has not been adequately proven. If an intermediate age set is chosen before testing, it is not possible to test the hypothesis logically and with validity. 3 references

515 Cowgill, Ursula M. "Changes in the Fertility Span of Man," in Perspectives in Biology and Medicine, Vol. 15, 141-146, Autumn 1971.

The fertility span of man is increasing and data are presented to show this.   Menarche begins at an earlier age and menopause is beginning later.   Ways of controlling the fertility span are discussed. 18 references

516   Diamond, Milton (ed.).   Perspectives in Reproduction and Sex-
        ual Behavior.   Bloomington, IN: Indiana University Press,
        1968.   (Proceedings from a symposium and discussion on se-
        lected topics within the field of reproduction and sexual behav-
        ior.)
        This book is divided into several parts: 1) symposium, 2) discussion, 3) volume contributions, 4) dinner, and 5) after.   An au-thor and name index is included as well as a subject index.   It is a technical resource useful primarily to graduate students and research-ers.   Many of the papers consider aging and sexuality in animals. Of particular interest to those interested in humans are Chapter 23 and Chapter 24.   Chapter 23 is entitled "Human Sex Behavior Re-search," by Paul H. Gebhard; and Chapter 24 is entitled "Human Sex-ual Inadequacy and Some Parameters of Therapy," and is written by William H. Masters and Virginia E. Johnson.   Chapter 13 by Robert W. Noyes, entitled "Perspectives in Human Fertility," is also quite relevant.

517   Ebanks, G. Edward.   "Users and Nonusers of Contraception,"
        in Population Studies, Vol. 24, No. 1, 85-92, 1970.
        In order to examine the nature of contraceptive use among clients of a family planning program, regression analysis is used. A good predictive equation is developed which relates the cumulated number of users and the years of operation of the program.   Over the period of twelve years, the transition probabilities are not con-stant.   The data are not homogeneous.   The transition probabilities are constant within each period when the twelve-year period is divided into three four-year periods.   Each of the three periods coincides with a distinctive period in the development of the program.

518   Friedman, Emanuel A. , and Sachtleben, Marlene R.   "Relation
        of Maternal Age to the Course of Labor," in American Journal
        of Obstetrics and Gynecology, Vol. 91, No. 7, 915-924, April
        1, 1965.   (This was presented at a meeting of the Chicago
        Gynecological Society, May 15, 1964.)
        Graphicostatistical techniques were used to determine the re-lationship between maternal age and labor.   Except for a progressive increase in the second stage of labor, no differences in the course of labor were attributable to advancing age.   A discussion ensues about factors leading to a clinical impression that older women have longer labor.   54 references

519   German, James.   "Mongolism, Delayed Fertilization and Human
        Sexual Behaviour," in Nature, Vol. 217, No. 5129, 516-518,
        February 10, 1968.
        The correlation of increased incidence of mongol births with higher maternal age might be explained by a decreasing amount of sexual intercourse which goes along with aging and length of marriage

thus setting up the condition of delayed fertilization.   (See also 513.)
16 references

520   Hafez, E. S. E. (ed.).   Aging and Reproductive Physiology.
        Vol. 2 of Perspectives in Human Reproduction.   Ann Arbor,
        MI: Ann Arbor Science, 1976.
        Seven chapters make up this book which is an outgrowth of a
colloquium held in December 1974 at the C. S. Mott Center of Wayne
State University School of Medicine.   Three of the total of nine authors were from West Germany.   The remainder were from the United
States.   A list of the contributors and their addresses are given after
the table of contents.   Chapter 1 is entitled "Reproductive Senescence"
(40 references).   Chapter 2 is entitled "Aging and Structural Changes
in Female Reproductive Tract" (21 references).   Chapter 3 is entitled
"Aging of Mammalian Ova" (54 references).   Chapter 4 is entitled
"Aging and the Hypothalamo-Hypophyseal-Gonadal Axis" (64 references).
Chapter 5 is entitled "Is Pregnancy a Risk in the Elderly Woman?"
(18 references).   Chapter 6 is entitled "Maternal Aging and Chromosomal Defects" (31 references).   Chapter 7 is entitled "Social and
Psychological Aspects of Sexual Behavior Among the Aged" (10 references).   A subject index is provided at the end of the book.

521   _____ .   "Reproductive Senescence," in his (ed.), Aging
        and Reproductive Physiology, Vol. 2 of Perspectives in Hu-
        man Reproduction, pp. 1-19.   Ann Arbor, MI: Ann Arbor
        Science, 1976.
        Topics discussed in this, Chapter 1 of the book, include: 1)
menopause, 2) clinical symptoms of menopause, 3) endocrine mechanisms of menopause (estrogens and gonadotropins), 4) the reproductive
organs, 5) fertility decline in women (menstrual cycles, pregnancy),
6) fertility decline in men (sexual behavior, spermatogenesis), 7) general effects of aging, and 8) concluding remarks.   A number of tables
and graphs are used to illustrate points.   40 references

522   Hook, Ernest B.   "Genetic Counseling for the Older Pregnant
        Woman," in New England Journal of Medicine, Vol. 299, No.
        15, 835-836, October 12, 1978.   (Letter to the editor.)
        With regard to maternal age being critical in the occurrence
of Down's syndrome (a letter by Lewis B. Holmes, M. D.), the author states that a substantial fraction of Down's-syndrome cases are
of paternal origin.   However, an independent paternal-age effect may
be weaker than the maternal-age effect.   5 references

523   Kajanoja, Pauli, and Widholm, Olof.   "Pregnancy and Delivery
        in Women Aged 40 and Over," in Obstetrics and Gynecology,
        Vol. 51, No. 1, 47-51, January 1978.
        During a seven-year period from 1969-1975, 558 women aged
40 and over gave birth to 564 babies at the Helsinki University Central Hospital.   The cesarean section rate was high and the mean duration of labor for vaginal deliveries was short.   Perinatal mortality
was 28/1000 compared with 19/1000 for women under 40.   A temporary reduction of pregnancies in older women (approximately 50
percent) was attributed to the liberalized Abortion Act of 1970 in

Finland. During the last two years, the percentage of older primi-
gravidas increased. It was concluded that an older woman who has
had a safe pregnancy has a good chance of giving birth to a healthy
child. 13 references

524   Klebanow, David, and MacLeod, John. "Semen Quality and Cer-
         tain Disturbances of Reproduction in Diabetic Men," in Fertil-
         ity and Sterility, Vol. 11, No. 3, 255-261, 1960.
         Semen quality was studied in 28 diabetic men taking insulin.
No serious disturbances in spermatogenesis were observed. In about
50 percent of the men, the sperm motility was diminished. Impotence
was common even to the men taking insulin. Failure to ejaculate is
common in diabetic men even if they are able to achieve orgasm.
The authors present a theory linking erectile impotence and ejaculatory impotence in diabetic men. 15 references

525   Koen, Ann L. "Maternal Aging and Chromosomal Defects,"
         Chapter 6 in Hafez, E. S. E. (ed.), Aging and Reproductive
         Physiology, Vol. 2 of Perspectives in Human Reproduction,
         pp. 75-88. Ann Arbor, MI: Ann Arbor Science, 1976.
         A discussion on experimental observations follows an introduc-
tory section on genetics pertaining to chromosomal defects. Theories
supporting evidence and deficiencies are presented along with pictures
of chromosomes (not detailed). A discussion follows. 31 references

526   Koren, Z.; Zuckerman, H.; and Brezinski, A. "Pregnancy and
         Delivery After Forty," in Obstetrics and Gynecology, Vol. 21,
         No. 2, 165-169, February 1963.
         Hadassah University Hospital in Jerusalem had 395 women over
40 years of age give birth. This covered a period of ten years between 1952-1961 during which time 23,939 women delivered. Grand
multiparity and some specific pathological conditions were attributed
to the higher age of the mother. A link was suggested between fertility period length and pregnancy numbers. Mothers of nonoriental
and oriental origin showed significant differences. 22 references

527   Kuppe, G.; Metzger, H.; and Ludwig, H. "Aging and Structural
         Changes in Female Reproductive Tract," Chapter 2 in Hafez,
         E. S. E. (ed.), Aging and Reproductive Physiology, Vol. 2 of
         Perspectives in Human Reproduction, pp. 21-34. Ann Arbor,
         MI: Ann Arbor Science, 1976.
         Aging changes of the vulva, the vagina, the uterine cervix, the
endometrium, the myometrium, the fallopian tube, and the ovary are
covered in separate sections. Photographs and a drawing are used
to illustrate points. 21 references

528   McCauley, Carole Spearin. Pregnancy After 35. New York:
         E. P. Dutton and Co., Inc., 1976.
         Contains information on medical, genetic, and psychological
topics for women or couples over 35 who may be expecting or planning a child. Some attention is given to single parenting and to
fathering.

529 Mariona, Federico G. "Is Pregnancy a Risk in the Elderly
     Woman?" Chapter 5 in Hafez, E. S. E. (ed.), Aging and Re-
     productive Physiology, Vol. 2 of Perspectives in Human Re-
     production, pp. 67-74. Ann Arbor, MI: Ann Arbor Science,
     1976.
     The chapter begins by stating that pregnancy is a definite risk
for older women (40 and over). Tables with data are present to illustrate this fact. Prenatal complications are discussed as well as
intrapartum performance. Newborns and maternal and fetal mortality are also discussed in short sections. Conclusions are offered.
18 references

530 Moran, P. A. P.; Novitski, E.; and Novitski, C. "Paternal
     Age and the Secondary Sex Ratio in Humans," in Annals of
     Human Genetics (London), Vol. 32, 315-316, 1969.
     Paternal age influences sex ratio to a small extent. This con-
firms Novitski and Sandler's 1956 conclusion. 2 references

531 Mosley, W. Henry (ed.). Nutrition and Human Reproduction.
     New York: Plenum Press, 1978. (Proceedings of a Confer-
     ence on Nutrition and Human Reproduction, supported and or-
     ganized by the National Institutes of Child Health and Human
     Development, held at the National Institutes of Health, Bethesda,
     MD, February 14-16, 1977.)
     Sections under which the papers presented at this conference
were placed include: 1) Introduction, 2) Nutrition and Endocrine Function, 3) Nutrition, Fertility and Infant Mortality, 4) Nutrition, Breast-
Feeding, and Fertility, 5) Analytical Models of Nutrition-Fertility Relationships, 6) Field Studies. A list of contributors and an index appear at the end of the book. Section 5 contains most of the pertinent
information on aging.

532 Natter, Carl E. "Pregnancy After Fifty," in Obstetrics and
     Gynecology, Vol. 24, No. 4, 641-643, October 1964.
     The incidence of women aged 50 to 100 years giving birth is
very low. By checking public health records, the incidence was determined to be between 1/20,000 to 1/60,000. The maternal and
fetal complications which occur with pregnancy after fifty are probably the same as those which occur in women from 40-45 years of
age. Mongolism and other congenital malformations are more common to births after fifty. After menopause, it is very rare for pregnancy to occur. One case of a woman delivering two viable infants
after fifty is discussed. 24 references

533 Newcombe, Howard B., and Tavendale, Olwyn G. "Effects of
     Father's Age on the Risk of Child Handicap or Death," in
     American Journal of Human Genetics, Vol. 17, No. 2, 163-
     178, March 1965.
     Risks to children depending on the ages of the fathers were
studied using a special file of 8,928 registrations of deaths and handi-
caps among individuals born between 1953-58 in British Columbia,
Canada. It was found that there was an increased risk among children of fathers who were 45 years of age and older. Older fathers

who married very young wives showed a very strong relationship with the effect shown by pooled data for all causes of diseases in the children.   Respiratory disease of children of older fathers is not seen when data for North American Indians and non-Indians are looked at separately.   The reason for the increased risk of child handicap or death with older fathers may be due to the presence of more mutant genes or chromosomes in these fathers.   10 references

534   Novak, Edmund R.   "Ovulation After Fifty," in Obstetrics and
       Gynecology, Vol. 36, No. 6, 903-910, December 1970. (This
       was presented at the 18th Annual Meeting of the American Col-
       lege of Obstetricians and Gynecologists, April 12-18, 1970,
       New York, N. Y.)
          In women past age 50, viable pregnancy is rare.   An increas-
ing anovulation has been thought to be the cause of this.   Ovulation
incidence in the aging woman is hard to determine.   This study was
conducted on 200 women over age 50.   These women had undergone
oophorectomy and hysterectomy for bleeding problems which were not
hormonally induced and weren't malignant.   Pathological study was
done as was correlation of endometrium and ovaries.   Histological
evidence revealed corpus luteum within six months in 23 percent of
the women.   Infertility at this age is most likely caused by an inade-
quate corpus luteum rather than anovulation.   13 references (author
abstract modified)

535   Peluso, John J.   "Aging of Mammalian Ova," Chapter 3 in Ha-
       fez, E. S. E. (ed.), Aging and Reproductive Physiology, Vol.
       2 of Perspectives in Human Reproduction, pp. 35-50.   Ann
       Arbor, MI: Ann Arbor Science, 1976.
          Pictures and graphs are generously used by the author to dis-
cuss his topic.   Sections include chronological aging of mammalian
ova (hamsters, mice), tubal aging of mammalian ova, follicular aging of mammalian ova (human, rat), and a conclusion section.   This
is primarily an article on animals not humans.   54 references

536   Potter, Robert G. ; New, Mary L. ; Wyon, John B. ; and Gordon,
       John E.   "Applications of Field Studies to Research on the
       Physiology of Human Reproduction," in Journal of Chronic
       Disease, Vol. 18, 1125-1140, 1965.
          This study focused upon lactation and its effects upon birth inter-
vals in eleven Punjab villages in India.   Postpartum amenorrhea was
prolonged by lactation.   Fetal wastage doubled and menstruation intervals were increased when the mothers passed early twenties to late
thirties and early forties.   25 references

537   Schneider, Edward L. (ed.).   The Aging Reproductive System.
       Aging, Vol. 4, New York: Raven Press, 1978.   (Book review
       by Herman T. Blumenthal in Journal of Gerontology, Vol. 34,
       No. 1, 124, 1979.)
          A comprehensive view of human reproductive aging ranging
from the behavioral sciences to clinical medicine.   Topics considered
include the clinical aspects of aging of the female and male reproductive systems and accessory organs, the effects of aging on the neuro-

endocrine control of the reproductive system, and the genetic effects on offspring of reproductive aging. The chapters on human reproductive aging are interspersed with animal studies.

538 Schneider, Jan. "The High-Risk Pregnancy," in Hospital Practice, Vol. 6, 133-136, 141-143, October 1971.
The most important factors in high-risk pregnancy, according to the author, are socioeconomic in origin even including the medical risks. It is important to identify the patient where complications might be expected and to give her services which she needs. Consolidation of facilities is suggested. No references (author abstract modified)

539 Selvin, Steve, and Garfinkel, Joseph. "The Relationship Between Age and Birth Order with the Percentage of Low Birth-weight Infants," in Human Biology, Vol. 44, No. 3, 501-509, September 1972.
Birth order, as defined by this article, is the number of children previously born to the mother plus the present one. New York State birth certificates (N=1,515,443) were used to determine the association between low weight (less than 2501 grams) and age of parents. The percentage of "premature" infants was minimum at birth order three but was highest at birth order one and six plus. Strong interaction between birth order and maternal age. The proportion of low-birthweight infants was high for young mothers whose infants were in increasing birth order. Mothers older than forty-five had the opposite tendency. A change in association occurred in the age ranges from young mothers to older mothers. Paternal age was shown to have an effect on the number of infants with weights lower than 2501 grams. 7 references

540 Shipley, Paul W.; Wray, Jo Ann; Heckter, Hyman H.; Arellano, Max G.; and Borhani, Nemat O. "Frequency of Twinning in California. Its Relationship to Maternal Age, Parity and Race," in American Journal of Epidemiology, Vol. 85, No. 1, 147-156, 1967.
All multiple births in the state of California since 1905 were studied to analyze the influence of demographic factors on twinning. The occurrence of dizygotic twins is closely related to maternal age and parity. Maximum twinning for whites occurred between ages 35-39 of the mother. No evidence of decline existed among older black mothers. Maternal age operates independently as does parity. When holding these two factors constant, black mothers still have much higher dizygotic twinning rates. 19 references

541 Spencer, Geraldine M. "Fertility Trends in Australia," in Demography, Vol. 8, No. 2, 247-259, May 1971.
Several time series were compiled from the Australian vital registration and census systems. The series included: 1) crude birth rates from the 1860's, 2) fertility rates from the 1880's, 3) age-specific and parity-specific measures from the 1910's, 4) cumulative fertility measures by birth year of parent beginning with the 1890's, and 5) cumulative fertility measures for marriages by year

120   Sexuality and Aging

contracted from the 1910's. Both generation and annual measures show
a decrease in childlessness, fewer large families, and a younger age
at parenthood. Generation fertility is projected to be 2. 5 children or
about 20 per 1000 for the next 15 years. 10 references (author abstract modified)

542   Steger, R. W. "Aging and the Hypothalamo-Hypophyseal-Godadal
      Axis," Chapter 4 in Hafez, E. S. E. (ed.), Aging and Repro-
      ductive Physiology, Vol. 2 of Perspectives in Human Reproduc-
      tion, pp. 51-65. Ann Arbor, MI: Ann Arbor Science, 1976.
      This chapter begins with an introduction and then proceeds to
cover ovarian function and reproductive senescence (including oocyte
population), endocrine function (including corpora lutea function), pituitary function in aged animals (including morphology, gonadotropin
regulation and pituitary responsiveness), hypothalamus function in
aged animals, steroid feedback, and a summary section. Animals
and humans are both discussed. 64 references

543   Stoeckel, John, and Choudhury, Moqbul A. "Differential Fertil-
      ity in a Rural Area of East Pakistan," in Milbank Memorial
      Fund Quarterly, Vol. 47, 189-198, 1969.
      Social and economic development affects status groups' fertility
differences. Late marriages have a higher fertility rate. Marital
fertility was found to be 7. 2 births. The IUD and sterilization are
suggested as effective methods of contraception. 30 references

544   Sweetser, Frank L. , and Piepponen, Paavo. "Postwar Fertility
      Trends and Their Consequences in Finland and the United
      States," in Journal of Social History, Vol. 1, No. 2, 101-118,
      Winter 1967.
      Tables are presented which show postwar fertility trends in
Finland and the United States. Age structure affects fertility and
sustained periods of low fertility and high fertility affect age structure. Periods of high fertility produce large age-cohorts who will
move from childhood to old age over time. These large age-cohorts
will have many far-reaching effects in the continuing social history
of nations. 4 footnotes

545   Teitelbaum, Michael S. ; Mantel, Nathan; and Stark, Charles R.
      "Limited Dependence on the Human Sex Ratio on Birth Order
      and Parental Ages," in American Journal of Human Genetics,
      Vol. 23, 271-280, 1971.
      A reanalysis of a study by Novitski and Kimball (1958) does
not support the same conclusions. Using the data from the Novitski
and Kimball (1958), the researchers in this paper used the extended
Mantel-Haenszel X^2 (chi squared) procedure and found no significance
for paternal age as causing a birth-order effect. A reversal of birth-
order effect may occur as paternal age increases. Race may also
affect data analysis. 21 references

546   Weg, Ruth B. "Normal Aging in the Reproductive System: Sex-
      uality of Age," in Burnside, Irene Mortenson (ed.), Nursing
      and the Aged, pp. 99-112. New York: McGraw-Hill, 1976.

The author begins the chapter with historical and cultural perspectives of aging and reproduction.   Sexuality and the whole person
and sexuality in old age including the role of sex and sexuality in
later life follow.   Physical changes in the male and female reproductive systems are presented.   Some attention is given to the climacteric.   Bases for sexual dysfunction are covered.   Eight implications
for the helping professions wrap up the chapter.   55 references

547   Wharton, Lawrence R.   "Normal Pregnancy with Living Children
      in Women Past the Age of Fifty," in American Journal of Ob-
      stetrics and Gynecology, Vol. 90, No. 5, 672-681, November
      1, 1964.   (Presented at the Eighty-seventh Annual Meeting of
      the American Gynecological Society, Hot Springs, Virginia,
      May 25-27, 1964.)
      There is no way to place an upper limit on the age of a woman
who can possibly have a baby even though the possibility is negligible
after 50.   There have been a number of authentic cases of healthy
births by women over 50.   Therefore, the author suggests that contraception be continued for about a year after menstruation has stopped.
Discussion follows by Dr. M. Edward Davis of Chicago, Illinois; Dr.
R. Gordon Douglas, New York, New York; and Dr. Nicholson J. East-
man, of New York, New York.   27 references

548   Woolf, Charles M.   "Stillbirths and Parental Age," in Obste-
      trics and Gynecology, Vol. 26, No. 1, 1-8, July 1965.
      A covariance method was used to analyze stillbirths in the
state of Arizona from 1958-1961 to determine if parental age had any
effect on this outcome.   Controls were the live births which occurred
during 1960.   Increased maternal and paternal age is associated with
stillbirths in certain coded groups.   Increased paternal age is important for stillbirths coded as ill-defined cause of death.   Father's age
should be included in vital statistics and obstetrics records.   10 references

SEXUAL PROBLEMS AND AGING

549   Beck, Aaron T.   "Sexuality and Depression," in Medical Aspects of Human Sexuality, Vol. 2, No. 7, 44-51, July 1968.
      Depression is defined in the beginning of this discussion.   Loss of libido in depression and causes of libido loss are covered next.   The relationship of promiscuity is pointed out.   Sexual arousal can be an antidote to depression.   Forced abstinence can bring on depression.   Emotion-laden imagery can be an antidote to anxiety or depression.   Reduced sex drive and enjoyment can be a manifestation of depression.   2 references.

550   Bellak, Leopold.   "Crisis Intervention in Geriatric Psychiatry," pp. 175-189 in Bellak, Leopold; Karasu, Toksoz B.; and Birenbaum, Caroline (eds.), Geriatric Psychiatry: A Handbook for Psychiatrists and Primary Care Physicians.   New York: Grune and Stratton, Inc., 1976.
      One of many problems which may require crisis intervention includes sexual acting-out.   10 references

551   _____; Karasu, Toksoz B.; and Birenbaum, Caroline.   Geriatric Psychiatry: A Handbook for Psychiatrists and Primary Care Physicians.   New York: Grune and Stratton, 1976.   (Reviewed by Martin Merowitz in Journal of Geriatric Psychology, Vol. 11, No. 1, 89-90, 1978.)
      Two sections are relevant and are reviewed separately in this annotated bibliography.   The sections are concerned with 1) sexual decline and impotence, and 2) crisis intervention.   The section on sexual decline and impotence was written by Alex Louis Finkle.   The section on crisis intervention was written by Leopold Bellak.   Masturbation and female sexuality in the aging are not covered.   These sections are annotated separately in this bibliography.

552   Benjamin, Harry.   "Impotence and Aging," in Sexology, Vol. 26, 238-243, November 1959.
      Several case studies are presented to show that proper treatment of impotence can lead to a satisfying and healthy life for aging men.   No references

553   _____.   "The Role of the Physician in the Sex Problems of the Aged," in Advances in Sex Research, Vol. 1, 143-150, 1963.   (S.A., Vol. 12, No. 6, B 2164, 1964.)
      Medical and psychological support should be given by the physician to the older person with regard to any sex problems they

might have. In providing permissive support, the physician should
take into consideration the psychosexual personality and general state
of health of the patient. Unless hormone treatment is contraindicated,
it can improve the patient's state of health and sexual performance.
There is no better preservation of youth for older people than to
enjoy sexual activity.

554 Bergevin, Patrick R. "The Increasing Problems of Malignancy
     in the Elderly," in Medical Clinics of North America, Vol.
     60, No. 6, 1241-1251, November 1976.
        Problems of malignancy including cancer of the prostate, can-
cer of the breast, colon and rectal cancer, and cancer of the uterine
endometrium are covered. 12 references

555 Bowers, L. M.; Cross, R. R., Jr.; and Lloyd, F. A. "Sex-
     ual Function and Urologic Disease in the Elderly Male," in
     Journal of the American Geriatrics Society, Vol. 11, No. 7,
     647-652, July 1963.
        Incidence of impotence was reported for 157 males from ages
60 to 74 years. The incidence of impotence rose from 30 percent to
60 percent. Males who were potent had intercourse 20 times during
the year. Incidence of disease or urological disease as well as non-
urologic disease was the same for both the group of impotent men
and the group of potent men. According to this report, impotence is
independent of the physical condition of the male. 3 references

556 Brenton, Myron. "How I Overcame Impotence: As Told to
     Myron Brenton," in Forum: The International Journal of Hu-
     man Relations, Vol. 8, No. 3, 18-22, December 1978.
        A personal account of how a man overcame impotence with
the help of an understanding and sympathetic woman in conjunction
with psychotherapy.

557 _____. Sex and Your Heart. New York: Coward-McCann, 1968.
        Topics of discussion include sexual intercourse--possible strain
on heart, the adjustments of heart patients to sex lives, the heart
patient's spouse, and what happens to the heart during sexual intercourse. Both healthy men and women and heart patients were clin-
ically studied for the information contained here.

558 Burnap, Donald W., and Golden, Joshua S. "Sexual Problems
     in Medical Practice," in Journal of Medical Education, Vol.
     42, 673-680, July 1967.
        The population for this study was 87 physicians who were ran-
domly selected. A semistructured interview technique was used to
obtain information on the importance of sexual problems in medical
practice. Sexual problems related to what was considered "normal"
intercourse were more common than those about perversions and
homosexuality. The physicians dealt with sexual problems of their
patients but had little training in sexuality. 11 references

559 Calderone, Mary Steichen. "Sexual Problems in Medical Prac-
     tice," in Journal of the American Medical Women's Association,

Vol. 23, No. 2, 140-146, February 1968. (This was a paper
given at the 1st Alice Stone Woolley Memorial Lecture of the
American Medical Women's Association before the Ohio State
Medical Association at Columbus, Ohio, May 17, 1967.)
    Sexual problems can be primary or secondary: primary mean-
ing those of the sexual system; and secondary meaning those resultant
from other system disturbances in the body. Dr. Calderone classi-
fies sexual problems as 1) sexual anatomical anomalies and ambigui-
ties, 2) sexual problems secondary or incidental to another health
problem, 3) sexual problems occurring during the change of the life
cycle, 4) sexual problems relating to contraceptive techniques, and
5) sexual problems stemming from childhood conditioning. Sex should
be a source of joy to an individual and society instead of a source of
problems. 8 references

560 Carr, Charles M. "Sexual Problems Seen in Family Practice,"
     in Journal of the Tennessee Medical Association, Vol. 69,
     No. 12, 847-848, December 1976.
     Some of the most difficult marital problems are ones coming
to a head in a marriage which has lasted for 25 years. Impotence
can be a result of drug use including Aldomet, Reserpine, and In-
deral. Sometimes Chlorthalidone can give some men a limp erection.
A physician should be sensitive to the patient's sex life and be prepared to change drugs accordingly. Sympathy and understanding
should be used in the office treatment of sexual problems. No references

561 Claman, A. D.; Swartz, David; Kinch, R. A. H.; Hirt, Norman
     B. "Sex Difficulties After 50: Panel Discussion," in Canad-
     ian Medical Association Journal, Vol. 94, No. 5, 207-217,
     246-247, January 29, 1966. (A panel discussion which was
     presented at the 97th Annual Meeting of the Canadian Medical
     Association, Vancouver, British Columbia, June 23, 1964.)
     Dr. A. D. Claman provides the "Introduction." Dr. David
Swartz provides "Sexual Difficulties After 50: The Urologist's View."
In this presentation, he covers the male climacteric, frequency of
coitus in older men, the anatomical basis of erection and ejaculation,
and prostatectomy and potency. R. A. H. Kinch provides "Sexual
Difficulties After 50: The Gynecologist's View." It deals with some
general sexual problems after 50 and quotes the Duke University and
Kinsey studies which relate to sexuality and aging and women in particular. Dr. Norman B. Hirt provides "Sexual Difficulties After 50:
The Psychiatrist's View." He makes the important point that the
psychiatrist is often involved in iatrogenic sexual problems in older
people mainly because of the attending physician's inability to explore
these areas. Three cases are presented to illustrate the relationship
of expressed symptoms to the hidden fears concerning sexuality. General discussion follows (pp. 215-217, and 246-247).

562 Cole, Theodore M., and Cole, Sandra S. "Sexuality and Phys-
     ical Disabilities: The Physician's Role," in Minnesota Medi-
     cine, Vol. 60, No. 7, Part I, 525-529, July 1977.
     Medical treatment should include establishing sexual health.

Information is available to physicians on including sexuality in the treatment of disabled patients. Physical disabilities fall into four groups depending upon the different influences on the sexuality of the patient. 7 references

563   Coleman, Vernon. Everything You Want to Know About Ageing, pp. 66-70. London: Gordon and Cremonesi, n. d.
      A discussion on sexual problems of older people including problems of impotence and problems during the menopause. Remarriage in retirement is encouraged as is sex in the later years for those who want it. Sexual aids for older men and women with sexual problems are suggested for specific problems.

564   Cooper, Alan J. "Outpatient Treatment of Impotence," in Journal of Nervous and Mental Diseases, Vol. 149, No. 4, 360-371, 1969.
      Of 57 patients who had psychogenic (primary) impotence or impotentia ejaculandi, 44 (77 percent) satisfied the "treated" criterion by going to at least 20 sessions in one year. Therapy included participation by both partners whenever possible. Only 19 subjects (43 percent) were improved or recovered and 25 (57 percent) stayed the same or got worse. Profiles for both good responders and poor responders are set forth. 30 references.

565   Denber, Herman C. B. "Sexual Problems in the Mature Female," in Psychosomatics, Vol. 9, 40-43, July-August, Section 2, 1968.
      Topics discussed by Dr. Denber include the sexual act, marriage, frigidity, and the changing period (menopause). Psychotherapy and pharmacotherapy are suggested to treat the anxiety, tension, restlessness, depression, autonomic and somatic symptoms which may plague the woman at this time. 12 references

566   Dlin, Barney M. , and Perlman, Abraham. "Emotional Response to Ileostomy and Colostomy in Patients over the Age of 50," in Geriatrics, Vol. 26, No. 6, 112-118, June 1971.
      At least one year of recovery is needed for the average ostomate. A good indicator of the patient's degree of recovery is the return of sexual interest and function. Patients with a poor sexual adjustment should be referred for psychiatric treatment. 2 references

567   Eton, Bruce. "Gynecologic Surgery in Elderly Women," in Geriatrics, Vol. 28, No. 11, 119-123, November 1973.
      Contains important considerations in selecting patients for surgery, and sections on prolapse of the uterus, incontinence, and cancer. General principles in gynecologic surgery are presented including preoperative assessment, operative precautions, immediate postoperative care, thromboembolism, and pulmonary collapse. Age doesn't have to be a contraindication to radical surgery if the patient is healthy, in good physical condition, and the prospects of cure justify the procedure.

568   Fellman, Sheldon L. ; Hastings, Donald W. ; Kupperman, Herbert

S.; and Miller, William M., Jr. "Viewpoints: Should Androgens Be Used to Treat Impotence in Men over 50?" in Medical
Aspects of Human Sexuality, Vol. 9, No. 7, 32-43, July 1975.
A discussion by four physicians on the benefits of the use of
androgens to treat impotence in men over 50. No references

569   Finkle, Alex Louis. "Sex Problems in Later Years," in Med-
      ical Times, Vol. 95, No. 4, 416-419, April 1967. (Presented
      March 20, 1965, in a symposium entitled "Sex Disorders in
      Clinical Practice," at the University of California Medical
      Center, San Francisco, California.)
      Aging men desire and should have sex. Physicians should en-
courage sexual activity in their patients. 7 references

570   _____; Moyers, Thomas G.; Tobenkin, Mark I.; and Karg,
      Sara J. "Sexual Potency in Aging Males: 1. Frequency of
      Coitus Among Clinic Patients," in Journal of the American
      Medical Association, Vol. 170, No. 12, 1391-1393, July 18,
      1959.
      A study of 101 men between the ages of 55 and 86 is presented.
Clinical questions were asked as well as questions on sexual activity.
The men were ambulant patients whose complaints did not prevent
sexual activity. Some 65 percent or 33 of 51 patients 69 years old
or less were potent. That is, they had intercourse at least one time
during the previous year. Some 34 percent or 17 of 50 patients who
were over 70 years of age were potent. Sexual activity was reported
by two men over 80, and they had coitus an average of ten times during the year. A general decline in sexual activity occurs with age,
but great differences are seen among individuals. 10 references

571   _____, and Prian, Dimitry V. "Sexual Potency in Elderly
      Men Before and After Prostatectomy," in Journal of the Amer-
      ican Medical Association, Vol. 196, No. 2, 139-143, April 11,
      1966. (This was read before the Oregon Urological Society,
      Portland, June 11, 1965.)
      Patients treated in private practice were reviewed for sexual
activity before and after prostatectomy. A total of 102 males were
reviewed. A majority (67 percent) of the men were potent before the
operation and 84 percent retained potency after the operation no matter what surgical route was used for the prostatectomy. The most
important factor in maintaining sexual potency after prostatectomy is
a willing sexual partner. Physicians need to understand the sexual
functioning of prostatectomy patients. 12 references

572   Finkle, Joan E.; Finkle, Paul S.; and Finkle, Alex Louis. "En-
      couraging Preservation of Sexual Function Postprostatectomy,"
      in Urology, Vol. 6, No. 6, 697-702, December 1975. (Pre-
      sented at Tenth International Congress of Gerontology, Jeru-
      salem, Israel, June 23, 1975.)
      Prostatectomy patients (N=128), most of whom had undergone
perirenal prostatectomies, were reviewed concerning their sexual
function. These patients were treated in private practice over a
twenty-year period by a urologist biased toward retaining sexual

function after the operation. A prostatectomy need not impair sexual potency. The urologist and/or physician should encourage post-operative sexual function. 63 references (author abstract modified)

573   Freeman, Joseph T. "John S. --Widower," in Journal of the American Geriatrics Society, Vol. 18, No. 9, 736-742, September 1970.
      Dr. Freeman presents a paper written by a surgeon in 1895 entitled "Old Age a Myth." It was published in the Toledo Medical and Surgical Reporter Series of 1895, No. 3, and was written by James A. Duncan, M.D. He describes a surgical procedure which helped "John S., aged 66, widower" have erections. The original title of the 1895 article was misnamed. Re-potentiation is not exactly the same as rejuvenation. 8 references (author abstract modified)

574   Freese, Arthur S. Protecting Yourself from Prostate Problems. New York: Public Affairs Pamphlet No. 532, 1976.
      This illustrated pamphlet discusses evolution and the prostate, anatomy of the prostate, its function, warning signals about impending problems, the diagnosing of prostate problems, cancer of the prostate, and sexual effects and concerns connected with prostate problems.

575   Gaitz, Charles M., and Scott, Judith. "Analysis of Letters to 'Dear Abby' Concerning Old Age," in Gerontologist, Vol. 15, No. 1, 47-50, 1975.
      Over 300 letters to Dear Abby were analyzed to ascertain the prime concerns of older people. One of the topics of most concern was sexual problems.

576   Galton, Lawrence. "Impotence: What Medicine Can Do for It Now," in Parade, p. 20, April 23, 1978.
      This is a general discussion of the problem of impotence. Alcohol and diabetes as well as common tranquilizers and antidepressants can cause impotence. Nocturnal penile tumescence (NPT) monitoring is a way of determining whether impotence is organic or psychological.

577   Glover, Benjamin H. "Disorders of Sexuality and Communication in the Elderly," in Comprehensive Therapy, Vol. 3, No. 6, 21-25, June 1977.
      Sexual problems of older people are covered in this article aimed primarily at physicians. The importance of counseling is emphasized as well as counseling methods and treatment of communication problems.

578   _____. "Problems of Aging: Sex in the Aging," in Postgraduate Medicine, Vol. 57, No. 6, 165-169, 1975.
      This article was adapted from a course on problem solving in clinical geriatrics held at the University of Wisconsin, Madison. Many elderly are deprived of sex due to social restraints. This sexual activity would benefit them emotionally and physically. Sections include 1) social restraints on the elderly, 2) sex after a heart attack, 3) the widower's syndrome, 4) effects of aging on sex drive, 5) drugs

that affect potency and libido, 6) sexual adequacy at different ages,
7) more and better sex with age, 8) conclusion. A good mental,
emotional, and physical status can be maintained through the encouragement of sex activity in the elderly. 15 references

579   Gold, Fred M. , and Hotchkiss, Robert S. "Sexual Potency Fol-
      lowing Simple Prostatectomy," in New York State Journal of
      Medicine, Vol. 69, 2987-2989, December 1, 1969.
        Sexual potency in 94 men was examined one year following
prostate surgery. The postoperative diminished potency was said to
be unrelated to type of prostatectomy but was a function of age. Statistical data are presented which support these conclusions. 5 references

580   Golden, Joshua S. "Management of Sexual Problems by the
      Physician," in Obstetrics and Gynecology, Vol. 23, No. 3,
      471-474, March 1964.
        Human sexuality has not been adequately studied. In dealing
with sexual problems, two things come into play: 1) patient problems
and 2) problems which the physician brings to the situation. Much
of the current available information on sexuality is wrong. The physician should be a resource of sexual information for the patient. 4
references

581   Hartman, William E. , and Fithian, Marilyn A. The Treatment
      of Sexual Dysfunction: A Bio-Psycho-Social Approach. New
      York: Jason Aronson, 1974.
        Presents an approach to dealing with the sexual problems of
people.

582   Hastings, Donald W. "Problems of Impotence," in Sexology,
      Vol. 31, 90-92, September 1964.
        Impotence is most often caused by psychological or emotional
problems. Some impotence is due to drugs and a few cases are due
to actual physical disease. No references

583   Herschcopf, Berta R. "Impotence: A Case Study," in Nursing
      Care, Vol. 10, No. 7, 14-15, 1977.
        This case study involving Eunice and John B. suggests that
many different factors can cause sexual dysfunction. A process which
involves facing and solving problems should be used in order to cure
patients with this problem. No references

584   Johnson, G. Timothy. Everyman's Guide to Prostate Trouble.
      New York: Newspaperbooks, 1977.
        Contains general information on the prostate with accompanying
diagrams. The pamphlet goes on to explain infectious prostatitis,
chronic prostatitis, prostatosis, and benign prostatic hyperplasia. In
addition, cancer of the prostate and methods of treatment are presented as well as sex and the prostate.

585   Johnson, John. Disorders of Sexual Potency in the Male. Ox-
      ford: Pergamon, 1968.

Topics covered by this book include: 1) literary and historical aspects of disorders of sexual potency, 2) biology of disordered potency in the male, 3) definition, incidence and legal aspects of impotence including causation of impotence, 4) clinical investigation of disorder of potency, 5) disorders of ejaculation, 6) disorders of sexual potency, constitution and psychiatric illness, 7) prognosis and treatment of disorders of sexual potency, and 8) a concluding chapter.

586   Kent, Saul. "Being Aware of a Patient's Sexual Problems Should Be the Concern of Every Physician," in Geriatrics, Vol. 30, No. 1, 140, 142, 1975.
Most sexual disorders are psychogenic in origin. Prevailing societal attitudes compound the sexual problems of aging men and women. Results of a survey of 60 physicians are reported to determine how they dealt with their patients' sexual problems. Very few physicians are trained to manage sexual problems even though the problems are quite common. Physicians should project a self-assured, understanding, and professional attitude toward their patients with sexual problems.

587   _____. "Impotence as a Consequence of Organic Disease," in Geriatrics, Vol. 30, No. 9, 155, 157, September 1975.
Fifty percent of diabetic men are affected by loss of potency. Loss of potency is probably due to neurologic complications. 2 references

588   _____. "Impotence: The Facts Versus the Fallacies," in Geriatrics, Vol. 30, No. 4, 164, 169, 171, April 1975.
If physiologic changes can be separated from psychogenic factors of impotence, the problem can be solved. Fear of failure is a self-fulfilling prophecy which is the root of the problem. Some men can be sexually reactivated by use of steroid replacement therapy. No references

589   _____. "Urinary Tract Problems in Women Are Linked to Sexual Activity," in Geriatrics, Vol. 30, No. 7, 145-146, July 1975.
Sexual and urologic dysfunction can result from bacteria and bacterial irritation which is transmitted through sexual intercourse. Causes of dysfunction, therapy for recurrent infection, and suggestions for counseling are given. No references

590   Kentsmith, David K., and Eaton, Merrill T., Jr. Treating Sexual Problems in Medical Practice. New York: Arco Publishing, 1979. (Reviewed by Daniel H. Labby in SIECUS Report, Vol. 8, No. 2, 11-12, November 1979.)
The book is mainly aimed at medical care personnel and includes information on sexual activity in later life, extramarital affairs, menopause, divorce and sexual problems. Also, there is a section on "Sex During Illness."

591   Kleegman, Sophia J. "Female Sex Problems," in Sexology, Vol. 31, 226-229, November 1964.

130   Sexuality and Aging

A series of eight questions are answered by Dr. Kleegman on
the sexual difficulties of the wife. Specific topics of the questions
and answers include 1) removal of ovaries when a woman has a hysterectomy, 2) development of cancer in ovaries, 3) estrogen therapy,
4) the possible susceptibility of older women to cancer if given estrogen, 5) recommendations of the physician to a woman so that she
might enjoy a continued sex life in the later years, 6) time differences of intercourse in producing a male baby or female baby, 7) artificial insemination, and 8) reply to criticism of artificial insemination. No references

592 _____ . "Frigidity in Women," in Quarterly Review of Sur-
        gery, Obstetrics, and Gynecology, Vol. 16, 243-248, October-
        December 1959.
        Parents need to be educated to have healthy attitudes toward
marriage and sex. Medical students and physicians also need to be
educated. A premarital examination and interview should be done;
and as a result of this, somatic causes of dyspareunia may be detected. Postmenopausal atrophy and dyspareunia should be prevented
by the physician in order that sex might be enjoyed during this year.
General practitioners are the ones who can help prevent these problems as they see most of the problems. A loving potent man can be
the best prescription for a frigid woman. 5 references

593 Kolodny, Robert C. "Sexual Dysfunction in Diabetic Females,"
        in Diabetes, Vol. 20, No. 8, 557-559, August 1971.
        Caucasian women were the only ones studied in this research.
Diabetic women (N=125) and nondiabetic women (N=100) ranging in age
from 18 to 42 were interviewed. The purpose of the interviews was
to determine the incidence of sexual dysfunction in the two groups.
Complete nonorgasmic function during the preceding year was reported
by 44 of the 125 diabetic women and by 6 of the 100 nondiabetic women.
That is, 35.2 percent of diabetic women and 6 percent of nondiabetic
women were nonorgasmic. The difference was significant at the
$p < .01$ level. Duration of diabetes was strongly correlated with sexual dysfunction. Very little association was found between sexual dysfunction and age, dose of insulin, neuropathy, vaginitis, retinopathy
or nephropathy. In cases where sexual dysfunction is felt to be on
an organic basis but appears after normal sexual functioning, the term
"secondary orgasmic dysfunction" is used. 8 references

594 _____ ; Kahn, Charles B.; Goldstein, H. Howard, and Barnett,
        Donald M. "Sexual Dysfunction in Diabetic Men," in Diabetes,
        Vol. 23, No. 4, 306-309, April 1974.
        Sexual functioning in 175 diabetic males was studied. The pa-
tients were chosen at random. Medical, sexual histories, blood count,
urinalysis, physical examination, T4, 12-channel chemistry screening
profile and plasma testosterone determination were tests used to col-
lect data. Impotence was found in 85 of the 175 men (49 percent) and
4 had premature ejaculation (2 percent) while 2 had retrograde ejaculation (1 percent). Impotence came on gradually (in the impotent
group) from about six months to a year. More than 90 percent of the
impotent males showed patterns of organic impotence development.

Androgen deficiency was not an etiologic factor in the group of impotent men. 15 references (author's abstract modified)

595 Laver, M. C. "Sexual Behaviour Patterns in Male Hyperten-
       sives," in Australian, New Zealand Journal of Medicine, Vol.
       4, No. 1, 29-31, February 1974.
       Male patients in a hypertensive clinic were systematically sur-
veyed. Eighty-eight patients were studied, and it was found that 40
men had decreased potency which was blamed on drug therapy. Severe hypertensives and large doses of all drugs resulted in a higher
incidence of potency decrease. 6 references (author's summary modified)

596 Leader, Abel J. Elective Vasectomy. Norwich, NY: Eaton
       Laboratories, n. d.
       This is a 14-page booklet which describes different methods
of contraception but presents the vasectomy as the simplest, least
expensive, and most dependable method. A series of questions and
answers are presented about vasectomies. Instructions are presented
for the patient who is preparing himself for vasectomy and instructions are also presented for the patient to follow after vasectomy.
The technique of vasectomy is presented in 16 steps, presumably as
a guide to the physician and also to let the patient know exactly what
will happen to him. Seven illustrations are provided to clarify the
operative procedure. Advantages of the technique which is presented
and illustrated are given. Finally, on the last page, a consent for
sterilization operation form is provided. No references

597 Leviton, Dan. "The Intimacy/Sexual Needs of the Terminally
       Ill and the Widowed," in Death Education, Vol. 2, 261-280,
       Fall 1978.
       The author's discussion is limited to the widow. After pre-
senting definitions, the author presents a social-demographic picture
of widowhood as well as health status of the widowed and sexual behavior of the widowed. He then presents some research on intimacy
and discusses death as stress. Seven implications for death education and counseling are presented. 31 references

598 Lilius, H. G.; Valtonen, Erkki J.; Wikström, Juhani. "Sexual
       Problems in Patients Suffering from Multiple Sclerosis," in
       Journal of Chronic Disability, Vol. 29, 643-647, 1976.
       Some 302 patients with multiple sclerosis (MS) filled out anony-
mous questionnaires concerning their sexual lives. More than half
had a nonexistent or unsatisfying sexual life. In 91 percent of the
males and 72 percent of the females, the sex life was changed. Most
of the patients were in poor physical condition. Only 20 percent of
the men had normal erections with 62 percent having problems with
erection. Women had orgasm loss (33 percent), spasticity (12 percent), and loss of libido (27 percent). Duration of multiple sclerosis
and incidence of sexual disturbances were not correlated. Symptoms
of spinal origin occur concomitantly with neurological problems in sex
life. Different ways of having intercourse under these conditions are
discussed. 3 references

599   Martin, Maurice J.   "Frigidity, Impotence and the Family," in
        Psychosomatics, Vol. 9, No. 4 (2 sections) 2nd section, 8-11,
        July-August 1968.   (This was read at the meeting of the Acad-
        emy of Psychosomatic Medicine, Houston, Texas, November
        30 to December 2, 1967.)
            Frigidity or impotence rarely exists as a problem by itself
but may be symptomatic of other problems of daily life.   These problems may be relieved by the solving of the basic problems of basic
life.   If the patient's physician can provide reassurance and support,
the frigidity and impotence may be ameliorated.   Importance should
be placed on stressing three main points; namely 1) physicians must
be nonjudgmental in the treatment of sexual problems, 2) the sexual
problem may be a reflection of other parts of life which are not going
well, 3) impotence in the man and frigidity in the woman can have
many causes.   7 references

600   Masters, William H. , and Johnson, Virginia E.   Human Sexual
        Inadequacy.   Boston: Little, Brown and Co. , 1970.
            Contains two chapters of importance.   Chapter 12 entitled
"Sexual Inadequacy in the Aging Male" and chapter 13 entitled "Sexual
Inadequacy in the Aging Female. "   Both are annotated separately in
this bibliography.

601   Mozes, Eugene B.   "Impotence: What the Wife Can Do," in Sex-
        ology, Vol. 26, 176-181, October 1959.
            A case study begins this article to illustrate what the wife can
do psychologically and physically to help her husband overcome impotence.   No references

602   Nicholas, Leslie, and Lentz, John W.   "Diagnosis of Syphilis
        in Geriatric Patient," in Geriatrics, Vol. 23, 169-174, Sep-
        tember 1968.
            The problem of diagnosing syphilis in the geriatric patient is
compounded by the multiplicity of syphilitic manifestations, the less
frequent routine tests of blood serum for the syphilis, and the diminished index of suspicion.   15 references

603   Oberleder, Muriel.   "Crisis Therapy in Mental Breakdown of the
        Aging," in Gerontologist, Vol. 10, 111-114, 1970.   (This is
        based on a paper presented at the 21st Annual Meeting of the
        Gerontological Society, Denver, November 1, 1968.)
            Crisis therapy was used to treat a random selection of "senile"
State Hospital patients.   Life crises had brought on institutionalization
in all of the cases, but six months of treatment resulted in a return
to normal.   Twelve patients diagnosed as having chronic brain syndrome (CBS) or arteriosclerosis with psychosis were involved in the
treatment.   The average age of the patients was 76. 4 years.   Staff,
family, and community worked together to facilitate a speedy discharge.
Recovery potential of these patients was studied after discharge.   Symptoms originally associated with senility can be prevented and treated
differently.   Distorted drawings were produced by some of the more
intact patients.   An explanation for this was suggested.   The drawings may have been a dissociative mechanism to manage sexual and

aggressive feelings. There was free expression without fear with sex as a favorite subject. Only a small amount of embarrassment was exhibited when talking about masturbation. There were some sexual "acting-out" reactions. Non-acting out patients would complain about bizarre physical symptoms centering around the genital or urinary areas. 5 references

604 _____. "Managing Problem Behaviors of Elderly Patients," in Hospital and Community Psychiatry, Vol. 27, No. 5, 325-330, 1976.
    Management of behavior problems of older people is covered including inappropriate sexual behaviors.

605 Peberdy, Geoffrey. "Sex and Its Problems. X. Sexual Adjustment at the Climacteric," in Practitioner, Vol. 199, 564-571, October 1967.
    The practitioner's aim is to provide encouragement to the patient about the normality of sexuality in middle and later years. Coital rates decline and middle life problems can affect sexuality. Marital adjustments need to be made in the middle years. Contraception can also be a problem but contraception should continue one year after the last period of women over 45 years. Psychosexual adjustments may need to be made. Domestic and social pressures can decrease sexual interest. Cessation of menstruation does not have to affect sexual response, but sexual drives may increase due to lack of fear of pregnancy. Depression can easily occur during the climacteric. Hysterectomies can cause depression and sexual problems. Hormonal changes can cause emotional instabilities. Middle life finds inner emotional changes occurring for both men and women. No references

606 Pilmer, Gordon A. Chronic Prostatitis: "Prostate Trouble." Norwich, NY: Eaton Laboratories, 1962, 1974.
    This ten-page booklet was written for men who suffer from chronic prostatitis. Some general points are first presented. The cause of chronic prostatitis is then discussed and three illustrations are used to clarify the discussion. Finally, symptoms and signs of chronic prostatitis are presented. No references

607 _____. Chronic Urethritis in the Female. Norwich, NY: Eaton Laboratories, 1963.
    This is a pamphlet that a general practitioner or urologist would give a chronic urethritis patient. It provides space for an appointment schedule and special instructions to be written by the doctor. The pamphlet explains what chronic urethritis is, the causes of it, and provides three illustrations for clarification. Finally, infection is explained as well as treatment of the infection and symptoms of chronic urethritis are given. No references

608 Pollak, Gertrude K. "Coping with Sexual Needs After Divorce or Death of Spouse," in her Leadership of Discussion Groups: Case Material and Theory, pp. 225-251. New York: Spectrum Publications, Inc., 1975.
    Contains the proceedings of a seminar for the separated, di-

134   Sexuality and Aging

vorced, and widowed members of the Single Parents Society of Philadelphia, which is actually a local equivalent of Parents Without Partners. Emphasis was on the adults' problems as related to their plans
for remarriage or other ways to rebuild their lives. The seminar
focused on the attitudes and emotions of group members who took
great responsibility for planning and organizing the seminar. The
sexual needs after divorce or death of a spouse may vary widely depending on the individual person. The sexual problems of this group
are well discussed in the seminar but solutions and resolutions are
not given a great deal of time perhaps due to the variety of needs of
the participants.

609   Post, Felix. "Management of Senile Psychiatric Disorders," in
        British Medical Journal, Vol. 4, 627-630, December 7, 1968.
        A section on sexual problems is included in this article. The
author suggests that anxiety and distress can be avoided by reassurance from the physician based on knowledge of the patient's sexual situation and the possible effects of sexual activity in his or her physical
state.   8 references suggested for further reading

610   _____. "Sex and Its Problems: IX. Disorders of Sex in the
        Elderly," in Practitioner, Vol. 199, 377-382, September 1967.
        Although sexual interests and activities decline with age, they
can be retained until shortly before death. Advice can be given to
elderly patients with serious physical disease about sexual adjustment.
Counseling can be provided before and after urogenital operations.
Changes in sexual patterns of the aged may indicate depression or
other psychiatric disorders. Sympathetic counseling for sexual anxieties in the elderly can be very helpful. 15 references

611   Proctor, Richard C. "Impotence--A Defense Mechanism," in
        Journal of the American Geriatrics Society, Vol. 17, No. 9,
        874-879, September 1969.
        A paper focusing primarily on the psychological factors leading
to impotence; however, organic factors are mentioned. 4 references

612   Raboch, Jan. "Two Studies of Male Sex Impotence," in Journal
        of Sex Research, Vol. 6, No. 3, 181-187, August 1970.
        A presentation of two studies is given. Potency difficulties in
a group of 600 men were examined in the first study. Analysis indicated that 66 percent of these men failed after going through a number of good sexual relations. Thirty-three percent sought help for
their sexual difficulties very early. The second study focused on
functional disturbances in the sexual lives of 2,087 men. Chronological age was correlated with pathological symptoms. Subgroups around
20 years old had the most anxieties about sexual inadequacy. Premature ejaculation was highest in these men from 26 to 30 years old.
Male sexual frigidity was highest between 46 and 50 years old. Failure to achieve erection was the most common problem and was experienced by 50 percent of the cases. Failure to achieve erection
increased with age.   3 references

613   Renshaw, Domeena C. "Sexuality and Depression in Adults and

the Elderly," in Medical Aspects of Human Sexuality, Vol. 9,
No. 9, 40-62, September 1975.
Depression can cause sexual problems. When it does, the
problems can be reversible by medical treatment if treated quickly.
16 references

614   Robinson, William J.   "Sexual Impotence and Mental Decay: The
        Confession of a Man of Seventy," in Journal of Sexology and
        Psychoanalysis, Vol. 1, No. 2, 118-120, March 1923.
        A case study of a man of 70 who questions his physician about
mental decay following his impotence.   Impotence is not followed by
mental decay; in fact, the case study patient was satisfied with impotence and enjoyed several positive afteraffects: 1) he had improved
health, 2) he ate better, 3) he slept better, and 4) accomplished much
more than before the onset of impotence.   Many men can show a new
lease of life after their climacterium.   No references

615   Rodgers, David A.; Ziegler, Frederick J.; and Leyy, Nissim.
        "Prevailing Cultural Attitudes About Vasectomy: A Possible
        Explanation of Postoperative Psychological Response," in Psy-
        chosomatic Medicine, Vol. 29, No. 4, 367-375, 1967.
        If a couple have derogatory attitudes about vasectomy as a
method of contraception, adverse personality changes may be reinforced or initiated.   Two cultural subgroups with common cultural attitudes ascribed less favorable characteristics to couples using vasectomy as contraception than those using ovulation suppression.   Negative personality changes after vasectomy are discussed along with this
study's findings.   14 references (author's abstract modified)

616   Rubin, Isadore. "Climax Without Ejaculation," in Sexology,
        Vol. 30, 694-696, May 1964.
        Diabetes, prostate surgery after-effects, and the use of certain
drugs can cause retrograde ejaculation; that is, backward ejaculation
into the bladder.   This type of ejaculation has no effect on sexual
ability or gratification.   No method of treatment is known.

617   _____.   "Diabetes and Impotence," in Sexology, Vol. 30,
        83-85, September 1963.
        A great number of diabetics do not become impotent and dia-
betes can be controlled by diet or a combination of drugs and diet.
Sexual inadequacy can be the first sign of developing diabetes in the
male.   If a man becomes impotent because of diabetes, the potency
can be restored when the condition is controlled.

618   Runciman, Alexander P. "Problems Older Clients Present in
        Counseling About Sexuality," in Burnside, Irene Mortenson
        (ed.), Sexuality and Aging, pp. 54-66. Los Angeles: Univer-
        sity of Southern California, 1975.
        Very similar to the citation in the Solnick book.   3 references

619   _____.   "Sexual Problems in the Senior World," in Solnick,
        Robert Lewis (ed.), Sexuality and Aging (revised), pp. 78-95.
        Los Angeles: University of Southern California, 1978.

Counselors of the aged with sex problems would find this chapter relevant.   He speaks of the paucity of research data on aged sexuality and very few books on the subject.   Generally, the chapter addresses the common problems with sex that men and women have in their later years and makes some counseling suggestions.   3 references

620   Rutledge, Aaron L.   "Sexual Failure in the Male," in Sexology, Vol. 29, 804-807, July 1963.
Fear of sexual failure can be the major cause of the failure. Mechanical aids are usually not helpful in the treatment of sexual failure.   Older males require manipulation or touch to achieve erection.   Husbands and wives should communicate openly about what continues to please them or what does not.   Men need variety of sexual experience.   No references

621   Schneidman, Barbara, and McGuire, Linda.   "Group Therapy for Non-Orgasmic Women: Two Age Levels," in Archives of Sexual Behavior, Vol. 5, No. 3, 239-247, 1976.
The appropriateness of a group method of therapy was determined for ten women under and ten women over 35 years of age for treatment of primary orgasmic dysfunction.   A Masters and Johnson style of behavioral therapy was combined with a self-stimulation therapy.   Individual treatment may be more successful than group therapy for older women.   10 references

622   "Senile Vaginal Atrophy," in British Medical Journal, Vol. 3, 518, August 30, 1969.
In response to the question about what form of local estrogen (except by mouth because of nausea) could be used to treat dyspareunia due to senile vaginal atrophy, this anonymous answer suggested local treatment of estrogen as suppositories (stilboestrol, dienoestrol, or estrone) or as cream by an applicator.   Regular sexual intercourse should be maintained to prevent the vagina from becoming progressively narrow.

623   "Sex After 50 Held a Matter of Attitude, Not Age," in Medical World News, Vol. 7, No. 18, 68-69, May 13, 1966.
This is a general summary of an article by Claman, A. D.; Swartz, David; Kinch, R. A. H.; and Hirt, Norman B. entitled "Sex Difficulties After 50: Panel Discussion," in Canadian Medical Association Journal, Vol. 94, No. 5, 207-217, 246-247, January 29, 1966. This article is annotated in this bibliography under sex problems.   No references

624   Smith, James W.; Lemere, Frederick; and Dunn, Robert B. "Impotence in Alcoholism," in Northwest Medicine, Vol. 71, 523-524, July 1972.
Alcohol abuse can cause sexual impotence.   Androgenic hormone replacement therapy does not always correct this problem. Glandular deficiency can thus be ruled out as a prime factor.   At the first sign of sexual failure, the heavy drinker should abstain from drinking.   If this isn't done, permanent impotence might result.   2 references

625 Steffl, Bernita M. "Sexuality and Aging: Implications for
     Nurses and Other Helping Professionals," in Solnick, Robert
     Lewis (ed.), Sexuality and Aging (revised), pp. 132-153. Los
     Angeles: University of Southern California, 1978.
     Bernita Steffl's chapter here did not originally appear in Burn-
side's Sexuality and Aging. She covers the problems which health care
professionals who work with the elderly usually encounter. Some
common problems include arthritis and sex and sex after hysterectomy. Common gynecological problems discussed include senile vaginitis, vulvitis, peritoneal pruritis, cystocele and rectocele. Prostatectomies and impotence are common problems for men. Cardiovascular conditions, strokes, Parkinson's Disease are common problems
to both sexes. Suggestions for resumption of sexual activity after illness are given as well as variation of positions for intercourse. Remaining topics covered include organic brain syndrome, sexual acting-
out, aphrodisiacs, drugs and sexuality, sexercise, what to teach old
people, sexuality and the institutionalized elderly and counseling guidelines for professionals. 20 references

626 Weg, Ruth B. "Sexual Inadequacy in the Elderly," in Goldman,
     Ralph, and Rockstein, Morris (eds.), The Physiology and Path-
     ology of Human Aging, pp. 203-227. New York: Academic
     Press, Inc. , 1975.
     A short background section begins this paper. Sexuality must
include the whole personality of a person because it is not separable
from its influence on anatomy and physiology. Sexuality and old age
and the role of sexuality in later life is considered in a broad context.
The behavior and physiology of sexuality for older men and women is
discussed. There is a section on the climacteric. Sexual responsiveness is described by stages. Bases for sexual dysfunction including
coronary disease, hypertension, and diabetes are explained as is potency. A summary section makes suggestions for future work. 68
references

627 Whitehead, Tony. "Self-Distressing Love Affairs in the Elderly,"
     in World Medicine (London), Vol. 10, No. 16, 27-29, 1975.
     Three cases are used to illustrate emotional problems which
are a manifestation of love affairs in older people. The cases were
treated as manifestations of disease. Older people may have many
sexual problems and awareness of this fact by the physician can lead
to more useful diagnoses.

628 Wood, Robin Young, and Rose, Karla. "Penile Implants for
     Impotence," in American Journal of Nursing, Vol. 78, No. 2,
     234-238, February 1978. (Reviewed by Mary Steichen Cal-
     derone in SIECUS Newsletter, Vol. 7, No. 1, 15, Septem-
     ber 1978.)
     Two types of implants are discussed: 1) inflatable penile pros-
thesis and 2) Small-Carrion rod prosthesis (non-inflatable). Other
topics include postoperative care, treatment for pain, use of catheters
for elimination, physical activity, discharge planning, and psychological concerns. 9 references

629   Zimring, Joseph G.   "Sexual Problems of Geriatric Patient,"
          in <u>New York State Journal of Medicine</u>, Vol. 79, No. 5, 752-
          753, April 1979.
          Covers psychologic and physiologic factors involved in sexual
problems of the geriatric patient.   Sexual activity among older people
is not unnatural and the activity may give serenity to older people.
7 references

CHEMICAL INFLUENCE ON SEXUALITY AND AGING
OTHER THAN ESTROGEN TREATMENT
FOR THE CLIMACTERIC

630   Anderson, T. W.   "Oral Contraceptives and Female Mortality
      Trends," in Canadian Medical Association Journal, Vol. 102,
      No. 11, 1156-1160, May 30, 1970.
      Conditions in which there is firm evidence of increased inci-
dence among women using oral contraceptives are cerebral thrombosis and venous thromboembolism.   According to the author, there is
no firm evidence of an increase in death rates from cancer of the
breast, ischemic heart disease, cancer of the uterus, and the overall
death rate has declined.   Other forms of contraception should be considered if dependability and convenience are not paramount.   Summary
is also in French.   14 references

631   Cherkin, Arthur, and Eckardt, Michael J.   "Effects of Dimethy-
      laminoethanol upon Life-Span and Behavior of Aged Japanese
      Quail," in Journal of Gerontology, Vol. 32, No. 1, 38-45,
      1977.
      In this investigation, sexual mounting response to a female quail
was one of three behavioral studies carried out.   No detectable differences in latency to mount were found.   29 references

632   De Leon, George, and Wexler, Harry K.   "Heroin Addiction:
      Its Relation to Sexual Behavior and Sexual Experience," in
      Journal of Abnormal Psychology, Vol. 81, No. 1, 36-38, 1973.
      Male residents of a Phoenix House Therapeutic Community
(N= 31) who were drug free heroin addicts were interviewed.   The
nonaddict male interviewer questioned each addict separately about
seven sexual variations.   Reduced frequencies of masturbation, nocturnal emissions, and intercourse were reported during addiction periods.   Ejaculation time was long, proportion of orgasm went down,
and ratings of desire and quality of orgasm were low.   After addiction was over, the residents recovered sexuality at the same level or
higher than pre-addiction levels.   There seems to be clear changes
in sexuality when a male becomes addicted to heroin.   6 references
(author abstract modified)

633   Doroshow, Jack.   "How to Live to a Ripe Old Age and Stay Young
      Enough to Enjoy It," in Forum: The International Journal of
      Human Relations, Vol. 3, No. 1, 50-57, October 1973.
      The author examines the latest elixirs of life including Gero-
vitol (Rumanian KH3), cell therapy, injections of chorionic gonadotro-

pin and other hormones, and treatment with aromatics.   These treatments are said to cure impotence.   Impotence is suggested to be
psychologically based in 90 percent of cases and hormonally based in
10 percent of the cases.   The business of providing "cures" for impotence is becoming very lucrative.   Many questions remain in the
scientific community as to the validity of the "cures."   No references

634   Ellis, William J., and Grayhack, John T.   "Sexual Function in
        Aging Males After Orchiectomy and Estrogen Therapy," in
        Journal of Urology, Vol. 89, No. 6, 895-899, June 1963.
        Eighty-two patients who had metastatic or locally extended car-
cinoma of the prostate which was treated by estrogens or by orchiectomy or both were checked for potency.   Out of 32, 38 or 46 percent
of these were potent before treatment.   After treatment, 16 of the
original potent males retained a portion of normal sexual activity.
Greater potency was found among the men who were treated with estrogens alone than those who had both orchiectomy and estrogen or
orchiectomy alone.   Both treatment groups had some potent men after
treatment.   17 references (authors' summary modified)

635   Farrell, Alice; Gerall, Arnold A.; and Alexander, Mary J.
        "Age-Related Decline in Receptivity in Normal, Neonatally
        Androgenized Female and Male Hamsters," in Experimental
        Aging Research, Vol. 3, No. 2, 117-128, 1977.
        Exposure to perinatal androgen was related to the pattern of
female sexual behavior shown by both aging male and female hamsters.
High doses of endogenous or exogenous perinatal testosterone had the
effect of suppressing receptivity throughout the animal's life span.
It did not, however, accelerate the rate of decline in female behavior
over time.   The greatest decrease in receptivity with advanced age
was exhibited by nonandrogenized animals.   19 references

636   Geller, Jack.   "The Role of Sex Hormones in Problems of the
        Mature Years and Beyond," in Journal of the American Ger-
        iatrics Society, Vol. 17, No. 9, 861-873, 1969.
        One aspect of male climacteric, that is, prostatism, can be
treated with progestational hormones.   Large excess amounts of rel-
ative or absolute estrogen may cause prostatism and lower sexual
vigor.   Hormone assays in the future may establish more knowledge
about testosterone and estrogen metabolism.   14 references

637   Green, Michael.   "Inhibition of Ejaculation as a Side-Effect of
        Mellaril," in American Journal of Psychiatry, Vol. 118, 172-
        173, August 1961.
        Dr. Green provides a probable mechanism for the mentioned
side-effect.   He suggests "the peristalsis of the vasa deferentia, seminal vesicles, and ejaculatory ducts which discharge semen into ure-
tha is induced by efferent impulses from hypogastric plexuses which
derive from the thoracolumbar (sympathetic) outflow.   A potent sym-
patholytic agent would produce failure of ejaculation by blocking these
adrenergic impulses at the neuro-effector junction."   No references

638   Greenberg, Harvey R.   "Erectile Impotence During the Course

of Tofranil Therapy, " in American Journal of Psychiatry, Vol. 171, 1021, 1965.
    A case history is presented in which a man became impotent during treatment with tofranil. Reducing the dosage of tofranil to a lower maintenance level was enough to return sexual function to normal. 2 references

639   Greenblatt, Robert Benjamin. "The Psychogenic and Endocrine Aspects of Sexual Behavior," in Journal of the American Geriatrics Society, Vol. 22, No. 9, 393-396, 1974. (This was presented as a part of the Symposium on Sexuality in the Aging Individual; 31st Annual Meeting of the American Geriatrics Society, Royal York Hotel, Toronto, Canada, April 17-18, 1974.)
    Psychogenic and endocrine factors play a role in sexual behavior. Problems in sexuality can best be understood by realizing that these two factors play a part in sexuality. Topics discussed include maleness and femaleness, sex interest in the female, sex inadequacy, and sexual gluttony. A distinction must be made between psychogenic and endocrine factors before sexual problems can be dealt with. No references (author abstract modified)

640   Heller, Joseph. "Another Case of Inhibition of Ejaculation as a Side Effect of Mellaril," in American Journal of Psychiatry, Vol. 118, 172-173, August 1961.
    A case is presented of a 40-year-old male who developed an inability to ejaculate after treatment with Mellaril. He was switched to meprobamate and returned to normal sexual activity and ejaculation. No references

641   Herr, Harry. W. "Preservation of Sexual Potency in Prostatic Cancer Patients After [125]I Implantation," in Journal of the American Geriatrics Society, Vol. 27, No. 1, 17-19, January 1979.
    Fifty-one men with prostatic cancer were sources of data. The sexual histories of these men and their spouses were obtained before and after pelvic lymphadenectomy and retropubic [125] I implantation. The patients' average age was 64.7 years. Of the forty-one patients who were sexually active before the operation, forty retained their sexual activity. Four of the patients had diminished potency before the operation and six had complete erectile impotence. The sexual dysfunction was most often psychogenic in origin. When reassurance, encouragement and education were provided, five of the patients with sexual dysfunction were able to resume sexual intercourse. The use of [125] I implantation to treat local prostatic carcinoma seems to have the advantage over other therapeutic modalities in that it can preserve sexual potency. 2 references (An almost identical article appeared in Journal of Urology, Vol. 121, 621-623, May 1979, and was a paper which was read at the Annual Meeting of the American Urological Association, Washington, D. C., May 21-25, 1978.)

642   Hughes, J. M. "Failure to Ejaculate with Chlordiazepoxide,"

in American Journal of Psychiatry, Vol. 121, 610-611, December 1964.
A case is presented in which Librium (chlordiazepoxide) treatment caused a man failure to ejaculate. The suggestion for why this
was so was because the drug depresses spinal reflexes.   5 references

643   Jakubczak, Leonard F. "Effects of Testosterone Propionate on
       Age Differences in Mating Behavior," in Journal of Gerontology,
       Vol. 19, No. 4, 458-461, October 1964. (This article is based
       on a dissertation submitted to the Graduate School of Arts and
       Sciences, Washington University, St. Louis, Missouri, in par-
       tial fulfillment of the requirements for the Ph. D. degree.   A
       preliminary report of this study was given at the meeting of
       the American Psychological Association, 1961.)
       Two groups of male guinea pigs were observed weekly.   One
group was young (6 months) and the other group was mature (30
months).   Nine guinea pigs in each group were injected with testosterone propionate daily.   Seven guinea pigs of each group were given
placebo injections.   The old males ejaculated much less frequently
than the young males.   The rate of intromission for old males was
less than that of young males.   Contact latency and rates of mounting
and nuzzling were the same for both groups.   The only effects of testosterone were to decrease the rates of abortive mounting by old animals.   A lack of endogenous androgen cannot explain age differences
in mating behavior.   17 references

644   Jancar, V. G. ; Arony, A. J. ; and Hrachovec, J. P.   "Recent
       Clinical Experience with Treatment of Depression with Gero-
       vital H3 Tablets," in Gerontologist, Vol. 15, No. 5, Part 2,
       34, 1975. (This was a paper given at the 28th annual meeting
       of the Gerontological Society, Louisville, Kentucky, October
       1975.)
       Gerovital H3 (GH3) which contains procaine HCl, has been re-
ported by a number of studies to be beneficial in various complaints
of old age.   A report is given on the first half of the researchers'
clinical studies on 16 patients.   All were over 45 years of age and
suffered from depression.   The patients received an increasing dosage over six weeks, starting with three tablets a day of 100 mg. of
procaine per tablet.   Not more than six tablets a day were given to
obtain optimum response.   Sexual libido was improved in the patients.

645 Kent, Saul. "Neuroendocrine Changes That Come with Age Do
       Not Spell the End to Sexual Fulfillment," in Geriatrics, Vol.
       30, No. 3, 184, 186, 188, 1975.
       The neuroendocrine system is explained in general.   Neuro-
endocrine changes are separately discussed for men and for women.
Regular sexual expression is important for sexual consistency.   No
references

646   _____. "Neurotransmitters May Be Weak Link in the Aging
       Brain's Communication Network," in Geriatrics, Vol. 31, No.
       7, 105-106, 110-111, 1976.
       It is suggested that declining sexual functions with age might

be directly related to fluctuations in levels of dopamine and serotonin
in the brain.   36 references

647 _____ .   "On the Trail of an Authentic Aphrodisiac," in Ger-
       iatrics, Vol. 30, No. 12, 96, 99, December 1975.
       Traditional aphrodisiacs such as Spanish fly, yohimbine, and
ginseng are discussed.   Alcohol and marijuana are also mentioned.
Nature's aphrodisiac, pheromones, has real potential as an aphrodisiac.   Chemical controls on the brain and direct stimulation on the
brain need more research for clinical use as aphrodisiacs.   11 references

648 Lemere, Frederick, and Smith, James W.   "Alcohol-Induced
       Sexual Impotence," in American Journal of Psychiatry, Vol.
       130, No. 2, 212-213, February 1973.
       Even after years of sobriety, the sexual impotence which was
brought on by alcohol abuse can persist.   The alcohol has a destruc-
tive effect on the neurogenic reflex arc which serves the process of
erection.   That this damage may be irreversible is demonstrated by
inability to regain potency even after abstaining from alcohol use.

649 Mann, T.   "Effects of Pharmacological Agents on Male Sexual
       Functions," in Journal of Reproduction and Fertility, Vol. 16
       (Supplement 4), 101-114, 1968.
       Pharmacological agents discussed include opiates and other
psychotomimetic drugs, psychotherapeutic drugs, amphetamines, and
alcohol.   Passage of drugs and other substances into semen is discussed.   Sympathicomimetic, parasympathicomimetic and autonomic-
blocking agents, antispermatogenic, spermiostatic, and finally spermi-
cidal agents and their effects on male sexual functions round out the
discussion in this article.   73 references

650 Money, John, and Yankowitz, Robert.   "The Sympathetic-Inhibit-
       ing Effects of the Drug Ismelin on Human Male Eroticism,
       with a Note on Mellaril," in Journal of Sex Research, Vol. 3,
       No. 1, 69-82, February 1967.
       Six patients being treated with Ismelin for hypertension exper-
ienced changes in orgasm and ejaculation.   Doses of Ismelin had
ranged from 10 to 75 mg. per day.   One patient couldn't experience
orgasm and became impotent.   Two men experienced a lessening of
intensity and clarity of orgasm.   Three men had dry-run orgasms.
Ismelin and Mellaril seem to have a blocking effect on the sympathet-
ics of genitopelvic sexual functioning.   18 references

651 Ostfeld, Adrian; Smith, Cedric M.; and Stotsky, Bernard A.
       "The Systemic Use of Procaine in the Treatment of the Elderly:
       A Review," in Journal of the American Geriatrics Society,
       Vol. 25, No. 1, 1-19, 1977.
       A review and evaluation of world literature concerning the sys-
temic use of procaine in the treatment of aging.   Procaine (or Gero-
vital of which procaine is the major component) may have an antidepressant effect.   Other than that, there seems to be no other value
in it for the treatment of disease.   Decreased complaints in the sexual

and other systems may be due to the antidepressant effect.   148 references

652   Rubin, Isadore.   "The Search for Rejuvenation," in Sexology,
          Vol. 25, 558-561, April 1959.
          Despite all the advances which have been made in gerontology
we still do not have the long-sought "elixir of youth" which would lead
to sexual rejuvenation.   Scientists who have worked on developing
"elixirs of youth" include Professor Leon Binet, Dean of the Faculty
of Medicine of the University of Paris, Dr. Colette Jaramec-Tchernia,
Dr. N. Ischlondski, Dr. Paul Niehans, Professor Carroll M. Williams,
Dr. O. H. Robertson, and Dr. A. C. Leopold.

653   Shader, Richard I.   "Sexual Dysfunction Associated with Thiori-
          dazine Hydrochloride," in Journal of the American Medical
          Association, Vol. 188, No. 11, 1007-1009, 1964.
          Three cases are presented to illustrate the effects of thiorida-
zine hydrochloride on male patients.   Results included failure to ejaculate, sexual dysfunction, or the passage of sperm-containing urine.
Other phenothiazines were used without the same effect.   The adrenergic blocking properties of thioridazine hydrochloride might be causing these effects.   A mechanism needs to be found to clearly link
these effects of the drug.   15 references

654   _____, and DiMascio, Alberto.   "Endocrine Effects of Psycho-
          tropic Drugs. VI.   Male Sexual Function," in Connecticut
          Medicine, Vol. 32, No. 11, 847-848, November 1968.
          A short review of the literature on the effects of psychotropic
drugs on gonadotropin excretion and sperm production.   The authors
suggest that it is impossible to draw conclusions from the limited data
available.   14 references

655   Singh, Harbhajan.   "A Case of Inhibition of Ejaculation as a
          Side Effect of Mellaril," in American Journal of Psychiatry,
          Vol. 117, 1041-1042, 1961.
          A case report is presented showing the side effect of inhibition
of ejaculation as a result of treatment with Mellaril (Thioridazine).
No references

656   Wesson, Miley B.   "The Value of Testosterone to Men Past
          Middle Age," in Journal of American Geriatrics Society, Vol.
          12, 1149-1153, December 1964.
          This report presents clinical follow-up data on older men seen
in private practice by one doctor.   A period of 54 years was used
for observations.   Twenty-two years before testosterone therapy and
thirty-two years after the therapy were used as observation periods.
All of the men were over 50.   They all received a weekly intramuscular injection of 50-100 mg. of testosterone propionate.   The process
of urination was improved due to increased bladder tone from hyper-
trophy of the bladder musculation.   It is suggested that the testosterone
does not speed up the growth of cancer.   Testosterone usage coupled
with psychotherapy and prostatic massage can bring potency to the
impotent man.   14 general references

657 Young, William Caldwell. "Patterning of Sexual Behavior," in
     Bliss, Eugene L. (ed.), Roots of Behavior, pp. 115-122.
     New York: Harper and Row, 1962. (Facsimile reproduction
     1968 by New York: Hafner Publishing Co.)
          Most of the studies reported in this chapter were done on an-
imals. Areas covered include 1) resultant mating behavior from pre-
natally administered androgen, 2) effect of androgen on developing
genital tracts, 3) effect of hormonal factors on masculine and feminine behavior patterns, and 4) rules of hormonal action on the neural
tissues mediating mating behavior and on the genital tracts.   51 references

658 Young, William Caldwell; Goy, Robert W.; and Phoenix, Charles
     H. "Hormones and Sexual Behavior," in Money, John (ed.),
     Sex Research: New Developments, pp. 176-196. New York:
     Holt, Rinehart and Winston, 1965.
          Gonadal hormones have a broad role in the determination of
sexual behavior. During a period of differentiation and organization
(prenatal in the monkey and guinea pig and postnatal in the rat) the
hormones effect a differentiation or organization of neural tissues
identical to the principles which operate during the differentiation of
the genital tracts. More research on the hormonal action on the sexual behavior in man needs to be done. Discussion touches almost entirely on animal studies.   44 references and notes

THE CLIMACTERIC AND ESTROGEN THERAPY

659 Acken, Henry S. , Jr. "Estrogen Replacement Therapy," in Obstetrics and Gynecology, Vol. 34, No. 1, 46-49, July 1969.
  A group of 479 women of menopausal age [age not specified] who were estrogen-deficient were treated with a form of orally administered conjugated estrogens. Regularly scheduled examinations and diagnostic curettage is urged as a precaution for even the slightest evidence of uterine bleeding. The estrogen-treated women did not show an increase in the incidence of breast and endometrial cancer compared with the incidence in author's other patients. No references

660 Anderson, Helen C. Newton's Geriatric Nursing (5th edition), pp. 41-44, 166, 256, 267-276. St. Louis, MO: C. V. Mosby Co. , 1971
  Companionship and its importance to the elderly are discussed (pp. 41-44). Involutional psychotic reaction is discussed (p. 166) where preoccupation with sexual activities as great sin may exist. Emotional conflicts may occur in men who undergo urologic surgery (p. 256). Gynecologic diseases are presented in Chapter 22 (pp. 267-276).

661 Avioli, Louis V. "Senile and Postmenopausal Osteoporosis," in Advances in Internal Medicine, Vol. 21, 391-415, 1976.
  A knowledgeable physician should be able to rule out subtle forms of demineralizing disorders such as apathetic or T_3-thyrotoxicosis, hyperparathyroidism, malabsorption and osteomalacia or multiple myeloma. These diseases can mimic postmenopausal or senile osteoporosis radiologically. Short-term estrogen therapy should be used to treat the senescent or postmenopausal osteoporotic patient. A diet with vitamin D and calcium content should be continued for skeletal mobilization. Extreme caution should be used if the addition of sodium fluoride and/or calcitonin is considered. 164 references

662 Bakke, J. L. "A Double-Blind Study of a Progestin-Estrogen Combination in the Management of the Menopause," in Pacific Medicine and Surgery, Vol. 73, 200-205, May-June 1965.
  Women with ovarian failure should be given a trial of hormone replacement--estrogen and progestin. One-third of the women should respond favorably. For women with a uterus, the hormone replacement is important to control periodic shedding of the endometrium. 13 references

663 Barnes, Allan C. "Climacteric," in Obstetrics and Gynecology, Vol. 32, No. 3, 437-439, September 1968.

A short general discussion of the origin of the word climacteric and its philosophical concept. An important point that is made is that the mythology surrounding a rung on life's ladder (a climacteric) is much worse than making the step. No references

664 Bart, Pauline B. "Depression in Middle Aged Women," in Cox, Sue (ed.), Female Psychology: The Emerging Self, pp. 349-367. Chicago: Science Research Associates, 1976.
A small section on depression and menopause is included in this article. 16 references for the article

665 Bedford, J. R. "An Attempt to Eliminate the Menopause and Its Consequences," in Postgraduate Medical Journal, Vol. 43 (December Supplement), 51-54, 1967.
This article is a discussion of ovarian failure and the menopause. A trial to treat this condition is described. The author suggests that there is no reason for not treating ovarian deficiency. The treatment can make life more pleasant and less uncomfortable. 26 references

666 Block, Marilyn R.; Davidson, Janice L.; Serock, Kathryn E.; and Grambs, Jean D. Uncharted Territory: Issues and Concerns of Women over 40, pp. 41-49. College Park, MD: University of Maryland Center on Aging, August 1978.
Unit 3 entitled "Menopause and Sexuality" covers the definition of menopause, symptoms of menopause, estrogen replacement therapy, and sexuality after 40. Discussions, questions, and suggested activities are also provided. 54 references

667 Bolton, William. "That's a Good Question--Menopause," in Today's Health, Vol. 44, No. 7, 6, 9, July 1966.
Menopausal changes can be irregular or temporarily halted. Complete ending of menstruation for one-half year is a satisfactory length of time to assume that pregnancy is not possible. Contraception should be used for at least one-half year after the last period.

668 _____. "That's a Good Question--No Change of Life," in Today's Health, Vol. 44, No. 2, 8, February 1966.
No "change of life" is produced by hysterectomy since ovaries were left in place. When uterus is removed, menstruation ceases; but ovaries continue to function until age of menopause. Symptoms of menopause can appear due to nervousness that occurs after hysterectomy.

669 Campbell, Stuart (ed.). The Management of the Menopause and Post-Menopausal Years. Baltimore, MD: University Park Press, 1976. (The Proceedings of the International Symposium held in London, 24-26 November 1975. Arranged by the Institute of Obstetrics and Gynaecology, The University of London, London, England.)
The book consists of 10 sections and a total of 39 papers. Section A contains four papers on epidemiology. Section B contains four papers on endocrinology. Section C contains six papers on psy-

chological aspects.   Section D contains three papers on lipid metabolism.   Section E contains two papers on calcium metabolism.   Section F contains four papers on skin.   Section G contains three papers
on urinary tract.   Section H contains four papers on the risks of estrogen therapy subdivided into two sections: one on thromboembolism
(two papers) and one on cancer (two papers).   Section I contains four
papers on therapeutic problems.   Section J contains five papers on
the management of the menopause.
        A list of contributors and their addresses, a foreword by the
editor, and an index is provided.   Two presenters, Dr. Charles B.
Hammond and Dr. M. Dorothea Kerr, were American.   The rest of
the total of 47 were European.

670   Carson, Ruth.   Your Menopause.   New York: Public Affairs
        Pamphlets No. 447, 1974.
        Contains basic information on menopause including symptoms,
sex during menopause, the use of estrogen, and what the woman can
do about menopause.

671   Cherry, Sheldon H.   The Menopausal Myth.   New York: Ballan-
        tine, 1976.
        The medical and physical aspects of menopause are well cov-
ered in this book.   The author dispels the myth that menopause
changes women into miserable "hags."   The emotional symptoms which
appear during the menopause are brought about psychologically, according to author.

672   Clay, Vidal S.   Women: Menopause and Middle Age.   Pitts-
        burgh, PA: Know, Inc. , 1977.   (A book review of this is done
        by Laura J. Singer in SIECUS Newsletter, Vol. 7, No. 1, 8,
        September 1978.)
        An anti-estrogen feminist book on menopause.   It is optimistic,
woman-positive and suggests alternatives to estrogen therapy.

673   Coope, Jean; Thompson, Jean M. ; and Poller, L.   "Effects of
        'Natural Oestrogen' Replacement Therapy on Menopausal Symp-
        toms and Blood Clotting," in British Medical Journal, Vol. 4,
        No. 5989, 139-143, October 18, 1975.
        Thirty patients with menopausal symptoms served as a sample
for this double-blind study.   The value of "natural" estrogens (equine)
in treating the symptoms was examined as well as possible adverse
effects.   Women were randomly selected into two groups of 15.   Then
they were given hormone treatment for three months and then a placebo for three months or just the opposite.   Both groups showed improvement in the first three months, although the group which took
estrogen deteriorated after switching back to placebo.   The group
taking the placebo first didn't deteriorate when switching to the estrogen.   More long-term studies need to be done before estrogen therapy can be suggested on a large scale.   12 references

674   Cooper, William H.   Husband's Guide to Menopause.   New York:
        Simon and Schuster, 1969.
        One of very few resources directed at men.   This book con-
tains illustrations.

675 Crawford, Marion P. , and Hooper, Douglas. "Menopause, Ag-
     ing, and Family," in Social Science and Medicine, Vol. 7,
     469-482, 1973.
       Middle-aged women go through many psychosocial transitions.
Menopause can be considered one such transition.   One hundred and
six women were used as a sample.   Menopause was investigated for
relationships with physical health, sex identity and age and post-parenthood, grandparenthood, and marriage in the middle years.   Some relationship was found between menopause and health (subjective) and
sexual identity, but age identity was not related.   Post-parenthood,
especially giving up of a daughter, was more stressful than being a
grandparent.   25 references

676 Daly, Michael Joseph.   "Sexual Attitudes in Menopausal and Post-
     menopausal Women," in Medical Aspects of Human Sexuality,
     Vol. 2, No. 5, 48-53, May 1968.
       Dr. Daly suggests that mastery of psychological reactions to
the climacteric is very difficult.   Sexuality need not end, however.
Factors affecting the climacteric include cultural background, parental influences, physiological changes and psychological influences on
sexual attitudes.   Some other factors affecting the menopause are
mentioned.   Sexual responsiveness of climacteric women are discussed
as well as the physician's role in treating the climacteric woman.   9
references

677 Davidson, Bill [William].   "Menopause--Is There a Cure?" in
     Saturday Evening Post, Vol. 240, 70-72, 1967.
       Estrogen can't solve all the problems of middle age; but it can
relieve vaginal irritation, hot flushes and sometimes depression, head-
ache and fatigue.   It will not make a woman young again.

678 Davis, M. Edward, and Meilach, Dona Z.   A Doctor Discusses
     Menopause and Estrogen.   Chicago: Budlong Press, 1977.
       This booklet presents an objective statement on several aspects
of the menopause including symptoms, physiology, and treatment.   The
authors discuss estrogen as an alternative to menopause but no other
alternatives are offered.

679 Detre, Thomas.   "Severe Emotional Reactions Precipitated by
     the Climacterium," in Psychosomatics, Vol. 9, No. 4, Two-
     Sections, Section 2, 31-35, July-August 1968.
       Six principles must be observed when a physician undertakes
psychotherapeutic management of depressed patients: 1) always be
available, 2) strong support, 3) premature decisions should be avoided,
4) frequent visits to provide very close supervision, 5) keeping the
family involved, and 6) hospitalization immediately if family can't
provide the proper support.   The following of these principles will
guard against the suicidal threat.   Trust and confidence must exist
between patient and physician.   No references

680 Dunlop, Edwin H.   "Emotional Imbalance in the Premenopausal
     Woman," in Psychosomatics, Vol. 9, No. 4, Two Sections,
     Section 2, 44-47, July-August 1968.

Dr. Dunlop discusses the critical years just before the menopause. He strongly emphasizes three points: 1) anxiety and depression must be recognized and treated together, 2) medication must be correctly and carefully chosen, 3) the physician must provide continued guidance and a supportive atmosphere. Very brief psychotherapy is often the best. No references

681   Estrogen: For a Few Years--For a Few Months--or Not at All. New York: Ayerst Laboratories, March 1978.
       Basically, this is an earlier version of The Menopausal Woman Whose Time Has Come ... Now She Needs Your Support.

682   "Estrogen Therapy: The Dangerous Road to Shangri-La," in Consumer Reports, Vol. 41, No. 11, 642-645, November 1976.
       Some recent research reports on estrogens and cancer are presented. Additional hazards of estrogen are also listed. Then the article covers the biology of menopause, osteoporosis and estrogen therapy, and ways of reducing the risk. Women's responsibilities in the safe use of estrogen replacement therapy are listed. No references

683   "Feminine Forever," in Newsweek, Vol. 69, No. 14, 55, April 3, 1967.
       Advancement of hormone pills by Dr. Robert A. Wilson is discussed. By taking routine annual cervical-smear tests, a woman may find out what her "femininity index" is, or actually her estrogen level. When the index drops, estrogen replacement therapy begins. Some opposition to estrogen replacement therapy is voiced by Dr. Edmund R. Novak who suggests that most menopausal problems are psychological and not physical. Although there is a cancer scare concerning estrogen replacement therapy, this article states that the number of patients who develop such problems is very small.

684   Flint, Marcha. "The Menopause: Reward or Punishment?" in Psychosomatics, Vol. 16, No. 4, 161-163, 1975.
       Menopause is not described cross-culturally by many authors. Some foreign populations are mentioned in which a woman's status is elevated upon reaching menopause. In our culture, however, menopause is a kind of punishment. Several ways of alleviating the problems many women suffer include: 1) psychotherapy, 2) hormone therapy, and 3) exchanging ideas about the problems of menopause and dispelling of myths about menopause that have been enculturated.   22 references

685   Forman, Joseph B. "Hormonal vs. Psychosomatic Disturbances of the Menopause," in Psychosomatics, Vol. 9, No. 4, Two Sections, Section 2, 17-21, July-August 1968.
       Dr. Forman states that the major features of menopause are the neuroses. The fear of menopause begins at forty and time and patience must be taken to listen to the complaints of the menopausal woman. He concludes that the menopausal woman benefits from estrogen replacement therapy but that emotional symptoms should be treated with psychotherapeutics, including certain drugs. No reference

686   Gaitz, Charles M.   "Middle Age and Postmenopausal Sexual Ad-
      justment," in Medical Record and Annals, Vol. 61, 299-302,
      1968.
      A short paper which contains sections on menopause, sexual
adjustment of middle-aged women, and implications for the physician.
Physicians should be sensitive to the sexual needs of their patients,
especially if they are older or in the menopausal stage.   Love between mature people should be looked at with understanding.   A physician can help a patient who is middle-aged deal with many sources
of conflict by being open, understanding, and supportive.   2 references

687   Galloway, Karen.   "The Middle Years: The Change of Life,"
      in American Journal of Nursing, Vol. 75, No. 6, 1006-1011,
      June 1975.
      Presents information on what to expect during menopause.   In-
cluded in the discussion are physical changes, psychological changes,
and sociocultural changes.   Males often go through a psychological
change which could be referred to as the "male menopause."   Nurses
can be a great help in preventing the menopause from becoming a
crisis by emphasizing health maintenance and by providing counseling
about the change of life.   5 references

688   Galton, Lawrence.   "Estrogen for Menopause: Easing Pain--
      Without Fear," in Parade, 12-13, August 27, 1978.
      Estrogen can be safe if used properly.   Estrogen when used
in combination with the hormone progesterone can be cancer-free
without harmful side effects.

689   Goldberg, Minnie B.   Medical Management of Menopause.   New
      York: Grune and Stratton, 1959.
      This thin book covers 1) menstrual function and the menopause,
2) the physiology of menstruation and etiology of the menopausal syndrome, 3) physiologic, metabolic and pharmacologic aspects of gonadal steroids, 4) symptomatology of the menopause, 5) diagnosis and
diagnostic procedures, 6) therapeutic armamentarium, 7) hormonal
and hormone-like agents for the treatment of the menopause, 8) choice
of therapy and management, 9) problems in therapy, and 10) recapit-
ulation.   32 references

690   Goldfarb, Alvin F.   "The Climacteric and Some of Its Prob-
      lems," in Geriatrics, Vol. 24, No. 5, 107-116, May 1969.
      Individual needs should be considered before starting estrogen
replacement therapy for loss of ovarian function.   Sequential cyclic
administration of estrogens and progestins during premenopausal and
menopausal years is better than usage of unopposed estrogens.   Continuous small doses of estrogens should be used when needed during
the post-menopausal period.   4 references

691   _____.   The Female Climacteric: Current Guidelines on
      Managing Menopausal Patients (A discussion with Alvin F.
      Goldfarb, M.D.).   New York: Ayerst Laboratories, 1977.
      The first part of this publication is in question-and-answer
format.   He makes the point that every woman in the climacteric

should be treated as an individual.   When estrogen therapy is needed,
the smallest dose necessary to get rid of symptoms should be used.
Personal counseling should be used to treat a woman's depression.
Vaginal smears are used to determine estrogen levels, but treatment
should focus on the whole patient not just results of a smear.   Patients
should participate in the decision-making process to use a drug and
be told of the risks involved.   Premarin (conjugated estrogens tablets,
U. S. P. and vaginal cream in a nonliquefying base) is discussed as a
possible drug for treatment of estrogen deficiency.   Warnings and pre-
cautions in the drug's use are presented.   Information for the patient
about estrogens is presented.

692   Goodman, Madeleine; Stewart, Cynthia J.; and Gilbert, Fred, Jr.
        "Patterns of Menopause," in Journal of Gerontology, Vol. 32,
        No. 3, 291-298, 1977.
        This is a study of certain medical and physiological variables
among Caucasian and Japanese women living in Hawaii.   Comparisons
of physical changes and clinical symptoms of the menopause were
made.   For the Caucasians, 170 menopausal women and 162 nonmenopausal women were analyzed.   Multiphasic screening records were
used in the analysis.   For the Japanese, 159 menopausal women and
187 nonmenopausal women were analyzed.   Physiological, anthropo-
metric, and medical variables were examined with discriminant function analysis.   The two significant discriminant variables were surgery
and medication.   Even though clinical conditions due to the effect of
aging were the only ones associated with menopause, medical and
surgical procedures were significantly related.   26 references

693   Graber, Edward A., and Barber, Hugh R. K.   "The Case For
        and Against Estrogen Replacement Therapy," in American
        Journal of Nursing, Vol. 75, No. 10, 1766-1771, October 1975.
        Estrogen therapy should be used rationally to treat specific
symptoms.   Patients should be made aware of the pros and cons of
using estrogens.   Estrogens need not be prescribed for all menopausal
women.

694   Gray, Madeline.   The Changing Years: The Menopause Without
        Fear.   New York: Doubleday and Co., 1970.
        Recent research and literature is absent from this book.   Bas-
ically, the book promotes the use of estrogen.   On the whole, it is
rather dated.

695   Greenblatt, Robert Benjamin.   "Estrogen Therapy for Post-
        Menopausal Females," in New England Journal of Medicine,
        Vol. 272, No. 6, 305-308, 1965.
        Describes treatment procedures for estrogen therapy including
combination with methyltestosterone.   4 references

696   _____, and Emperaire, Jean C.   "Changing Concepts in the
        Management of the Menopause," in Medical Times, Vol. 98,
        No. 6, 153-164, June 1970.
        Post-menopausal problems increase as a woman's life span
increases.   Hormone replacement therapy can get rid of autonomic

imbalance, psychogenic disturbances, and metabolic disorders. The catabolic:anabolic ratio can also be brought into better balance. 58 references

697 _____; Mahesh, Virendra B.; and McDonough, Paul G. (eds.). The Menopausal Syndrome. New York: MEDCOM Press, 1974. (This is a collection of the proceedings on an international symposium held in Augusta, Georgia.)
Proceedings presented in three sections: 1) basic science concepts in the menopause (ten papers), 2) problems of the menopause (fifteen papers), and 3) management of the menopause (four papers).

698 _____, and Scarpa-Smith, Clorinda J. "Nymphomania in Post-Menopausal Women," in Journal of the American Geriatrics Society, Vol. 7, 339-342, April 1959.
Two menopausal women were studied gynecologically, neurologically, and endocrinologically to determine organic bases for nymphomania. No organic basis for nymphomania was found. Treatment of both women with progestational agents resulted in a good response by one. Even though anatomical, psychological, and sentimental factors affect sex drive, a large part of sex drive is chemically controlled. Androgens increase sex drive in women. Corticoids (progesterone), over time, can decrease the sex drive. 13 references

699 Her Complaints Suggest Postmenopausal Atrophic Vaginitis ... But What If She Doesn't Complain? New York: Ayerst Laboratories, September 1977.
Premarin (conjugated estrogens, U.S.P.) Vaginal Cream is suggested to control symptoms of atrophic vaginitis. Risks and warnings of its use are discussed. 41 physician references

700 Hertz, Dan G.; Steiner, Jacob E.; Zukerman, Henryck; and Pizanti, Sara. "Psychological and Physical Symptom-Formation in Menopause," in Psychotherapy and Psychosomatics, Vol. 19, 47-52, 1971. (Read at the 8th European Conference on Psychosomatic Research, May 25-29, 1970, Knokke, Belgium.)
Correlations exist between menopausal women's subjective symptoms and the vaginal and oral mucosa condition. Thirty women were evaluated. Methods of evaluation included gynecological and oral physiological examinations and through psychiatric interviews. The psychiatric interviews included anxiety scales and a brief psychiatric rating. The "dry mouth syndrome" during menopause is due to personality and psychosocial factors. 13 references

701 Hoover, Robert; Gray, Laman A., Sr.; Cole, Philip; and MacMahon, Brian. "Menopausal Estrogens and Breast Cancer," in New England Journal of Medicine, Vol. 295, No. 8, 401-405, August 19, 1976.
Forty-nine women out of 1,891 women who were given conjugated estrogens for the treatment of menopause were found to have

breast cancer.   The expected rate which was computed was 39.1.
Excess risk increased after ten years.   Women using higher-dose
tablets and women taking medication on other than daily basis had
a higher risk.   Estrogen use, concludes the authors, is related to
a high risk of breast cancer after use of it has begun.   33 references

702   Hutchin, Kenneth C.   "The Change and What Husbands Should
        Know About It," in Today's Health, Vol. 44, No. 9, 54-56,
        79-80, September 1966.
            This article, aimed at husbands, is adapted from How Not to
Kill Your Wife by Kenneth C. Hutchin, M.D., Hawthorn Books, Inc.,
70 Fifth Avenue, New York, New York (copyright by George Allen
and Unwin, Ltd., 1965).   General kinds of problems that women
have during the climacteric are discussed.   The author suggests
that life can begin after the change.   A full sex life can occur without having to worry about contraception.   The couple can enjoy each
other without fear and also without the distraction of a family.   No
references

703   Jern, Helen Z.   Hormone Therapy of Menopause and Aging.
        Springfield, IL: Charles C. Thomas, 1973.
            The first book on menopause written by a woman physician.
Many years of research and treatment of thousands of climacteric
women provide the author with the basis for this book.   Case histories based on office visits, taped interviews, and written stories
are presented.   The book is pro estrogen as a way of alleviating
climacteric problems.

704   Kaufman, Sherwin A.   "Limited Relationship of Maturation In-
        dex to Estrogen Therapy for Menopausal Symptoms.   An Anal-
        ysis of 200 Patients," in Obstetrics and Gynecology, Vol. 30,
        No. 3, 399-407, September 1967.   (Presented at the 15th An-
        nual Clinical Meeting of the American College of Obstetricians
        and Gynecologists, Washington, D.C., April 15-20, 1967.)
            Two hundred women who related their complaints to menopause
were studied.   Data collected included severity and duration of complaints, relationships in family and marriage, and an initial examination.   The examination included a vaginal smear and maturation
count.   Maturation count was repeated every three to six months.
Estrogen therapy was given to every woman and was individualized.
Forty-six complaints were received, and all but three were abolished
by estrogen therapy.   Maturation count is not the best guide for therapy.   The symptoms of the patient and individual therapy response
should be the main guide.   27 references

705   _____.   "Menopause and Sex," in Sexual Behavior, Vol. 1,
        No. 2, 58-63, May 1971.
            Physical and emotional problems can plague a couple during
menopause.   Physical problems can be dealt with by using estrogen
replacement therapy.   Psychological problems may bring on depression and loss of sexual interest and activity.   Through a combination
of estrogen replacement therapy and sympathetic counseling, these
problems can be managed.   No references

706 _____. "Pleasure Without Pain," Chapter 11 in his The
    Ageless Woman: Menopause, Hormones and the Quest for
    Youth, pp. 111-124. Englewood Cliffs, NJ: Prentice-Hall,
    Inc. , 1967.
        Vaginal discomforts are the focal point of this discussion
with suggestions given to get rid of pain and anxiety.

707 Kelly, G. Lombard. A Doctor Discusses Menopause. Chicago:
    Budlong Press, 1959.
        This is a pamphlet for both husbands and wives to inform
them of the changes which occur during menopause.

708 Kent, Saul. "Balancing the Pluses and the Minuses of the
    Menopause," in Geriatrics, Vol. 30, No. 5, 160, 165, 1975.
        A short and general article on menopause covering involutional
changes, estrogen replacement, and beneficial aspect of sex to well-
being. No references

709 Klein, Thomas, and Charles, David. "The Administration of
    Quinestrol to Postmenopausal Women," in Journal of Repro-
    ductive Medicine, Vol. 9, 50-54, 1972.
        Thirty-three postmenopausal women served as the sample for
this study. Quinestrol (ethynylestradiol-3-cyclopentyl ether) was given
to these women in doses of 25-50 micrograms daily in varying periods from 4 weeks to 14 months. Vaginal cytology and endometrial
morphologic changes displayed the estrogenic properties of the Quinestrol. Some patterns seen in the endometrium included: tubal meta-
plasia, reacting hyperplasia, and occasionally the appearance of sub-
nuclear vacuoles in gland cells. Hepatic function was not altered.
15 references

710 Kupperman, Herbert S. "The Menopausal Woman and Sex Hor-
    mones," in Medical Aspects of Human Sexuality, Vol. 1,
    No. 9, 64-68, September 1967.
        Symptoms of the climacteric are presented as well as the in-
adequacy of nonhormonal treatment. A chart showing the effect of
various preparations on menopausal symptoms is given. Estrogen
can be used continuously, but progestin has to be given at the proper
intervals to reduce the effects of estrogens on the uterus and the
breasts. Nuclear atypism is prevented by the use of progestin in
women with an intact uterus. 2 references

711 Lanson, Lucienne. From Woman to Woman: A Gynecologist
    Answers Questions About You and Your Body. New York:
    Alfred E. Knopf, 1975.
        A gynecologist, the author uses a question-and-answer format
to present information on women's health. Included is a chapter on
menopause.

712 Lauritzen, Christian, and van Keep, Pieter A. (eds.). Estro-
    gen Therapy, The Benefits and Risks. Frontiers of Hormone
    Research, Vol. 5. Series editor T. B. van Wimersma Grei-
    danus. Basel, Switzerland: S. Karger, 1977. (Reviewed by

Herman T. Blumenthal in the Journal of Gerontology, Vol.
34, No. 1, 124, 1979.)
The book is derived from the Third International Workshop
on Estrogen held in Geneva, Switzerland in 1977.   It is concerned
with the use of long-term estrogen therapy in the treatment of the
post-menopause and osteoporosis.   The role of estrogens in endometrial and mammary cancer is presented.   Contains 16 chapters,
each followed by discussion.

713   Lindsay, Hamlin B.   "The Male and Female Climacteric," in
      Diseases of the Nervous System, Vol. 23, No. 3, 149-151,
      March 1962.
      The author suggests that heterosexual hormones are useful in
treating the male and female climacteric, respectively.   Chorionic
gonadotropin was effective in relieving loss of sexual interest, decreased libido, depression, nervousness, irritability, dizziness,
absentmindedness, impotence, and fatigue for men experiencing the
male climacteric.   Fortified testosterone was useful in relieving
dizziness, loss of sexual interest, depression, fatigue, irritability,
nervousness, and frigidity for women experiencing the female climacteric.   17 references

714   McCarter, Susan.   Menopause.   Washington, DC: Women's
      Medical Center, Inc. , n. d.
      This seven-page booklet is an excellent overview which can
easily be understood by the layman.   There is an absence of medical jargon; it is clear and to the point.   The format is one of question and answer with eighteen questions covering what menopause is,
estrogen therapy (pro and con), and sexual desire and function during and after menopause.   The author is an R. N. , and the publication may be obtained from: Women's Medical Center, 1712 "I"
Street, N. W. , Washington, D. C. 20006 (202-298-9227).

715   _____ (comp.).   Selected Annotated Menopause Bibliography.
      Washington, DC: Women's Medical Center, Inc. , November
      1977.
      This six-page annotated bibliography was compiled by an R. N.
It is woman-centered and objective.   The sections include General
(eleven citations); Medical, Estrogen Replacement Therapy (eight citations); Sexuality (five citations); Psychology, Mental Health (five
citations); and Miscellaneous (four citations).   A total of 34 references are cited in this excellent resource to begin investigating the
menopause.   It is available from: Women's Medical Center, 1712
"I" Street, N. W. , Washington, D. C. 20006 (202-298-9227).

716   Mack, Thomas M. ; Pike, Malcolm C. ; Henderson, Brian E. ;
      Pfeffer, Robert I. ; Gerkins, Vibeke R. ; Arthur, Mary; and
      Brown, Sandra E.   "Estrogen and Endometrial Cancer in a
      Retirement Community," in New England Journal of Medicine,
      Vol. 294, No. 23, 1262-1267, 1976.
      Controls chosen from a roster of all women in the same com-
munity were compared with all cases of endometrial cancer developed
among the residents of an affluent retirement community.   Three

sources were used to obtain estrogen and other drug use: 1) medical records of the principal care facility, 2) interviews, and 3) records of the local pharmacy. An increased risk of endometrial cancer was found for invasive as well as noninvasive cancer. A dose-response effect was demonstrated. For women using estrogen, the risk of endometrial cancer appeared to greatly exceed the base-line risk from any other single cancer. 22 references (author abstract modified)

717 McKinlay, Sonja M. , and McKinlay, John B. "Selected Studies of the Menopause," in Journal of Biosocial Science, Vol. 5, No. 4, 533-555, October 1973.
        A selective review of literature on menopause from the past three decades. It is presented in annotated form in three sections: 1) clinical observation or experience, 2) the survey, 3) clinical trial. A short discussion precedes each section. Further research suggestions are given.

718 Maoz, Benjamin; Dowty, Nancy; Antonovsky, Aaron; and Wijsenbeek, Henricus. "Female Attitudes to Menopause," in Social Psychiatry, Vol. 5, No. 1, 35-40, 1970.
        Psychiatrists have not studied the climacterium enough except for extreme emotional reactions. A broad range of women was studied to find out what the women's responses to the climacterium were. The sample size was 52, including women of various ethnic backgrounds. Questions asked in semistructured psychiatric interviews focused on femininity, menopause, psychosexual history, and associated family and social problems. Eleven different independent variables were associated to the menopause response and there was a control for ethnicity. Only one independent variable had a positive response to menopause and that was no desire to have any more children. The Oriental-Arab gave this response. The summary is given in English, French and German. 14 references

719 Marley, Faye. "Sex and the Older Woman--Hormones," in Science News, Vol. 91, No. 17, 413, April 29, 1967.
        Several opinions on estrogen therapy are presented. Dr. Robert A. Wilson, Dr. Caroline Jackson, and Dr. Robert W. Kistner point out the positive aspects of estrogen therapy. Others who use the therapy, Dr. Henry S. Acken and Dr. M. Edward Davis are concerned about the possibility of estrogen therapy causing cancer. Dr. Roy Hertz points out the need to be concerned about the possibility of endometrial cancer in long-term therapy. No references

720 Masters, William H. , and Ballew, John William. "The Third Sex," in Geriatrics, Vol. 10, No. 1, 1-4, January 1955.
        (Presented at the 3rd International Congress of Gerontology in London, July 1954.)
        Persons of old age are rapidly multiplying in our society and can be called a "third sex" or a "neutral gender." The article covers various aspects of long-range sex steroid replacement therapy. 12 references

721 _____; Greenblatt, Robert Benjamin; Wilson, Thomas A.;
        Kannel, William B.; and Davis, M. Edward. "Should Estro-
        gens Be Given to Menopausal and Post-Menopausal Patients?"
        in Modern Medicine, Vol. 36, No. 13, 177-180, June 17, 1968.
        Discussion about relieving menopausal symptoms by giving es-
trogen therapy. Long-term exogenous estrogen replacement is suggested for complete gonadal failure. The quality of living will be
improved. No references

722 The Menopausal Woman Whose Time Has Come ... Now She
        Needs Your Support. New York: Ayerst Laboratories, August
        1978.
        This is a booklet describing Premarin (conjugated estrogens
tablets, U.S.P.) Tablets. Sections include management of the menopause, surgical menopause, postmenopausal bone loss, and vasomotor
symptoms. The complete text of the package circular is presented
with 41 physician references. Last page contains information for the
patient.

723 Midwinter, Audrey. "The Management of the Menopause," in
        Practitioner, Vol. 202, 372-379, March 1969.
        Menopausal symptoms can be treated with estrogen which will
also alter cardiovascular disease and osteoporosis when used for life.
Uterine cancer in patients on long-term estrogen therapy is less than
in patients who use it short term. When hormonally dependent can-
cers and fibroids exist in the patient, treatment is contraindicated.
Sample treatment schedules are suggested. 19 references

724 Mozley, Paul D. "Woman's Capacity for Orgasm After Meno-
        pause," in Medical Aspects of Human Sexuality, Vol. 9, No.
        8, 104-105, 109-110, August 1975.
        Sexual problems occur after menopause because sexual desire
can no longer be equated with reproductive desire. Hysterectomy
patients fearing loss of uterus contractions and equating orgasm with
this alone actually became nonorgasmic from anxiety and fear. The
contraction of the uterus doesn't cause orgasm; it is a manifestation
of orgasm. The husband should be involved in evaluation of postmenopausal or postoperative problems. Maturity can encourage sexuality
and release inhibitions. No references

725 Nachtigall, Lila, and Heilman, Joan Rattner. The Lila Nachti-
        gall Report. New York: G. P. Putnam's Sons, 1977.
        A book written for women who are experiencing menopause.
Dr. Nachtigall is for estrogen, with certain reservations and precau-
tions, for most women who need it after menopause. She presents
results of a ten-year study which she and other researchers completed
on the effects of long-term estrogen replacement. The study, according to Dr. Nachtigall, was prospective, double-blind and totally controlled. Menopause can be managed by properly administered estrogen replacement. On the basis of the study, she suggests that incidence of cancer is not any greater among women on properly administered hormones for ten years than it is among a normal population.

726 Naismith, Grace. "Common Sense and the Femininity Pill," in Reader's Digest, Vol. 89, No. 533, 99-102, September 1966.
Estrogen therapy can help 25 percent of women over 50 according to this article. A woman will not be made young again, however; and there may be risks involved with taking the hormone.

727 Neugarten, Bernice L. "Dynamics of Transition of Middle Age to Old Age: Adaptation and the Life Cycle," in Journal of Geriatric Psychiatry, Vol. 4, No. 1, 71-87, Fall 1970. (This was presented at an Interdisciplinary Meeting of the Boston Society for Gerontologic Psychiatry, December 6, 1969. An earlier version of this paper was presented at a conference on "Adaptation to Change," sponsored by the Foundation for Research in Psychiatry, June, 1968.)
The article deals with adaptation through time. Life time was thought of as different from calendar or historical time. An unanticipated life event is likely to be a traumatic event. These traumatic events upset the rhythm and sequence of the life cycle. Psychology of the life cycle is more a psychology of timing rather than a psychology of crisis behavior. A section is included on how menopause affects sexuality. 10 references

728 _____, and Kraines, Ruth J. "'Menopausal Symptoms' in Women of Various Ages," in Psychosomatic Medicine, Vol. 27, No. 3, 266-273, 1965.
A symptom checklist was filled out by 460 women. Data from this sample were examined across five age groups and between "menopausal" and "nonmenopausal" women within the same age group. What the investigators were looking for were symptoms usually associated with menopausal change. Two points, adolescence and menopause, were where the highest incidence of symptoms occurred. Emotional symptoms were seen at adolescence and somatic symptoms were seen at menopause. A weighted instrument, the Blatt Menopause Index, measured endocrine-related changes and clearly separated the "menopausal" groups from the others. 10 references

729 _____; Wood, Vivian; Kraines, Ruth J.; and Loomis, Barbara. "Women's Attitudes Toward the Menopause," in Vita humana, Vol. 6, 140-151, 1963. (This appears in abridged form in Neugarten, Bernice L. (ed.), Middle Age and Aging, pp. 195-200; Chicago: University of Chicago Press, 1968.)
Attitudes of women toward the menopause are measured by an instrument which the authors developed. The instrument consists of 35 statements to which a woman can either agree or disagree. Women (N=267) in four age groups: 21-30, 31-44, 45-55, and 56-65 participated in the study. The greatest differences were seen between the 21-30 and the 31-44 groups, and between the 45-55 and the 56-65 groups. Younger women had more negative attitudes. The summary is given in English, German and French. 9 references

730 Notelovitz, Morris. "Gynecologic Problems of Menopausal Women: Part 1. Changes in Genital Tissue," in Geriatrics, Vol. 33, No. 8, 24-30, August 1978.

During the menopause, the genital tissues undergo reproductive senescence. The vagina loses elasticity, shortens and narrows,
the vulva atrophies and the cervix shrinks. The use of estrogen can
help relieve vaginitis associated with menopausal vaginal changes.
An active sex life can also insure normal vaginal function and pli-
ability. Contraception should be continued beyond menopause because occasional ovulation can occur during the climacteric. Ovaries
are removed by some surgeons because of the risk of cancer and/or
benign disease requiring further surgery. 20 references

731 _____. "Gynecologic Problems of Menopausal Women: Part
        2. Treating Estrogen Deficiency," in Geriatrics, Vol. 33, No.
        9, 35-37, 41, September 1978.
Menopausal symptoms of estrogen deprivation include vasomotor symptoms, psychogenic problems, and urogenital disorders.
Lack of estrogen for many years after menopause may bring on spontaneous fractures or cardiovascular complications. Carefully selected
patients with estrogen-related symptoms and target tissue changes
should be considered for estrogen replacement therapy. Several con-
traindications need to be considered including liver or cerebrovascular
disease, previous myocardial infarction, and deep venous thrombosis.
No references

732 _____. "Gynecologic Problems of Menopausal Women:
        Part 3. Changes in Extragenital Tissues and Sexuality," in
        Geriatrics, Vol. 33, No. 10, 51-53, 57-58, October 1978.
The normal function of the urinary tract is affected by menopausal estrogen deficiency. Epithelium becomes thin and inflamed,
the distal urethra becomes thin and inflamed, the usual support of
pelvic organs is lost, and nerve conduction is altered in skeletal and
smooth muscle. Frequency, dysuria, and urgency are the urinary
symptoms which can be relieved by local or systemic daily treatment
with estrogen for two or three months. Breasts in postmenopausal
women involute, the alveoli begin to disappear, mammary ducts decrease, and connective tissue obliterates the lumina of the ducts if
deprived of cyclic stimulation of estrogen and progesterone. Con-
traindications for estrogen therapy include women with hormone-de-
pendent cancer of the breast or endometrium, a family history of
breast cancer or marked fibrocystic disease. Sexuality can be restored with proper counseling or treatment. 9 references

733 Novak, Edmund R. "Replacement Therapy of the Menopause,"
        in Johns Hopkins Medical Journal, Vol. 120, 408-415, 1967.
Ovaries play a crucial role in women's well-being. Retention
of ovarian tissue after hysterectomy leaves the possibility of subsequent ovarian cancer. The cystic ovary may also develop in the
posthysterectomy patient. Castration may lead to arteriosclerosis.
As a result of castration, post-menopausal osteoporosis may occur.
The author feels it is not wise to advocate routine replacement therapy because of the great variation in individual females. The postmenopausal person is not a sick person, and estrogen replacement
therapy is not the answer to all the problems aging has to offer.
23 references

734   Olds, Sally. "Menopause, Something to Look Forward To?"
        in Today's Health, Vol. 48, 48-49; 74-76; 79-80, May 1970.
        Points out the positive experiences which can occur in the
menopause after discussing some of problems which may be encountered by a woman.   An article which can be understood by the general public.   No references

735   Osofsky, Howard J. , and Seidenberg, Robert.   "Is Female Men-
        opausal Depression Inevitable?" in Obstetrics and Gynecology,
        Vol. 36, No. 4, 611-615, October 1970.
        Depression during menopause is a problem which has not been
adequately treated.   Female psychology is connected to female biology.
Treatment of menopausal symptoms has been backward.   Psychological treatment has been given for physiological symptoms and physiological treatment to psychological symptoms.   Current practices
need to be reexamined to include mature emotions and cognition.
20 references

736   Parks, John.   "Care of the Postmenopausal Patient," in Post-
        graduate Medicine, Vol. 42, 275-280, October 1967.
        Postmenopausal women need proper treatment to stay happy,
healthy and youthful.   Estrogen replacement therapy can help alleviate
many of the problems of postmenopause.   A sympathetic counseling
atmosphere should be provided also.   9 references

737   _____. "Womanhood After Fifty," in Medical Arts and Sci-
        ence, Vol. 13, 68-74, 1959.   (This was a paper presented
        at the Scientific Assembly of the Alumni Postgraduate Conven-
        tion of the College of Medical Evangelists School of Medicine
        in Los Angeles, March 10, 1959.)
        A dated, general discussion of the climacteric which stresses
periodic health examinations for the woman over 50.   14 references

738   Patrick, Maxine Lambrecht.   "A Study of Middle-Aged Women
        and Menopause," Unpublished doctoral dissertation, University
        of California, Los Angeles, 1970.   (D. A. , Vol. 32, 408-B,
        1971.)
        This study used a population of 155 women in menopause in
two groups: white upper middle-class women and black lower-class
women.   A control group of 55 nonmenopausal white and black women
in the same respective classes was used.   Symptoms of menopause
were studied with respect to life satisfaction, life changes, importance
of life changes, and life goals.   Life satisfaction scores showed no
difference of women in menopause or not in menopause in either
white upper middle-class women or black lower-class women.   Number of life changes reported in control group and study group showed
no significant difference between the groups.   Changes which occurred
to the white women in menopause were less important than those occurring in nonmenopausal white women.   In the life-cycle of black
women, menopause was accepted as just another event in the cycle.
Major life goals were self-expression and interesting experiences;
these applied to both ethnic groups.   Both ethnic groups rejected fame
and power as life goals.

739 "Pills to Keep Women Young," in Time, Vol. 87, No. 13, 50,
     55, April 1, 1966.
        A discussion of Dr. Robert A. Wilson's hormone therapy to
keep women young. Dr. Wilson's book, Feminine Forever, is mentioned; and Dr. William H. Masters of St. Louis believes the book
focuses on a problem that the medical profession has ignored.

740 Prados, M. "Emotional Factors in the Climacterium of Women,"
     in Psychotherapy and Psychosomatics, Vol. 15, 231-244,
     1967. (A seminar held at Vancouver, B. C. , Canada.)
        The climacteric is a normal process, and the biological as-
pect of it is not the cause of emotional problems which may occur
at this time but rather the precipitating factor for these changes.
Six cases are presented. The climacteric is a developmental phase
of a woman's personality. Disturbances at this time are usually
seen in depression, felt as the author calls a "narcissistic mortifi-
cation." Psychoanalytic-oriented psychotherapy can be used to treat
the depression. 2 references

741 Reitz, Rosetta. Menopause: A Positive Approach. Radnor,
     PA: Chilton Book Co. , 1978.
        Treats menopause as the beginning of a rich, satisfying part
of a woman's life. Contains information on symptoms of menopause,
vaginal ecology, masturbation, sex when you are older, hormones,
hormones and cancer, estrogen replacement therapy, an interview
with Dr. Saul B. Gusberg concerning the menopausal woman as hero,
nutrition and middle age (including food for sex), and a section on
male menopause. An extensive bibliography is included.

742 Rhoades, Francis P. "Continuous Cyclic Hormonal Therapy,"
     in Journal of the American Geriatrics Society, Vol. 22, No.
     4, 183-185, April 1974. (This was presented at a conjoint
     symposium on geriatric medicine by the Southern Medical
     Association and the American Geriatrics Society, San Antonio,
     Texas, November 11, 1973.)
        This article reports on 1, 200 postmenopausal women who re-
ceived estrogen replacement therapy. The study lasted two years.
Computerized data on 20 common symptoms suggested that 95 percent relief during the time period in which estrogen-progesterone
therapy was administered. No evidence was obtained that cancer
resulted from the treatment. It was concluded that benefits received
from the therapy outweighed any possible dangers. 9 references

743 _____ . "Minimizing the Menopause," in Journal of the
     American Geriatrics Society, Vol. 15, No. 4, 346-354, April
     1967.
        Menopause should be treated and not thought of as inevitable
where nothing can be done. Hormones should be used in estrogen-
progesterone combinations to control undesirable side effects. The
vaginal cytogram can be used to determine female hormone deficiency.
The latter half of a woman's life should be made as comfortable as possible. 10 references

744 Rice, Dabney. "Anti-Aging Pill," in Harper's Bazaar, No.
    3165, 78, 128B, August 1975.
        Premarin, one of the most widely used estrogen compounds,
is discussed. Hormone replacement therapy can help relieve menopausal symptoms, but it cannot turn back the hands of time. Estrogens and cancer and other disease are also covered.

745 Rogers, Joseph. "Estrogens in the Menopause and Postmeno-
    pause," in New England Journal of Medicine, Vol. 280, 364-
    367, 1969.
        Dr. Rogers, in review of the available evidence, suggests
estrogens help most menopausal women. Replacement therapy is
suggested for women who have negative calcium balances from gonadal hormone deficiency. Estrogens should be given to women with
hypercholesterolemia, diabetes or hypertension. The role of progestogens in this situation is not clear. 60 references

746 "The Role of Progestogens in Peri- and Post-Menopausal Hor-
    mone Replacement Therapy," in Postgraduate Medical Journal,
    Supplement (2), Vol. 54, 1-100, 1978. (Proceedings of a
    workshop held at Sussex University on 20 and 21 September
    1977. Edited by B. I. Hoffbrand, Professor M. Elstein,
    Dr. R. A. Wiseman, and Dr. P. G. T. Bye.)
        Contains four sessions: Session I--a review of oestrogen
replacement therapy, Session II--biochemical aspects, Session III--
endometrial factors, and Session IV--clinical and other studies.

747 Rose, Louise (ed.). The Menopause Book. New York: Haw-
    thorn Books, Inc., 1977. (Book Review of this by Eileen
    Stukane in Forum: The International Journal of Human Rela-
    tions, Vol. 7, No. 6, 74, March 1978. Book Review of this
    by Laura J. Singer in SIECUS Newsletter, Vol. 7, No. 1, 8,
    September 1978.)
        Eight women physicians have contributed to this book including
Barrie Anderson, M. D.; Elizabeth Connell, M. D.; Helen Singer Kaplan, M. D.; Nancy Kemeny, M. D.; Malkah T. Notman, M. D.; Johanna
F. Perlmutter, M. D.; Natalie Shainess, M. D.; and Mary Catherine
Tyson, M. D. A chapter on male menopause is included. Other
topics discussed include 1) what is menopause? 2) temporary symptoms and permanent changes, 3) the emotional element of menopause,
4) the use of estrogen, 5) hysterectomy, 6) breast cancer, 7) sex at
menopause, 8) diet, exercise, and cosmetic surgery during menopause, 9) women talk about menopause. A resource directory is
included.

748 "Roundtable: Sex and the Menopause," in Medical Aspects of
    Human Sexuality, Vol. 4, No. 11, 64-89, November 1970.
        A roundtable moderated by Alvin F. Goldfarb, M. D. Panel
members include Michael J. Daly, M. D.; Daniel Lieberman, M. D.;
and David M. Reed, Ph. D., M. P. H. Estrogens given to an estrogen-
deficient woman can give the vagina a better condition with which to
receive a penis. The sexual response of the woman may not be affected. Venereal disease is on the increase in middle-age women,

and the damage from it sometimes causes sexual problems. Vaginal
infection sometimes poses a problem by making intercourse difficult
to enjoy; prolapse of the uterus, cystourethrocele, rectocele, and
enterocele may result in painful intercourse. Carcinoma of the cervix and subsequent irradiation treatment can also make intercourse
painful if patient isn't treated with estrogen. Radical vulvectomy,
the treatment for carcinoma of the vulva, can for emotional and psychological reasons cause a woman to refrain from or not enjoy intercourse. Some discussion concerns how physicians might create problems in menopausal women.

749   Rutherford, Robert N. , and Rutherford, Jean J. "Menopause--
      Fear or Defeat," in Psychosomatics, Vol. 7, 89-93, March-
      April 1966. (This paper was presented at the annual meeting
      of the Academy of Psychosomatic Medicine, New York City,
      October 1964.)
        The female and male climacteric are described separately.
A small section discusses the family climacteric. Treatment programs for both men and women are described. The physician should
counsel and suggest avenues to enrich the life of the patient. 9 references

750   Ryan, Kenneth J. , and Gibson, Don C. (eds.). Menopause and
      Aging. Summary report and selected papers from a research
      conference May 23-26, 1971, in Hot Springs, Arkansas. Be-
      thesda, MD: U.S. DHEW, Public Health Service, Pub. No.
      (NIH) 73-319, 1973.
        Covers the topics of extraglandular estrogen in the postmeno-
pause, coronary heart disease and the menopause, menopausal effects
on calcium homeostasis and skeletal metabolism, and the relationship
between estrogens and progestogens and thromboembolic disease.

751   Schleyer-Saunders, E. "Results of Hormone Implants in the
      Treatment of the Climacteric," in Journal of the American
      Geriatrics Society, Vol. 19, No. 2, 114-121, February 1971.
        This study presupposed that climacteric is the result of de-
cline of sex gland function. One thousand women and three hundred
men (40-75 years of age) were treated by hormone implants during 35
years (1945-1970). Arguments for treatment are supported by the
facts that flushes were improved, general condition improved, depression and fatigue were improved, genital tract and skin improved, and
the patients had a more youthful look. Points against estrogen therapy included postmenopausal bleeding and the possibility that it might
cause cancer. Cancer and bleeding were lower in hormonally treated
women than ones who didn't receive it. Patients, the author concludes, should not be deprived of hormonal therapy. 23 references

752   Seaman, Barbara, and Seaman, Gideon. Women and the Crisis
      in Sex Hormones. New York: Rawson Associates Publishers,
      Inc. , 1977.
        Suggests women use alternatives to estrogen in enduring men-
opause and preventing pregnancy. The book explores the alternatives.

753 Shafer, Nathaniel. "Helping Women Through the Change of
        Life," in Sexology, Vol. 36, No. 1, 54-56, May 1970.
     Dr. Shafer discusses how a woman's climacteric can be one
of renewed vitality and increased sexual desire due to hormone therapy. No references

754 Sommers, Nancy, and Ridgeway, James. "Can a Woman Be
        Feminine Forever?" in New Republic, Vol. 154, No. 12,
        15-16, March 19, 1966.
     Presents Dr. Robert A. Wilson's point of view on estrogen
therapy which he published in his book, Feminine Forever. In his
study of 82 women, Dr. Wilson used the drug Enovid which was man-
ufactured by G. D. Searle and Company. He does not mention this
in his book, Feminine Forever. No references

755 Sonkin, Lawrence S., and Cohen, Eugene J. "Treatment of
        the Menopause," in Modern Treatment, Vol. 5, 545-563,
        1968.
     The discussion is organized on the following topics: 1) why
treat the menopause, 2) whom to treat (including symptomatic patients
with irregular or absent menses, symptomatic patients with regular
menses, prophylaxis, and control of appearance of aging), 3) how to
treat (including nonhormonal treatment, hormonal treatment and psychotherapy), 4) regulation of hormonal dosage (including use of the
vaginal smear technique, and the regulation of androgenic therapy),
and 5) who should administer treatment. Most menopausal women
don't require hormone therapy. 15 references

756 Spence, A. W. "Sexual Adjustment at the Climacteric," in
        Practitioner, Vol. 172, 427-430, April 1954.
     The female climacteric may cause a change of libido in some
women and dyspareunia may arise. Treatment for frigidity, changes
in libido and dyspareunia are covered. Hormone therapy for treatment
in women is discussed. Also covered is treatment of sterility and
impotence in the middle-aged man. 7 references

757 Stern, Francis H. "Use of a New Antidepressant in the Fe-
        male Climacteric," in Psychosomatics, Vol. 11, 464-466,
        1970.
     Dr. Stern has conducted an open investigation of the psycho-
stimulant pyrovalerone hydrochloride in treating climacteric emotional
symptoms. Further clinical evaluations are recommended. 3 references

758 Stopes, Marie Charlotte Carmichael. Change of Life in Men
        and Women. New York: G. P. Putnam's Sons, 1936.
     Although the book is dated in many ways, Stopes presents
some remarkably innovative ideas about sexual activity among older
adults. She stresses that the menopause should not mark the end of
sexual activity for women. She speaks of men having a climacteric
and that there are parallel happenings in both men and women during
the change which are similar in both sexes.

759   Sturgis, Somers H.   "Hormone Therapy in the Menopause: In-
       dications and Contraindications," in Medical Aspects of Human
       Sexuality, Vol. 3, 69-75, May 1969.
       Menopause affects different women differently.   One-third of
women have no estrogen deficiency symptoms.   One-third show symptoms which may require treatment, and one-third of women in menopause have conditions which contraindicate steroids without careful
consideration of the outcomes.   10 references

760   Taymor, Melvin L. , and Rizkallah, Tawfik H.   "Progestogen-
       Estrogen Therapy in the Menopause: A Double Blind Study,"
       in American Journal of Obstetrics and Gynecology, Vol. 97,
       No. 4, 460-464, 1967.
       Twenty patients were treated with a tablet containing 2. 5 mg.
of 17α-ethinyl-19-nortestosterone acetate and 0. 05 mg. of ethinyl es-
tradiol.   Nineteen of the patients received relief from the hot flashes
of menopause.   Only 1 of 17 patients experienced relief when all
were given a placebo.   The study was a double blind one.   However,
one-third of the patients received side effects which brought about
the need to cease medication.   The authors contend that this steroid
combination could be used in lieu of estrogen to avoid the problems
brought about by it.   16 references

761   U. S. National Institute of Child Health and Human Development.
       Menopause: The Experts Speak.   Bethesda, MD: National
       Institutes of Health, 1975.
       A summary of findings from a conference on the menopause.
It is in the form of question and answer.   Covers 1) signs and symptoms that are distinctly characteristic of the menopause, 2) the use
of estrogen in treating menopausal symptoms, 3) discussion on osteoporosis, 4) heart disease and estrogen, 5) estrogen and blood clot-
ting problems, 6) estrogen and cancer, and 7) recommendations regarding estrogen replacement therapy.

762   van Keep, Pieter A. ; Greenblatt, Robert B. ; and Albeaux-Fernet,
       Michel (eds.).   Consensus on Menopause Research: A Sum-
       mary of International Opinion.   Baltimore, MD: University
       Park Press, 1976.
       This volume contains the Proceedings of the First International
Congress on the Menopause held at La Grande Motte, France, in
June 1976, under the auspices of the American Geriatric Society and
the Medical Faculty of the University of Montpellier.   Section A contains 14 Consensus Reports by the Chairmen of the Workshops.   This
was primarily concerned with the chemical influence on the climacteric,
specifically estrogen therapy.   However, there was one report on the
climacteric syndrome and one on the psycho-social aspects of the
climacteric.   Section B contains selected papers presented at the
Congress, 11 in all.   Most of these were chemically oriented but one
by Marcha Flint was concerned with the cross-cultural factors which
affect the age of menopause.   Section C contains a comprehensive
list of all the papers presented at the Congress, the list of participants, and the address of each participant.   A topical index is also
included.

763 Weideger, Paula. Menstruation and Menopause: The Physiol-
     ogy and Psychology, the Myth and the Reality. New York:
     Alfred A. Knopf, 1976.
     The author talks about myths and taboos of menstruation and
the effects they had on women. Anatomy and physiology are covered
from menarche through menopause. She talks about women's self-
image during menstruation and menopause. This discussion is presented with authority as the writer did the study.

764 Williams, David. "The Menopause," in Nursing Mirror and
     Midwives Journal, Vol. 135, No. 25, 36, June 23, 1972.
     A general discussion of the topic including psychogenic dis-
turbances which may be encountered at the menopause. No references

765 Wilson, Charles B. "Menopause, Mental Illness and Meningio-
     mas," in Journal of the Kentucky Medical Association, Vol.
     63, 699-700, September 1965.
     This is a case discussion of a middle-aged woman who is
going through the menopause. A physical examination was undertaken. Two figures are given to illustrate findings: 1) a radioac-
tive mercury brain scan, 2) a right carotid arteriogram. Behavior
similar to that of a stereotypical menopausal woman was observed.
However, the physician suspected an organic process problem which
led to the discovery of a benign brain tumor. Organic disease can
be separated from functional mental disease by the appearance of
certain features in a stepwise fashion. No references

766 Wilson, Robert A. Feminine Forever. New York: M. Evans
     and Co. , Inc. , 1966.
     A book suggesting estrogen for the treatment of menopause.
Women's body chemistry is covered as well as discussion on sex
and birth control pills and menopause prevention. 78-item bibliography

767 _____, and Wilson, Thelma A. "The Basic Philosophy of
     Estrogen Maintenance," in Journal of the American Geria-
     trics Society, Vol. 20, No. 11, 521-523, 1972.
     Dr. Robert A. Wilson and Thelma A. Wilson, R. N. , stress
the importance of estrogen to women. Estrogen deficiency can be
monitored by the Maturation Index. Human or equine naturally occurring estrogens are best to use. If proper dosage is given, there
are no side effects. Estrogen maintenance can be carried on beyond
menopause. 9 references

768 Winn, Harold, and Daly, Michael Joseph. "The Change of Life
     in the Woman," in Geriatrics, Vol. 26, No. 6, 105-111,
     June 1971.
     When a woman passes through the climacteric, she may ex-
perience depression, loss of self-esteem, and regret. These emotions are all interrelated. These traumas, coupled with pre-existing
personality defects, can cause emotional illnesses. It is possible
that the climacteric can be a time of enrichment and new develop-

ment. A serious blow may be dealt to the self-esteem by the reduction of the roles of mother and sexual object.   6 references

769   Yannone, Michael E.   "The Use of Hormones in the Meno-
        pause," in Journal of the Iowa State Medical Society, Vol. 57,
        No. 11, 1099-1105, November 1967.   (This was a presenta-
        tion at the 1967 IMS Annual Meeting.)
        The author states that at the time of ovarian ablation all
women are estrogen deficient and that most are estrogen deficient
ten years past a spontaneous menopause.   This deficiency speeds
up adverse metabolic and tissue effects as well as menopausal symptoms.   Estrogen replacement therapy can be beneficial for certain
patients.   Further research and clinical experience will help improve
the therapeutic approach of estrogen substitution.   23 references

770   Ziel, Harry K. , and Finkle, William D.   "Increased Risk of
        Endometrial Carcinoma Among Users of Conjugated Estrogens,"
        in New England Journal of Medicine, Vol. 293, No. 23, 1167-
        1170, December 4, 1975.
        This study was an investigation to determine if the use of con-
jugated estrogens increases the risk of endometrial carcinoma.   A
twofold age-matched control series from the same population was
also used.   Conjugated estrogens (primarily sodium estrone sulfate)
use was monitored for 57 percent of 94 women with endometrial carcinoma.   Use was also recorded for 15 percent of controls.   Based
on the data, it was suggested that conjugated estrogens have an etiologic role in endometrial carcinoma.   22 references

SEXUALITY AND HEALTH

771 Berlin, Herman. "Effect of Human Sexuality on Well-Being from Birth to Aging," in Medical Aspects of Human Sexuality, Vol. 10, No. 7, 10-11, 14-15, 21, 23-25, 27, 31, July 1976.
Sexuality is important to human beings from the womb until the later years. Physicians should help their patients understand their own sexuality. 26 references

772 Busse, Ewald W. , and Pfeiffer, Eric. Mental Illness in Later Life. Washington, D. C. : American Psychiatric Association, 1973.
Life expectancy tables are presented (p. 23) and broken down by sex. Countertransference of sexual feelings by the patient (usually female) for a younger male therapist is touched upon briefly. The question "Can old people still be interested in sex?" is answered by Dr. Eric Pfeiffer. He suggests that sexual interest and activity in old age is normal and healthy.

773 Carpenter, Robert R. "Maintaining the General Health of Aging Women," in Clinical Obstetrics and Gynecology, Vol. 20, No. 1, 215-222, March 1977.
Dr. Carpenter provides a review of data on health detection and maintenance procedures. It is the responsibility of the physician to tailor the patient's health maintenance program in line with the patient's resources and needs. 38 references

774 Cole, Theodore M. "Sexuality and Physical Disabilities," in Rubinstein, Eli Abraham; Green, Richard; and Brecher, Edward (eds.), New Directions in Sex Research, pp. 67-81. New York and London: Plenum Press, 1976. (This paper is from the proceedings of a conference held at the State University of New York at Stony Brook, Stony Brook, New York, June 5-9, 1974. This material originally appeared in Archives of Sexual Behavior, Vol. 4, No. 4, July 1975.)
Covers spinal cord injury and sexuality (including male sexuality and spinal cord injury and female sexuality and spinal cord injury), other key points about sexual options for spinal injured adults, counseling, and future directions. Group discussion follows.

775 Felstein, Ivor. Sex and the Longer Life. Baltimore: Penguin Books, 1970.
Physical, psychological, and social changes which occur in the aged are described. A review of aging and sexuality as pre-

170   Sexuality and Aging

sented by Masters and Johnson, Freud, and Kinsey is given. Sex
in and out of marriage is covered.

776 "Heart Disease and Sex: Response to Questions," by Bakker,
     Cornelis B.; Bogdonoff, Morton; Hellerstein, Herman K.;
     Kraus, William L.; Naughton, John P.; Reiser, Morton F.;
     Rosenman, Ray H.; Schwab, John J.; and Wenger, Nanette
     K., in Medical Aspects of Human Sexuality, Vol. 5, No. 6,
     24, 28-29, 32-33, 35, June 1971.
     Sexual activity usually takes the same amount of energy as
it takes to climb stairs, take a walk, or scrub a floor. Sudden
death does not usually occur during sexual intercourse. The heart
disease patient must be reassured that he/she will be able to have
sex and be able to work. The patient's wife or husband must also
realize that the heart disease patient can have sex. No references

777 Hellerstein, Herman K., and Friedman, Ernest H. "Sexual
     Activity and the Post-Coronary Patient," in Medical Aspects
     of Human Sexuality, Vol. 3, No. 3, 70-96, March 1969.
     Up until now, cardiac patients did not know how much sexual
activity they could safely engage in. Studies of physiological changes
during intercourse hadn't focused on the cardiologic aspect. This
study examined the physiologic effects of intercourse on postcoronary
and coronary-prone individuals. Sexual habits of both these groups
were also studied. There doesn't seem to be any danger for middle-
aged and aged couples to have sex even if one or both is a postcoronary patient. 39 references

778 Hickman, Bonita Watson. "All About Sex ... Despite Dialysis,"
     in American Journal of Nursing, Vol. 77, No. 4, 606-607,
     April 1977.
     Even when sexual activity declines it is not necessary that
sexual satisfaction should decline. In counseling dialysis patients
about sex, three factors should be kept in mind: 1) confidentiality
and privacy should be provided; 2) empathy, reassurance and support
should be given to the patient who is likely to be anxious; 3) the
patients should be allowed to decide what is normal for them. 10
references

779 Jackson, Graham. "Sexual Instructions for Postcoronary Man,"
     in Medical Aspects of Human Sexuality, Vol. 13, No. 5, 135,
     May 1979.
     Suggestions are given to make coitus less stressful for the post
coronary man. The postcoronary patient should be able to resume his
normal precoronary sexual activity about six or eight weeks post infarction. Intercourse should be avoided within two hours of a meal or a bath
as they are likely to increase the cardiac output up to 20 percent. Most
coital deaths occur during extramarital sex, usually with a younger
woman in a strange environment and after a heavy meal. Physicians
should accurately counsel their patients concerning postinfarction sexual
activity. No references

780 Jacobson, Linbania. "Illness and Human Sexuality," in Nursing
     Outlook, Vol. 22, No. 1, 50-53, January 1974. (This is based

on a speech presented at a Conference on Human Sexuality,
sponsored by the Sex Information and Education Council of
the U.S. [SIECUS] held in New York, March 1973.)
Sexuality must be considered to care for the whole patient.
Health disorders and treatment of them can cause sexual problems.
Disorders that mutilate, special concerns of women, quality of counseling and repressive traditions are discussed. 16 references

781 Kalliomaki, J. L.; Markkanen, T. K.; and Mustonen, V. A. "Sex-
     ual Behavior After Cerebral Vascular Accident: A Study on
     Patients Below the Age of 60 Years," in Fertility and Steri-
     lity, Vol. 12, No. 2, 156-158, 1961.
Cerebral vascular accidents seem to decrease libido and intercourse frequency. Data from 105 patients under the age of 60
were used to determine this. Right-side paralysis seems to decrease libido more than left-side paralysis. The data are not sufficient to determine why this is so. However, patients who suffer
from cerebral vascular accidents don't have increased sex drives.
No references

782 Kent, Saul. "Continued Sexual Activity Depends on Health and
     the Availability of a Partner," in Geriatrics, Vol. 30, No.
     11, 142, 144, November 1975.
Women are less active than men in later life. This is a reflection of illness and impotence in men as well as their shorter life
spans. If a person is healthy and has a partner, sexuality can be
maintained into the later years. 4 references

783 _____. "The Intimate Relationship Between the Urinary
     System and Sexual Function," in Geriatrics, Vol. 30, No. 6,
     138, 143, 1975.
Among the topics discussed which are related to sexual function are included urethritis, prostatitis, benign prostatic enlargement,
prostatic cancer, prostatic surgery and impotence. Men can cam-
ouflage sexual problems by complaining about urological problems.
No references

784 _____. "When to Resume Sexual Activity After Myocardial
     Infarction," in Geriatrics, Vol. 30, No. 8, 151, 153, 1975.
Sex causes no more strain on the heart than normal daily
activities such as climbing stairs or walking briskly. The postcoronary patient should be counseled about resuming sexual activity
after recovery. No references

785 Oberleder, Muriel. "Emotional Breakdown in Elderly People,"
     in Hospital and Community Psychiatry, Vol. 20, No. 7, 21-
     25, July 1969. (Based on a paper presented at the 21st An-
     nual Meeting of the Gerontological Society, Denver, November
     1, 1968.)
Anxiety is more common to old age than any other age. Elderly people who have breakdowns can recover. Symptoms of senility, according to Dr. Oberleder, can actually be symptoms of psychosis. However, the double standard is often applied to old people:

the young with the same symptoms are designated psychotic but the
old people are said to be senile.   Sexual repression is a factor in
senile breakdown.   Patients, when given Rorschach tests, pointed
out areas which were pathologically sexual areas on card after card.
In order to fulfill needs for physical contact or sexual satisfaction,
patients use somatic complaints and relationships with the physician
to fulfill these needs.   No references

786   Osborne, David, and Maruta, Toshihiko.   "Sexual Adjustment
       and Chronic Back Pain," in Medical Aspects of Human Sex-
       uality, Vol. 14, No. 2, 94-95, 99, 102, 107, 113, February
       1980.
       Contains information on illness and sexual functioning includ-
ing pain and sexual avoidance, increased distance between partners,
anger and guilt, medication, emotional factors, and attitudinal factors.
There is a high frequency of sexual problems in chronic pain patients
and physicians should routinely discuss sexual adjustment with their
pain patients.   The author recommends different coital positions, a
rehabilitation program and presents a case study for illustration.   In
order to correct sexual problems in back pain patients, a total rehabilitation of the patient needs to occur including increased tolerance
for physical exercise, learning mechanisms to cope with chronic pain,
and involvement of the spouse in the process.   Commentary follows
by Lawrence W. Friedmann, M.D., and John E. Sarno, M.D.   3
references

787   Puksta, Nancy Sallese.   "All About Sex After a Coronary," in
       American Journal of Nursing, Vol. 77, No. 4, 602-605,
       April 1977.
       Recommendations are given to counselors in postcoronary sex-
ual counseling programs.   Direct approaches, openness and privacy
are suggested.   In addition, cultural and language barriers should
be overcome; and no pressure should be put on the patient to participate in the program.   All patients should be approached; and if the
patient agrees, the partner should be included in the discussions.
12 references

788   Reichert, Philip.   "Does Heart Disease End Sex Activity?" in
       Sexology, Vol. 29, 76-81, September 1962.
       The author is a heart specialist who says that married coup-
les can have a satisfying sex life even if one or both of them has had
a heart disease.   A chart is presented illustrating the heart action
in a husband and wife during sexual activity.   Sexual activity after heart disease will depend on the kind of heart disease and the
kind of sexual relationship.   Controlled sexual activity within the lim-
its of the disabled heart is far healthier than mental and emotional
problems which result from unsatisfied sexual needs.   No references.

789   Scheimann, Eugene.   "Sex Can Help You Live Longer," in
       Forum: The International Journal of Human Relations, Vol.
       8, No. 4, 28-31, January 1979.
       Dr. Scheimann begins this short article by quoting Dr. Stanley
R. Dean: "Aging is regarded as a demon that heralds approaching

death, whereas sex is equated with life. That is why sexuality is
especially significant for older persons' morale. It is an affirmation of life and a denial of death." Dr. Scheimann also quotes Dr.
Hans Franke: "If you want to reach one hundred, eat and work in
moderation and enjoy a regular sex life." He gives nine reasons
why he feels sexual activity is the secret of healthy longevity: 1)
sex balances body chemistry and hormones and this slows down the
aging process; 2) sex is an antidote to health hazards; 3) sex is
important in heart attack patient treatment; 4) marriage is enhanced
by good sex, 5) sex is a coping mechanism; 6) as exercise, sex is
great; 7) suicide and self-destructive behavior is discouraged by sex;
8) feelings of inadequacy and inferiority can be compensated for by
sex; 9) a positive frame of mind is enhanced by sex as are hope and
optimism.

790 _____. Sex Can Save Your Heart ... and Life. New York:
     Crown Publishers, Inc. , 1974.
     Sex can have a medicinal effect in healing. Ten reasons for
suggesting sex for his patients are presented. A five-point plan for
prevention of heart attacks and improvement of overall health is
given.

791 Scheingold, Lee Dresinger, and Wagner, Nathaniel N. Sound
     Sex and the Aging Heart. New York: Behavioral Publications,
     Inc. , 1974. (Also in abstract form in Aging, (239-240), 25,
     1974.)
     Sex after a heart attack is recommended despite possible
risks. The spouse of the heart attack patient is given suggestions.

792 Sha'ked, Ami. Human Sexuality in Physical and Mental Illnesses
     and Disabilities: An Annotated Bibliography. Bloomington:
     Indiana University Press, 1978. (The book is reviewed by
     Warren R. Johnson in SIECUS Report, Vol. 8, No. 1, 9,
     September 1979.)
     Contains a chapter on sex and the aging. The chapter has
91 citations covering general aspects of sexuality and aging, psychosocial aspects of sex and aging, sex and menopausal men and women,
rapid eye movement (REM) sleep and sex in the aged, sex in nursing homes, the aging homosexual, and the geriatric sex offender.
Most of the citations are on the general topic of sexuality and aging.

793 Tuttle, William B.; Cook, W. Leigh, Jr.; and Fitch, Edna.
     "Sexual Behavior in Post-Myocardial Infarction Patients," in
     American Journal of Cardiology, Vol. 13, 140, 1964.
     Total number of men questioned about their sexual activity
is not given. However, all had myocardial infarctions one to nine
years before the interview. Sexual activity had not been discussed
with two-thirds of the men. Vague advice was given to the rest.
Anginal pain was experienced by only two-thirds of the men who
were under 50. Permanent impotence was experienced by ten percent of all men, one-third resumed regular activity, and two-thirds
had a great decrease in sexual activity. Physicians need to give
specific recommendations to post myocardial infarction patients about
sexual activity. No references

794   Watts, Rosalyn Jones.   "Sexuality and the Middle-Aged Cardiac
      Patient," in Nursing Clinics of North America, Vol. 11, No.
      2, 349-359, June 1976.
         Topics covered include physiology of the male sexual response
(including the normal sex cycle in the male, effects of aging on male
sexuality, and adverse effects of drugs on the male sexual response);
cardiovascular response to sexual activity (including sexual intercourse, coital positions, cardiac cost of masturbation, energy expen-
diture of sexual activity, and counseling regarding specific activities);
psychosocial factors influencing sexuality (including middle age crises,
depression and sexuality, role of the spouse, and marital dynamics);
and rehabilitation.   17 references

795   Zimmerman, David.   "Sex Can Help Arthritis," in Forum:
      The International Journal of Human Relations, Vol. 5, No. 2,
      6-10, November 1975.   (Also reported about in Forum: The
      International Journal of Human Relations, Vol. 9, No. 5, 8,
      February 1980.)
         Sexual intercourse may have beneficial effects upon the pain
and discomfort of arthritis.   A number of illustrations appear which
show different positions for sexual intercourse for those couples with
arthritis or chronic disabling disease.   No references

MARRIAGE, FAMILY, AND SEX ROLES

796 Abse, D. Wilfred. "Sexual Disorder and Marriage," pp. 41-
73, Chapter 3 in Nash, Ethel M.; Jessner, Lucie; and Abse,
D. Wilfred (eds.), Marriage Counseling in Medical Practice.
Chapel Hill, NC: University of North Carolina Press, 1964.
Covers male potency disturbances with case examples, female
frigidity with case examples, paraphilia and marriage, homosexuality
and marriage with a case example, other paraphilias, and sexual
disorder as a medical problem. Some specific references to age
are made. 32 references

797 Akers, Donald S. "On Measuring the Marriage Squeeze," in
Demography, Vol. 4, No. 2, 907-924, 1967.
Single men have married at an increasing rate and single
women have married at a decreasing rate during the 1960's. The
"marriage squeeze" is the disproportion between men and women
at prime age of marriage and this is suggested as the reason for
the given rate differences. Two reasons for the "marriage squeeze"
are 1) women marry earlier than men, and 2) there was an increase
in births from 1939-47. More research is suggested to investigate
what the consequences of these changes in marriage patterns will be.
(Author's summary modified) Summary is also presented in Span-
ish. 9 references

798 Berlatsky, Marjorie N. "Some Aspects of the Marital Problems of the Elderly," in Social Casework, Vol. 43, No. 5,
233-237, May 1962.
A differential diagnosis is needed in order to treat marital
problems of elderly couples. This diagnosis is helpful to 1) find
out the character structure of the elderly married couple; 2) past
and current functioning evaluation of each partner; 3) separate problems inherent in aging processes, i. e., biological, physical and social; 4) determine what factors have kept the marriage together for
such a long time; 5) isolate factors in the marriage which are causing the problem. Supportive and sustaining environmental and psychological treatment can help save the marriage. Three case illustrations are presented. 12 references (author's summary modified)

799 Blau, David. "Normal Psychology of the Aging Process, Re-
visited--I: Discussion," in Journal of Geriatric Psychiatry,
Vol. 9, No. 2, 177-188, 1976.
Comments on article by Irving Kaufman in Journal of Geriatric Psychiatry, Vol. 9, No. 2, 161-175, 1976. Social changes in
attitudes toward sexuality are covered. 1 reference

176 Sexuality and Aging

800 Blau, Zena Smith. Old Age in a Changing Society. New York: New Viewpoints, Inc., 1973.
Suggests that decline of sexual capacity in aging men may be due to boredom with marital partner rather than age.

801 Blenkner, Margaret. "Social Work and Family Relationships in Later Life with Some Thoughts on Filial Maturity," in Shanas, Ethel, and Streib, Gordon F. (eds.), Social Structure and the Family: Generational Relations, pp. 46-59. New York: John Wiley, 1965.
Psychiatric and social-work theorists should conceive of a stage beyond genital maturity, perhaps a stage called filial maturity. This stage could be seen as part of the developmental sequence. The stage could represent the healthy transition from genital maturity to old age. Peck is mentioned as suggesting that old age has its own sequence of stages. Theory and values will determine whether family social workers can meet the challenge of the filial crisis. 48 footnotes

802 Bloom, Martin, and Monro, Alexander. "Social Work and the Aging Family," in Family Coordinator, Vol. 21, 103-115, January 1972.
The aged couple (including nonmarried persons) is covered. Types of problems and social work responses are presented. A selected review of the literature is presented.

803 Brigante, Mary Ellen. "A Trans-Generational Study of Sex-Roles in Marriage in Middle-Class America." Unpublished doctoral dissertation, Claremont Graduate School, Claremont, CA, 1972. (D.A., Vol. 33, 2160 A, 1972.)
There is a trend toward greater role-sharing preference with decreasing age. Older adults expressed the lowest role-sharing preference. Activity-categories covering child-rearing had a greater role-sharing preference over all generations than categories related to personal development in marriage. Change is always present in that very few activities have remained stable.

804 Broverman, Inge K.; Broverman, Donald M.; Clarkson, Frank E.; Rosenkrantz, Paul S.; and Vogel, Susan R. "Sex Role Stereotypes and Clinical Judgements of Mental Health," in Journal of Consulting and Clinical Psychiatry, Vol. 34, No. 1, 1-7, 1970.
Clinicians were given a sex-role Stereotype Questionnaire. This instrument was made up of 122 bipolar items. The clinicians were first asked to identify a socially competent, mature and healthy adult with no sex identification. Then, they were asked to identify a man with the same characteristics. Finally, they were asked to identify a woman with those same characteristics. Differences about healthy individuals were a function of sex and parallel stereotypic sex-role differences. Behaviors and characteristics seen as an ideal standard of health for an adult were similar to those judged as being ideal for men. 21 references

805   Cameron, Paul. "Masculinity-Femininity in the Aged," in
        Journal of Gerontology, Vol. 23, 63-65, 1968.
        A sample of young adults (N=162) from ages 18 to 40 and a
sample of older adults (N=117) all over age 50 were given the Berdie
Femininity Check List and Symonds Areas of Human Concern Interests Scale. The study indicated that while interests of the older
adult are more feminine compared to the young, their personality
style is more masculine. 10 references (author summary modified)

806   Campbell, Angus. "The American Way of Mating," in Psychol-
        ogy Today, Vol. 8, No. 12, 37-40, 42-43, May 1975.
        A national survey of 2,164 adults suggests that marrieds are
happier than singles, children cause many headaches for parents,
women get along without men better than the reverse, women report
less stress after marriage and men report more, the empty nest
makes it easier for married couples to enjoy each other. No references

807   Cantor, M., and Mayer, M. "Factors in Differential Utiliza-
        tion of Services by Urban Elderly," in Gerontologist, Vol. 15,
        No. 5, Part 2, 97, 1975. (This was a paper presented at
        the 28th annual meeting of the Gerontological Society, Louis-
        ville, Kentucky, October 1975.)
        Factors related to the likelihood of elderly utilizing major
services/entitlements are covered. Ethnicity, income, and sex
were most related to utilization.

808   Cavalli-Sforza, L. L.; Kimura, M.; and Barrai, I. "The
        Probability of Consanguineous Marriages," in Genetics, Vol.
        54, 37-60, July 1966.
        Prediction of frequencies of various types of consanguineous
marriages can be made using data about demography, migration patterns, age distributions, and the similarity of mates in the general
population. Theories were developed in this paper, and the Parma
Valley area was the region where the population was drawn and on
which probabilities were computed. Demographic information which
is available at this time is not adequate. Knowing the probabilities
of consanguineous marriages is important for those in the field of
human population genetics. 14 references

809   Clark, Alexander L., and Wallin, Paul. "The Accuracy of
        Husbands' and Wives' Reports of the Frequency of Marital
        Coitus," in Population Studies, Vol. 18, No. 2, 165-173,
        November 1964.
        The article reviews and evaluates previous studies on assess-
ing accuracy of data on the frequency of marital coitus. Spouses'
testimony about their coital frequency has a margin of error, but
this may not be easy to determine. The error may be due to the
couple members' level of satisfaction with the coital frequency.
More research on this and other errors in reporting of different
kinds of sexual behavior needs to be done. 11 footnotes

810   Cleveland, Martha. "Sex in Marriage: At 40 and Beyond,"

in Family Coordinator, Vol. 25, No. 3, 233-240, July 1976.
(P. A. , Vol. 57, Abstract No. 03087, 1977.)
The sexual dimension of marriage during middle age and beyond is considered as well as its importance.   An examination is
made of "traditional" and "new" norms concerning sexual behavior.
A discussion of implications for marriage counseling is presented.
28 references

811   "Cupid Comes to Older People," in Aging, No. 93, 8-10, July
        1962.
           In 1959, 1,494,000 marriages occurred in the United States.
About 35,300 or 2.4 percent of the total occurred in which the groom,
the bride, or both were 65 or over.   The number of marriages with
both grooms and brides over 65 was about 11,500.   Men who married brides under 65 numbered 21,700.   This was 65 percent of all
older grooms.   Brides who married grooms under 65 numbered
2,100 or 35 percent of all older brides.

812   de Ridder, Joyce Anna.   "Sex Related Roles, Attitudes, and
        Orientation of Negro, Anglo, and Mexican-American Women
        Over the Life Cycle," Dissertation done at North Texas
        State University, 1976.   (D.A., Vol 37 (4-A), 2442-2443,
        1976.)
           For women 65 and over, a significant positive association
exists between status occupancy combinations and attitudes favorable
to sex-based differentiation.   There was found to be a negative association between status occupancy combinations with age and age is
positively associated with orientation to housekeeping.   The sample
for study consisted of 727 women separated into age categories of
20-39, 40-64, and 65 and over.

813   Gebhard, Paul H.   "Post-Marital Coitus Among Widows and
        Divorcees," in Bohannan, Paul (ed.), Divorce and After,
        pp. 81-96, Garden City, NY: Doubleday, 1970 (paperback
        edition, Anchor Books, pp. 89-106).
           Two primary problems resulting from divorce include domes-
tic problems and sexual problems.   Postmarital coitus has received
very little scientific attention.   This study was based on 632 white
women.   These women were U.S. citizens who had never been imprisoned and who were interviewed by the staff of the Institute for
Sex Research between 1939 and 1956.   These women's marriages
had been terminated by death, separation, or divorce between ages
21 and 60.   Most women whose marriages have ended through widowhood, separation or divorce have coitus.   The postmarital coitus begins within one year following the end of the marriage.   Coital frequency ranges from 36 to 73 times a year up to age 40 when a sharp
decrease occurs.   Women who have postmarital coitus experience a
higher rate of orgasm during coitus than they did in their marital
coitus.   They also experience higher orgasm rates than wives of the
same age.   Divorced women exceed the widowed women in prior nonmarital sexual experience, in the percentage who have postmarital
coitus, in postmarital coital frequency, and in the quickness with
which the coitus was started after the termination of the marriage.

814 Gilmore, Anne. "Attitudes of the Elderly to Marriage," in
      Gerontologia Clinica, Vol. 15, 124-132, 1973.
      A subsample of 66 healthy elderly married people randomly
selected from a larger age-stratified sample of 300 subjects, aged
65-89 were interviewed. The subsample lived in their own homes.
They were interviewed about their attitudes about marriage and sex
lives. Most slept in the same room and had a satisfactory marriage.
Some, however, had separate rooms and separate beds. Most agreed
that age reduced the need for sex with 39 of 66 no longer having sex.
Of the 66, 63 felt they were healthy. (Author abstract modified) 7
references

815 Grauer, H.; Betts, D.; and Birbom, F. "Welfare Emotions
      and Family Therapy in Geriatrics," in Journal of the Amer-
      ican Geriatrics Society, Vol. 21, No. 1, 21-24, January 1973.
      Family therapy is described in a two-phase approach. Hos-
tile family members are separated in Phase 1. The patient can be
put in a Day Hospital. The family conflicts are ironed out in Phase
2. This is the most difficult task to accomplish. Admission to an
institution can be avoided if "welfare emotions" exist, and the marriage had been good and child rearing was successful. Satisfactory
retirement adaptation and a good work record are also linked to successful completion of Phases 1 and 2. 8 references

816 Hudson, R. Lofton. "Married Love in the Middle Years," in
      Journal of Religion and Health, Vol. 13, No. 4, 263-274,
      October 1974.
      Rev. Hudson presents six main problems confronting married
love in the middle years: 1) stress and grief attached to the child-
launching period, 2) relationship rebuilding with others and with each
other (including sexual response patterns, recreational experiments,
and new friends), 3) problems with new woman and dual-career families, 4) changing social and sexual practices in our culture, 5) the
"middlescent" rut of not-so-in-love crisis, and 6) couple must have
and/or develop ability to deeply care about each other and to cope
with stress. 7 references

817 Huyck, Margaret Hellie. "Sex, Gender, and Aging," in Hu-
      manitas, Vol. 13, 83-97, 1977. (A revision of this paper
      was presented at the Symposium on the Double Standard of Ag-
      ing: A Question of Sex Differences, Annual Scientific Meet-
      ings of the Gerontological Society, New York City, October
      1976.)   ,
      The paper focuses on the questions of 1) whether a person's
experience of aging is related to his or her gender and 2) how a
person's gender may be influenced by aging. A small section on
sexuality is included. 33 references

818 James, William H. "Marital Coital Rates, Spouses' Ages,
      Family Size and Social Class," in Journal of Sex Research,
      Vol. 10, No. 3, 205-218, August 1974.
      Two surveys on human sexual behavior were used to collect
data for this study. Four demographic variables--wife's age, hus-

band's age, parity, social class--were analyzed by holding three constant and examining marital coital rate with one variable. When social class and number of children (parity) were held constant, the rate of marital coitus dropped more rapidly with the husband's age rather than with the wife's age. When duration of marriage was held constant, there was a positive correlation with coital rate and parity. 22 references

819   Jewett, Stephen P. "Longevity and the Longevity Syndrome,"
        in Gerontologist, Vol. 13, No. 1, 91-99, Spring 1973.
        This paper is a report on a study of 79 people ranging in
age from 87 to 103. Hereditary factors are discussed. In addition,
personality characteristics, habit patterns, and traits were described.
The people interviewed were healthy, active, and creative thus fitting
them into the longevity syndrome. A personality profile of common
characteristics provided the climate for hereditary factors to operate
at their optimum. Marriage seems to be a factor in longevity; that
is, those who are married live longer. Many people who marry
past the age of 65 may do so to continue an active sex life. 11
references

820   Johnson, Ralph E. "Extramarital Sexual Intercourse: A Meth-
        odological Note," in Journal of Marriage and the Family, Vol.
        32, 279-282, May 1970.
        Extramarital sexual behavior of upper middle class, middle-
aged couples living in a midwestern community was examined. If
the methodological framework is carefully developed, representative
samples of the population are willing to yield data about coital activity. (Author abstract modified) 9 references

821   _____. "Some Correlates of Extramarital Coitus," in Jour-
        nal of Marriage and the Family, Vol. 32, 449-456, 1970.
        Middle class, middle-aged couples were studied (N=100) and
they were selected from two middle-class suburbs of a mid-west
city. Comparisons were made of individuals who have had affairs
outside of marriage and those who have not. Independent variables
which were used for comparison included: 1) opportunity for involvement, 2) perceived desire of others for involvement, 3) potential
involvement, 4) justification of involvement, and 5) marital sexual
satisfaction, marital adjustment and involvement. (Author abstract
modified) 13 references

822   Kassel, Victor. "Polygyny After 60," in Geriatrics, Vol. 21,
        214-218, April 1966.
        Dr. Kassel poses some advantages to polygyny after 60: 1)
the greater ratio of older women to older men, 2) reestablishment
of a meaningful family group, the family constellation, 3) married
couples have a more adequate diet than widowers and widows, 4)
living conditions are improved by the pooling of funds, 5) responsibility for care during sickness is shared, 6) housework can be shared,
7) unmarried older women can have a sex partner, 8) both women
and men would show more interest in grooming, 9) depression and
loneliness can be dispelled, and finally 10) group health insurance

is less expensive and has more advantages than individual policies.
No references

823 Kaufman, Irving. "Normal Psychology of the Aging Process,
     Revisited--I: Marital Adaptation in the Aging," in Journal
     of Geriatric Psychiatry, Vol. 9, No. 2, 161-175, 1976.
     (This was a paper presented at the Fifteenth Anniversary An-
     nual Scientific Meeting of the Boston Society for Gerontolog-
     ical Psychiatry, 1975.)
     An investigation of the relation between the social institution
of marriage, biological facts of aging, and the psychoanalytic implications of the interrelationship. A discussion of changing attitudes
about sexuality is included.

824 Kerckhoff, Alan C. "The Older Couple: Some Basic Consid-
     erations," in Simpson, Ida Harper, and McKinney, John C.
     (eds.), Social Aspects of Aging, pp. 133-137. Durham, NC:
     Duke University Press, 1966.
     The husband's retirement rather than age often leads to changes
in conjugal roles. It is difficult to know if the family life characteristics of older people are due to role changes or if they are the result of changed conditions within which the families function. This
chapter basically summarizes basic research considerations for the
older couple.

825 Klemer, Richard H. , and Klemer, Margaret G. Sexual Adjust-
     ment in Marriage. New York: Public Affairs Pamphlet No.
     397, 1976.
     Suggestions are given for making sexual adjustment in mar-
riage and improving sexual communication.

826 Kumamoto, Ryo, and Hiranuma, Hiroshi. "The Influence of
     Age and Sex on the Paroxysmal Activity in Various Activating
     Conditions," in Clinical Electroencephalography (Osaka), Vol.
     18, No. 4, 223-229, 1976.
     Sexual and age differences in the rate of abnormal paraoxys-
mal brain waves were noted in 2728 tested subjects. Of these subjects, 661 were epileptics, 1634 had head injuries, and 433 had head-
ache seizures. Female subjects had an overall rate of abnormal
waves at 8. 9 percent and males hand an overall rate of 4. 1 percent
15 references

827 Livsey, Clara G. ; Christ, Jacob; Kadis, Leslie B. ; and Tavris,
     Carol. "What Is the Relationship Between Sexual Satisfaction
     and the General Happiness of a Marriage?" in Medical As-
     pects of Human Sexuality, Vol. 12, No. 9, 170-171, 176-177,
     180, September 1978.
     Many well-adjusted couples don't have a good sex life while
others with a satisfying sexual life are very unhappy. More often
than not, the sexual and nonsexual aspects of marriage are disrupted
simultaneously. It is unusual for the sexual life to be intact when
other problems exist in the marriage. However, some clinical experiences have invalidated the perception that if the marriage is good,

sex is good; or if sex is good, the marriage is good. Another study
of 100,000 women (by Carol Tavris) suggests that a good sex life is
essential to a happy marriage.

828   McKain, Walter C.   "A New Look at Older Marriages," in
        Family Coordinator, Vol. 21, 61-69, 1972.
        Late marriages are usually successful especially when they
are reinforced by motivations of love and companionship, an adequate
income and approval of the adult children.   In addition, older people
tend to marry long-time acquaintances.

829   _____. Retirement Marriage. Storrs, CT: University of
        Connecticut Agricultural Experimental Station Monograph #3,
        1969.
        Couples who remarry in old age visit their children along a
same-sex line: the mothers will visit their daughters and the fathers
will visit their sons.   The older marriages have a better chance of
succeeding if the adult children approve of them.

830   Martin, Clyde E.   "Marital and Sexual Factors in Relation to
        Age, Disease, and Longevity," in Wirt, Robert D.; Winokur,
        George; and Roff, Merrill.   Life History Research in Psycho-
        pathology, Vol. 4, pp. 326-347.   Minneapolis, MN: Univer-
        sity of Minnesota Press, 1975.
        The author developed an interview to obtain information about
the marital and sexual lives of men taking part in the Baltimore Longitudinal Study of Aging.   Data from 603 interviews of men ranging in
age from 20-79 years of age are given in cross-sectional form.   A
history of marital dissolution and remarriage was found for those
men who were older at the interview.   In addition, for the older men,
there was a lesser amount of responsiveness to certain sexual stimuli,
a smaller amount in kind and quantity of sexual activity, and more
impotence.   There was no trend with age in response to the question
of whether the men would want a restoration of sexual vigor if it
were possible.   Older respondents reported much less sexual activity
between 20 and 40 years of age.   13 references

831   _____. "PHS-NIH Individual Project Report: Marital, Sex-
        ual and Social Factors in Aging," in Clinical Physiology,
        Brands Human Performance Section, Baltimore, MD: June/
        July 1973.
        The data on over 600 interviews with men indicated that coital
potency declines with advancing age.   The data do not provide evidence as to why some men become impotent and why others do not,
and the author suggests that other analytic approaches are needed
for etiological objectives.   No references

832   Nahemow, N. R.   "Loneliness in Old Age: The Ugandan Case,"
        in Gerontologist, Vol. 15, No. 5, Part 2, 46, 1975.   (A
        paper given at the 28th annual meeting of the Gerontological
        Society, Louisville, Kentucky, October 1975.)
        Accomplishments in early life and old age are looked on with
optimism by men while women are less optimistic.   It is suggested

that the sexual division of labor, which places a heavier burden on women throughout the life-cycle, is the reason for this difference.

833 Napier, Augustus Young. "Patterns of Growth and Stasis in
     Marriage over Several Generations." Unpublished doctoral
     dissertation, University of North Carolina at Chapel Hill,
     1970. (D. A. , Vol. 31, No. 5, 2999B, 1970.)
        A study of two younger married couples who were selected
from volunteers. The parents of each partner were also studied
and, in some cases, siblings were interviewed. Marriage is suggested as being the focus of an individual's attempt to change and
grow. This change is measured against patterns in the parental
marriage.

834 Oziel, L. Jerome. "Revitalizing Sexual Relations After Many
     Years of Marriage," in Medical Aspects of Human Sexuality,
     Vol. 10, No. 8, 7, 10, 13, 15-18, 23, August 1976.
        Some reasons for decline in sexual interest in one or both
marital partners after many years of marriage include: 1) loss of
physical attractiveness, 2) decreased intimacy, 3) decreased sexual
innovativeness, 4) extramarital affairs, 5) a lower libido, 6) changes
in self-perception, 7) disturbances in situation, 8) dissatisfaction with
the marriage, 9) sexual dysfunction, and 10) organic problems. Treatment processes recommended were: 1) retraining and sex education,
2) anxiety reduction, 3) communication training, 4) dynamic exploration, and 5) conflict resolution. 9 references

835 Peterson, James A. "Marital and Family Therapy Involving
     the Aged," in Gerontologist, Vol. 13, 27-31, Spring 1973.
        Cases are presented to illustrate group intervention as a way
of dealing with family and marital problems. Assessment and evaluation must be emphasized when using group intervention. 7 references

836 _____ . Marriage and Love in the Middle Years. Pamphlet
     No. 456. New York: Public Affairs Committee, Inc. , 1970.
        This pamphlet has been excerpted from the author's book en-
titled Married Love in the Middle Years. It focuses on complaints
and problems of the middle years by both men and women. Sexuality as the affirmation of tenderness and sexual adjustment and communication are covered.

837 _____ , and Payne, Barbara. "Sexual Achievement in Mar-
     riage in the Later Years," Chapter 5 in their Love in the
     Later Years, pp. 61-79. New York: Association Press,
     1975.
        A general and easy to understand chapter on what happens to
sexual response with age, the problems associated with this, and
some case studies for illustration. Suggestions are made for improving sex in marriage in the later years.

838 Pineo, Peter C. "Disenchantment in the Later Years of Mar-
     riage," in Neugarten, Bernice L. (ed.), Middle Age and Aging,

pp. 258-262. Chicago: University of Chicago Press, 1968.
(Abridged from Marriage and Family Living, Vol. 23, 3-11,
February 1961. Originally, this was a paper read at the
Eastern Canadian Sociological Conference on Kinship and the
Family sponsored by the Department of Sociology, McMaster
University, Hamilton, Ontario, February 1960.)
  Marital satisfaction goes down slowly over time although per-
sonal adjustment does not go down. Those who remain married and
those who get divorced have different rates of disenchantment.   12
references

839   Powers, Edward A., and Bultena, Gordon L.   "Sex Differences
      in Intimate Friendships of Old Age," in Journal of Marriage
      and the Family, Vol. 38, No. 4, 739-747, 1976.
  In order to assess the nature and prominence of intimate
friendships in the social world of older women and men, a statewide
sample was obtained. The sample consisted of 234 people who were
70 years of age or older. It was found that there were very few
sex differences in the characteristics of intimate friendships in late
life.   36 references

840   Puner, Morton.   "Sex and Marriage," Chapter 9 in his To the
      Good Life--What We Know About Growing Old, pp. 143-163.
      New York: Universe Books, 1974.
  Summaries of the Kinsey, Masters and Johnson, and Isadore
Rubin's studies are presented as they relate to the topic. The impor-
tance of sexual activity in the life of older people is stressed.

841   Reed, David M.   "What Is the Norm for Sexual Relations in
      Marriage?" in Medical Aspects of Human Sexuality, Vol. 1,
      No. 3, 6-9, November 1967.
  Some of the reasons for changes in marital sexuality include:
1) changes in family structure, 2) changes in sexual mores, 3)
changes in the role of women. There exists a great amount of sexual activity that occurs before marriage and outside of marriage.
The "sexual revolution" may not have reached the lower class yet.
13 references

842   Reedy, Margaret Neiswender.   "Age and Sex Differences in
      Personal Needs and the Nature of Love: A Study of Happily
      Married Young, Middle-Aged, and Older Adult Couples." Un-
      published doctoral dissertation, University of Southern Cali-
      fornia, 1977. (D.A., Vol. 38, No. 8, 3857-B, 1977.)
  One hundred and two happily married couples participated in
the study. The couples were divided into three age groups: young
adult (mean age 28 years), middle-aged (mean age 45 years), and
older adult (mean age 65 years). Older adults were lower in their
needs for Achievement, Heterosexuality, Aggression, Autonomy,
Dominance and they were found to be higher in needs for Deference
and Order compared to the other two age groups. The author suggests that neither sex nor age has to be a limiting factor in the experience and expression of love. This is similar to Margaret Neiswender Reedy, and James E. Birren's "How Do Lovers Grow Older

Together? Types of Lovers and Age," in Gerontologist, Vol. 18,
No. 5, Part 2, 115, November 16-20, 1978. (Paper presented at
the National Gerontological Society Meeting, Dallas, Texas, November 1978.)

843 _____. "What Happens to Love? Love, Sexuality and Ag-
    ing," in Solnick, Robert L. (ed.), Sexuality and Aging (re-
    vised), pp. 184-195. Los Angeles: University of Southern
    California, 1978.
       The need for love and intimacy exists throughout life. Data
for this chapter came from a larger study of the characteristics of
satisfying love relationships between men and women. She begins by
discussing the difinition of love and then relates love after parenthood to a second honeymoon. The author describes what love relationships are really like and the mellowing of love which occurs when
lovers grow old together. Cuddling and closeness are important di-
mensions to sexual intimacy. Expectations in relationships must
include commitment and mutual understanding. This was not included
in Irene Mortenson Burnside's Sexuality and Aging (1975). 5 references

844 Renne, Karen S. "Correlates of Dissatisfaction in Marriage,"
    in Journal of Marriage and the Family, Vol. 32, 54-67, Feb-
    ruary 1970.
       Adult respondents (N=5163) from 4452 households in Alameda
County, California, provided the data for this study. The respondents were all married and living with the mate. Sex survey questions
were responded to and were subsequently analyzed controlling for
race, sex, and age. The most dissatisfied were blacks, people with
low income, low education, low morale, physical illness, depression,
or heavy drinking problems. Also included in the most dissatisfied
were people with few intimate associations. Blacks were more dissatisfied than whites as a whole. Unhappy marriage can be thought
of as a disability. 12 references

845 Rollins, Boyd C., and Feldman, Harold. "Marital Satisfaction
    Through the Life Span," in Journal of Marriage and the Fam-
    ily, Vol. 32, 20-28, February 1970.
       Marital satisfaction over the family life cycle is examined.
Husbands and wives in 799 middle-class families were given separate
questionnaires. Data from these questionnaires suggest husbands
and wives are influenced in very different ways by life experiences.
Family life cycle experiences had an association with marital satisfaction for wives. This was not so strong an association for husbands. The wife gave negative evaluations of the marriage during
the dependent children stages. 32 references

846 Rutgers, Johannes. How to Attain and Practice the Ideal Sex
    Life. New York: Falstaff Press, Inc., 1937. (New York:
    Cadillac Publishing Co., 1940.) This book is a complete
    translation by Norman Haire, CH.M., M.B., of "Das Sexual-
    leben in seiner biologischen Bedeutung."
       Chapter 60 is entitled "The Dangerous Age in Man and Woman

and Ideal Sexual Life for Maximum Health," pp. 329-333 (1937); pp.
267-271 (1940). Chapter 61 is entitled "Practical Advice for Aged
Married Lovers," pp. 334-338 (1937); pp. 272-275 (1940). In Chapter 60 the author states that the sexuality of elderly men is almost
more dangerous than that of young people because when a man is
old, self-control deserts him. Takes a somewhat negative view of
sexuality and aging and speaks of sex only in the context of marriage.
Chapter 61 suggests that in the flower of his manhood a man should
glory in his sexual strength but that he should rest in old age.

847 Safilios-Rothschild, Constantina. "Sexuality, Power, and Free-
        dom Among 'Older' Women," in Troll, Lillian E. ; Israel,
        Joan; and Israel, Kenneth (eds.), Looking Ahead: A Woman's
        Guide to the Problems and Joys of Growing Older, pp. 162-
        166. Englewood Cliffs, NJ: Prentice-Hall, Inc. , 1977.
     A feminist article which includes comments on sex roles in
other cultures. A woman's sexual potential, desires, and urges
peak between the ages of 30 and 35 and remain stable from that
time on. Most older women experience sexual frustration. Women
should be able to feel comfortable with their sexual needs and desires
to fulfill them. 7 references

848 Schmitt, Robert C. "Age Differences in Marriage in Hawaii,"
        in Journal of Marriage and the Family, Vol. 28, 57-61, Feb-
        ruary 1966.
     Analysis was made of 16, 532 marriages which were per-
formed in Hawaii. Great variations in age between partners were revealed when classification was done by ethnicity, age level, previous
marital status, place of residence, and bride's or groom's occupa-
tion. The widest ranges were found for grooms of Filipino stock,
older people, remarriages, farm laborers, and interracial marriages.
Reasons for the differences are not given. 10 references

849 Schonfield, David. "Family Life Education Study: The Later
        Adult Years," in Gerontologist, Vol. 10, 115-118, Summer
        1970.
     People need to learn more about aging processes for general
awareness and also sympathy. Universities and schools should inte-
grate the aging aspect in the courses in sociology, physical education,
economics, biology and psychology. 12 references

850 Seidenberg, Robert. "Older Man-Younger Woman Marriages,"
        in Medical Aspects of Human Sexuality, Vol. 9, No. 11, 6-7,
        11-13; 17-18; 21; 25, November 1975.
     It is Dr. Seidenberg's opinion that older man-younger woman
marriages should not be condemned or recommended. No references

851 Sinnott, Jan Dynda. "Sex-Role Inconstancy, Biology, and Suc-
        cessful Aging: Dialectical Model," in Gerontologist, Vol. 17,
        No. 5, 459-463, 1977.
     This study, done in response to Kline (1975), looks at sex-
role inconstancy in association with life-span and successful aging.
Synthesis of conflicting role demands in the biological, cultural, and

psychological spheres may be adaptive, and a dialectical model is used to show this. Data are analyzed from studies dealing with sui- cide in middle-age, aging and mental health, social expectations, personality and aging, sexuality, and social change. The fuzzy dis- tinctions between male and female roles in old age are related to successful aging. Role flexibility could be a sign of a generalized trait, i. e. , adaptivity or intelligence. 26 references

852   Smith, Peter C. "Age at Marriage: Recent Trends and Pros- pects," in Philippine Sociological Review, Vol. 16, 1-16, 1968. (This was based on the author's M. A. Thesis, "Age at Marriage in the Philippines," completed at the University of the Philippines, 1966.)
        Any recent rise in age at marriage has been so small as to make measurement difficult. If these marriage patterns continue, they will have very little effect on Philippine fertility. 13 foot- notes

853   Stokes, Walter R. "A Widow's Sex and Marriage Prospects," in Sexology, Vol. 33, 439-441, February 1967.
        The sex life of a widowed woman is usually ignored. Mature, unmarried women have sex problems. Young, recent widows are often among the most marriageable of women since they are mature women who need and appreciate a man. These women are socially at ease with men and are sexually responsive to them. They can also make good mothers. The well adjusted woman who is widowed in middle or later life usually finds it difficult to make a suitable new marriage. A sound relationship for a woman in the later years will be determined more by affection and companionship than by sex- ual activity. No references

854   Sussman, Marvin B. "Family Relations and the Aged," in Hoff- man, Adeline Mildred (ed.), The Daily Needs and Interests of Older People, pp. 300-324. Springfield, IL: Charles C. Thomas, 1970.
        Kin supportive behavior can be important. Major role changes do not occur at the same time for women and men. Women are usually affected first when the children leave the home and sched- ules become less demanding. At the same time, males reach a peak of their activities in the work setting. This results in a great discrepancy between husband and wife. 56 references; 13 additional readings suggested

855   _____. Sourcebook in Marriage and the Family (3rd edition). Boston: Houghton Mifflin Co. , 1968.
        The fourth edition (1974) contains sections on marital sex and sex roles including origin, marriage and sex roles, social structure and sex roles, and change in sex roles. The third edition (1968) contains sections on age at first marriage, age and fertility, marital sex, sex differences, and sex roles. The second edition (1963) con- tains sections on age at first marriage and remarriage, marital status of aged, sex in marriage, and sex differences.

856   Swain, Mary Ann Price. "Husband-Wife Patterns of Interaction
      at Three Stages of Marriage." Unpublished doctoral disserta-
      tion, University of Michigan, 1969. (D. A. , Vol. 31, No. 2,
      904-B, 1970.)
      A study describing the differences in patterns of behavior
shown by 13 white middle-class, volunteer couples at three stages:
newlywed, pregnancy, and child development. It was found that general sex differences run counter to the instrumental-expressive theory
of sex-role differentiation.

857   Swensen, Clifford H. ; Eskew, Ron W. ; Kohlhepp, Karen A.
      "Factors in the Marriage of Older Couples." Research Re-
      port, NIMH Grant MH-26933, 1977.
      Two hundred and twenty-four couples over fifty years of age
and married 20 or more years were given an instrument measuring
the expression of love (Love Scale) and a scale measuring marital
problems (Scale of Marriage Problems) as well as interviews. The
purpose of this research was to examine the marriage relationship
as a function of sex and other factors. Sex was not related to marriage problems or to the expression of love in marriage. 55 references

858   Troll, Lillian E. "The Family of Later Life: A Decade Re-
      view," in Journal of Marriage and the Family, Vol. 33, 263-
      290, 1971.
      Dr. Troll makes the point that sexuality in middle and late
life has not received enough study. She cites the major studies which
suggest a decline in sexual activity in the later years and suggests
that a larger sample of older people need to be studied to determine
sexual behavior and attitudes. A major studies chart is included at
the end. Thirteen references out of a total of 160 pertain to sexuality
and aging.

859   _____ ; Miller, Sheila J. , and Atchley, Robert C. Families
      in Later Life. Belmont, CA: Wadsworth Publishing Company,
      Inc. , 1979.
      Contains a small general discussion on sexuality and aging.

860   Udry, J. Richard, and Hall, Mary. "Marital Role Segregation
      and Social Networks in Middle-Class, Middle-Aged Couples,"
      in Journal of Marriage and the Family, Vol. 27, 392-395,
      August 1965. (This was a paper presented at Pacific Socio-
      logical Association annual meeting, Salt Lake City, April
      1965.)
      Bott's hypothesis, originally developed on London families,
was tested in this study. Basically, Bott's hypothesis states that
married couples' social network interconnectedness is directly related to marital role segregation. A questionnaire was used to interview 44 members of a sociology class and the parents' friends.
No significant relationship was found to support Bott's hypothesis.
In couples with highly educated wives, role segregation was lowest.
The same was found to be true in couples where the wife worked most
outside the home. Bott's hypothesis may be relevant only to lower-

class couples or for middle-class couples for a small part of the
family cycle.   9 references

861 Wallin, Paul, and Clark, Alexander L.   "A Study of Orgasm
      as a Condition of Women's Enjoyment of Coitus in the Middle
      Years of Marriage," in Human Biology, Vol. 35, 131-139,
      1963.
         Questionnaire data were collected from over 400 women.   A
close association existed between orgasm frequency and their ratings
of the extent to which they enjoyed the coitus.   However, even a proportion of women who had no or few orgasms still enjoyed coitus
"very much" or "much."   Women can enjoy coitus even though they
don't have an orgasm.   More data need to be collected from women
who enjoy coitus without orgasm.   Interviews with non-clinical samples of women and men are recommended.   8 references

UNCLASSIFIED CITATIONS

Journal titles in this section have been abbreviated
as follows. Entries begin on page 192.

Acta med. , Fukuoka.   Acta medica.   Fukuoka.
Acta psychiat. , Kbh.   Acta psychiatrica et neurologica.   Copenhagen.
Aktuelle Geront.   Aktuelle Gerontologie.   Stuttgart.
Allg. ärztl. Zsch.   Psychotherap. , u. psych. Hygiene.   Allgemein
    ärztliche Zeitschrift für Psychotherapie und psychische Hygiene.
    Leipzig.
Andrologie.   Andrologie.   Berlin.
Ann. Méd. lég.   Annales de médecine légale.   Paris.
Ann. med. -psychol.   Annales médico-psychologiques.   Paris.
Arch. Gynaek.   Archiv für Gynaekologie.   Munich.
Arch. KrimAnthrop.   Archiv für Kriminalanthropologie und Kriminal-
    istik (Archiv für Kriminalogie).   Leipzig.
Arch. Psycho. , Genève.   Archives de psychologie.   Genève; Paris.
Arkhiv Patol.   Arkhiv Patologii.   Moscow.
Archives Mediterranéennes de Médecine.   Asnières, France.
Arzneimittel-Forschung.   Aulendorf, West Germany.
Bull. Acad. Méd. , Paris.   Bulletin de l'Académie de médecine.
    Paris.
Cas. Lek. čes.   Casopjs Lekaru Ceskych.   Prague.
Ceskoslov. Gynaek,   Ceskoslovenska Gynekologie.   Prague.
Cesk. Psychiatr.   Ceskoslovenska Psychiatrie.   Prague.
Clin. Endocr. , Tokyo.   Clinical Endocrinology.   Tokyo.
C. R. Acad. Sci. (D), Paris.   Comptes Rendus Hebdomadaires des
    Seances de L Academie des Sciences.   D: Sciences Naturelles.
    Paris.
Dtsch. med. Wschr.   Deutsche Medizinische Wochenschrift.   Leipzig.
Encéphale.   Encéphale; journal de neurologie et de psychiatrie.
    Paris.
Folia endocr. , japon.   Folia endocrinologica.   Kyoto, Japan.
Gin. polska.   Ginekologia Polska.   Łódź.
Gior. Geront.   Giornale di Gerontologia.   Florence.
Invest. Urol.   Investigative Urology.   Baltimore.
Jap. J. Geriat. Japanese Journal of Geriatrics.   Tokyo, Japan.
Krim. Abh.   Kriminalistiche Abhandlungen.   Leipzig.
Lakartidningen.   Lakartidningen.   Stockholm.
Maandbl. geest. Volksgezondh.   Maandblad voor de geestelijke volks-
    gezondheid.   Amsterdam.
Méd. and Hyg.   Médecine et hygiene; journal d'informations medicales
    et paramedicales.   Geneva.

Med. Bull., Bombay. Medical Bulletin. Bombay.
Med. geriat. Medicina Geriatrica. Florence.
Medicina, Madrid. Madrid.
Mens en Maatsch. Mensch en maatschappij. Deventer, Netherlands.
MMW (also Münch. med. Wschr.) Münchener medizinische Wochen-
    schrift. Munich.
Monatsberichte. Organ für internationale Altersforshung und alters
    Bakämfung. Rumänien-Chesnau. (Cont as Altersprobleme, Ki-
    shinev, USSR).
Monde méd. Monde médical. Revue international de médecine et
    de thérapeutique. Paris.
Münch. med. Wschr. see MMW
Ned. Tijdschr. Geneesk. Nederlandsch Tijdschrift voor Geneeskunde,
    Amsterdam.
Ned. Tijdschr. Geront. Nederlandsch Tijdschrift voor Deventer, Nether-
    lands.
Nervenarzt. Nevenarzt. Berlin.
Pakistan develop. Rev. Pakistan Development Review. Karachi.
Paris méd. Paris médical. La semaine des clinicien. Paris.
Pediat. Akush. Ginek. Pediatriia, Akusherstvo I Ginekologiia. Kiev.
Pol. Tyg. Lek. Polski Tygodnik Lekarski. Warsaw.
Prax. Psychother. Praxis der Psychotherapie. Munich.
Proc. Soc. exp. Biol., N.Y. Proceedings of the Society for Exper-
    imental Biology and Medicine. New York.
Psychiatr. Neurol. Med. Psychol. (Leipz). Psychiatrie, Neurologie
    und Medizinische Psychologie. Leipzig.
Psychoanal. Rev. Psychoanalytic Review. London.
Rev. franç. Géront., Paris. Revue Française de Gérontologie. Paris.
Rev. Gériat., Paris. La Revue de Gériatrie. Paris.
Rev. Med., Liege. Revue Medicale de Liege. Liege.
Revue de Gerontologie d'Expression Française. Paris.
Rif. med. Riforma medica. Naples.
Riv. Geront. Geriat. Rivista di gerontologia e geriatria. Fisio-
    patologia; clinica e sociologia dell'età avanzata. Rome.
Schweiz. Arch. Neurol. Neurochir. Psychiatr. Schweizer Archiv
    für Neurologie, Neurochirurgie und Psychiatrie. Zurich.
Schweiz. Zsch. f. Strafrecht. Schweizerische Zeitschrift für Stra-
    frecht. Bern.
Sem. méd., B. Aires. Semana médica. Buenos Aires.
Sessuologia. Turin, Italy.
Sexualmedica. Madrid, Spain.
Sexualmedizin. Wiesbaden, West Germany.
Wiadomosci lek. Wiadomosci lekarskie. Warsaw.
Z. Alternsforsch. Zeitschrift für Alternsforschung. Berlin, East Ger-
    many.
Zbl. Gynäk. Zentralblatt für Gynäkologie. Leipzig.
ZFA, Stuttgart. ZFA. Zeitschrift für Allgemeinmedizin. Stuttgart.
Z. ges. innere Med. Zeitschrift für die gesamte innere Medizin und
    ihre Grenzgebiete. Leipzig.
Zool. Zh. Zoologischeskii zhurnal. Moscow.
Z. Psychosom. Med. Psychoanal. Zeitschrift für Psychosomatische
    Medizin und Psychoanalyse. Gottingen.
Zsch. f. Sexualwiss. u. Sex.-pol. Zeitschrift für Sexualwissenschaft
    und Sexualpolitik. Bonn.

Zschr. Haut und Geschlkr.   Zeitschrift für Haut-und Geschlechts-
_____
   krankheiten. Berlin, West Germany.
Zsch. Sexualwiss. , Bonn. Zeitschrift für Sexualwissenschaft. Bonn.
_____

862   Abraham, Georges. "La Sexualité du Troisième Âge, " in Con-
      gres International de Sexologie Medicale, 113-117, Paris 1974.
      _____

863   _____ . "Lebensalter und Sexualität [Age and Sexuality], "
      in Sexualmedizin, Vol. 2, No. 10, 450-452, October 1973.
         _____

864   Afzal, M. , et al. "Estimation of Net Currently Married Life
      Within the Reproductive Period for Females in Pakistan, " in
      Pakistan develop. Rev. , Vol. 14, 85-99, 1975.
      _____

865   Allersma, J.   [Criminality in Old Age], in Nederlands Tijd-
                                                  _____
      schrift voor Gerontologie, Vol. 2, 285-293, 1971.
      _____

866   Alpatov, V. V. , and Gordeenko, N. A.   [Effect of Mating on
      the Longevity of Silkworms], in Zool. Zh. , Vol. 11, 60-65,
                                      _____
      1932.

867   Aresin, L.   [Sexual Behavior in Higher Age], in Z. ges. in-
                                                         _____
      nere Med. , Vol. 31, No. 4, 120-123, 1976.
      _____

868   Armaingaud. "Les amours des vieillards, au point de vue
      médical et social, " in Bull. Acad. Méd. , Paris, Vol. 81,
                              _____
      711-717, 1919.

869   Baranov, V. G.; Propp, M. V.; Savchenko, O. N.; and Stepanov,
      G. S.   "Some Factors of the Genesis of Aging and Climacteric
      in Women, " in Chebotarev, Dmitri Fyodorovich (ed.), The
                                                           ___
      Main Problems of Soviet Gerontology, pp. 182-198, Kiev:
      _____
      Ninth International Congress of Gerontologists, 1972.

870   Barnouw, V. , and Stern, J. A.   "Some Suggestions Concerning
      Social and Cultural Determinants of Human Sexual Behavior, "
      in Winokur, George (ed.), Determinants of Human Sexual Be-
                                 _____
      havior, Springfield, IL: Charles C. Thomas, 1963.
      _____

871   Barták, V. , and Ráboch, Jan.   "Beginnings of Heterosexual Life
      in Women of Two Different Age Groups, " (author's translation),
      in Casopis Lekaru Ceskych (Prague), Vol. 117, 1469-1471,
         _____
      1978.

872   Baruch, J. Z.   [Aging Man and Sexuality], in Maandbl. geest.
                                                     _____
      Volksgezondh. , Vol. 14, 403-408, 1959.
      _____

873   Belliveau, Fred, and Richter, Lin.   "Sex in the Aging, " Chap-
      ter 16 in their Understanding Human Sexual Inadequacy. pp.
                      _____
      207-216, New York: Bantam Books, 1970.

874   Benedek, Therese.   Psychosexual Functions in Women. New
                          _____

York: Ronald Press, 1952. (P.A., Vol. 27, No. 923, 1953.)

875 Benjamin, Harry. "Outline of Method to Estimate Biological
     Age, with Special Reference to Role of Sexual Function," in
     International Journal of Sexology, Vol. 3, No. 1, 34-37, Au-
     gust 1949.

876 Bianchini, M. L. "Psychologische und psychoanalytische Ein-
     fälle über die Klimakterium des Mannes," in Zsch. Sexualwiss.,
     Bonn, Vol. 14, 376-392, 1928. (P.A., Vol. 2, No. 3108,
     1928.)

877 Bien, E. "The Clinical Psychogenic Aspects of pruritus vul-
     vae," in Psychoanal. Rev., Vol. 20, 186-196, 1933. (P.A.,
     Vol. 7, No. 3884, 1933.)

878 _____. "Über Gerontophilie," in Allg. ärztl. Zsch. Psy-
     chotherap., u. psych. Hygiene, Vol. 1, 519-528, 1928.
     (P.A., Vol. 3, No. 4790, 1929.)

879 Biggers, J. E. "Problems Concerning the Uterine Causes of
     Embryonic Death, with Special Reference to the Effects of
     Ageing of the Uterus," in Journal of Reproduction and Fer-
     tility, Vol. 8, (Supplement 8), 27, 1969.

880 Birnbaum, S. J. "Geriatric Gynecology," in Chinn, A. B.
     (ed.), Working with Older People: A Guide to Practice.
     Volume IV. Clinical Aspects of Aging. United States Public
     Health Service, Publication, 1459, 149-155, 1971.

881 Bouquet, H. "Le vote sur la declaration obligatoire; les vieil-
     lards et l'amour," in Monde méd., Vol. 28, 177-181, 1919.

882 Braadbart, S. "Some Data on the Sexual Behavior of the Male
     Population of a Welfare Home," in Gerontologia Clinica, Vol.
     4, (Supplement), 120-122, 1962.

883 Buchmann, W. [Various Comments on Sexual Activity and the
     Climacteric], in Zbl. Gynäk., Vol. 96, 433-437, 1974.

884 Butler, Robert N. "Psychosocial Aspects of Reproductive Ag-
     ing," in Schneider, Edward L. (ed.), Aging. Vol. 4. The
     Aging Reproductive System, pp. 1-8, New York: Raven Press,
     1978.

885 _____. "Sex After 65," in Brown, Leo E., and Lewis, Ef-
     fie O. (eds.), Quality of Life: The Later Years, pp. 129-143.
     The American Medical Association. Acton, MA: Publishing
     Sciences Group, Inc., 1975.

886 Calvo-Melendro, J., and Sanchez-Malo de Calvo, P. "Marriage
     and the Aged," in Proceedings of the 7th International Congress
     of Gerontology. Vienna: Wiener Medizinischen Akademie, 6,
     87-88, 1966.

887   Cameron, D. Ewen. "Sexuality and the Sexual Disorders," in
      Rees, John Rawlings (ed.), Modern Practice in Psychological
      Medicine, pp. 223-238, New York: Paul B. Hoeber, 1949.
      (P. A. , Vol. 24, No. 1300, 1950.)

888   Canivet, H. "Enquête sur l'initiation sexuelle," in Arch. Psy-
      cho. , Genève, Vol. 23, 239-278, 1932. (P.A. , Vol. 7, No.
      308, 1933.)

889   Carriero, F. , and Torelli, O. "In tema di reati sessuali in eta
      senile," in Ospedale Psichiatrico, Vol. 38, No. 4, 504-507,
      1970.

890   Cendron, H., and Vallery-Masson, J. "Les Effets de l'Age Sur
      l'Activité Sexuelle Masculine. Incidences de Quelques Fac-
      teurs dont le tabac [The Effects of Age on Male Sex Activity.
      Incidence of Some Factors Including Tobacco]," in Presse
      Médicale, Vol. 78, No. 41, 1795-1797, October 3, 1970.

891   Chin, Y. [Aging and its Effects on Cerebral Contents of Ac-
      tive Amines and Sexual Behaviors], in Acta med. Fukuoka,
      Vol. 44, 416-437, 1974.

892   Cislak, I. ; Poradovsky, K. ; and Mihokova, M. [Sexual Feeling
      of Women After the Menopause (author's translation)], in
      Ceskoslov. Gynaek. , Vol. 39, 221-222, 1974.

893   Delore, P. "Prevenzione dell' impotenza negli anziani," in
      Riv. Geront. Geriat. , Vol. 5, 184-193, 1955.

894   De Martis, D. , and Weiss, G. "Problemi psichiatrici concer-
      nenti la sessualita nell'anziano [Psychiatric Problems of Sex-
      uality in the Elderly]," in Giornale di Gerontologia (Florence),
      Vol. 23, No. 4, 307-312, 1975.

895   Destrem, H. "La vie sexuelle des personnes âgées," in Maroc
      Medical (Casablanca), Vol. 52, 372-382, June 1972.

896   Dóka, V. ; Molčan, L. ; and Pontuch, A. [Comments to Sexual
      Life of Climacteric Women (author's translation)], in Cesko-
      slov. Gynaek. , Vol. 39, 591-593, 1974.

897   Doroshow, Jack. "La viellissement n'est plus l'ennemi de
      sexe," in Union, Vol. 22, 50-58, April 1974.

898   Eber, A. "Die Blutschande [Incest]," in Krim. Abh. Vol. 30,
      68, 1937. (P.A., Vol. 13, No. 2113, 1939.)

899   Ehrmann, Winston. "Social Determinants of Human Sexual
      Behavior," in Winokur, George (ed.), Determinants of Human
      Sexual Behavior, Springfield, IL: Charles C. Thomas, 1963.

900   Eitner, S. ; Ruhland, W. ; and Siggelkow, H. Praktische Gero-

hygiene: Handbuch de Komplexen Betreuung in Alter [Practical
Gerohygiene: Handbook for Complete Care of the Aged].
Dresden: VEP Theodor Steinkopff, 1975.

901 Ellis, Havelock. Psychology of Sex: A Manual for Students.
     Revised edition. New York: Emerson, 1938.

902 Ernst, Morris Leopold, and Loth, David. "The Adventure of
     Old Age," Chapter 8 in American Sexual Behavior and the
     Kinsey Report, pp. 89-98, New York: M.W. Drexler Book
     Co. , 1948.

903 Eysma, I.D. , and Stevens, N. L. [Sex and Gender in Later
     Life], in Ned. Tijdschr. Geront. , Vol. 10, 1-17, 1979.

904 Faber, John E. "Dyspareunia in Older Women," in Surgical
     Clinics of North America, Vol. 39, No. 4, 1105-1111, August
     1959. (Abstract in Geriatrics, Vol. 14, No. 11, 102A, 107A,
     November 1959.)

905 Fetscher, R. "Kriminalbiologische Erfahrungen an Sexualver-
     brechern," in Zsch. f. Sexualwiss. u. Sex. -pol. , Vol. 17,
     356-363, 1930. (P.A. , Vol. 5, No. 1948, 1931.)

906 Finkle, Alex Louis. "Diagnosis of Sexual Problems in Urology,"
     in Kaufman, J. J. (ed.), Advances in Diagnostic Urology.
     Boston: Little, Brown and Co. , 1964.

907 Fraschini, A. "Contribution to Therapeutics of Ejaculatio Prae-
     cox and of Some Forms of Sexual Impotence," in Proceedings
     of the 7th International Congress of Gerontology. Vienna:
     Wiener Medizinischen Akademie, 3, 127-129, 1966.

908 Frick-Bruder, V. [Sex in Old Age], in ZFA, Stuttgart, Vol. 55,
     724-725, 1979.

909 Frosch, J. , and Bromberg, W. "The Sex Offender--A Psychia-
     tric Study," in American Journal of Orthopsychiatry, Vol. 9,
     761-777, 1939. (P.A. , Vol. 14, No. 2033, 1940.)

910 Fürbringer. "Physiologie und Pathologie der Sexualität in der
     Involutionszeit," in Dtsch. med. Wschr. , Vol. 54, 605-607,
     1928.

911 Garay Lillo, José, and Monzonis, Vicente Monleon. "Aspectos
     psicosomaticos y psiquiatricos de la sexualidad en la tercera
     edad," in Sexualmedica, No. 9, 13-23, 66, 81, September 1974.

912 Geddes, Donald Porter (ed.). An Analysis of the Kinsey Re-
     ports on Sexual Behavior in the Human Male and Female.
     New York: Dutton, 1954.

913 Gelma, E. "La délinquance sexuelle primaire et tardive des

hommes âgés non déments," in Ann. Méd. lég. , Vol. 17,
926-931, 1937.

914   . "L'erotisme de l'âge avancé," in Paris méd. , Vol.
       4, 1, 1938.

915   . "L'érotisme de l'âge avancé," in Paris méd. , (an-
nexe), Vol. 108, 71-73, 1968.

916   . "L'érotisme sénile chez la femme," in Encéphale,
       Vol. 30, 737-752, 1935.   (P. A. , Vol. 11, No. 2690, 1937.)

917   Giese, H. "Das Altersbild sexueller Perversionen," in Ner-
      venarzt, Vol. 28, 553-554, 1957.

918   Giess, M. C. [Influence of Sexual Activity on Longevity in
      Adult Male Drosophila melanogaster], in C. R. Acad. Sci.
      (D), Paris, Vol. 285, 233-235, 1977.

919   Goda, G. [Sexology in Geriatrics], in Méd. and Hyg. , Vol.
      35, 1845-1846, 1977. (Abstract in Excerpta Medica, Vol. 21,
      Section 20, No. 1420, 1978.)

920   Göppert, Hans. "Rückbildung und Alter," in Die Sexualität des
      Menschen: Handbuch der Medizinischen Sexualforschung, 34-
      55, 1968.

921   . [The Sexual Problem of Aging], in Jahrbuch für
       Psychologie, Psychotherapie, und Medizinische Anthropologie,
       14 (2-4): 261-267, 1966.

922   Graber, Georgia, and Graber, Benjamin. Woman's Orgasm:
      A Guide to Sexual Satisfaction. Indianapolis, IN: Bobbs-
      Merrill Co. , 1975.

923   Grätz, H. D. , and Wiendieck, G. [Sociopsychological Problems
      of Aged Sexuality], in Actuelle Gerontologie, Vol. 2, 469-472,
      1972.

924   Gurewitsch, Z. A. , and Woroschbit, A. J. "Das Sexualleben
      der Bäuer in Russland," in Zsch. f. Sex. -wiss. u. Sex. -pol. ,
      Vol. 18, 51-74, 1931. (P. A. , Vol. 5, No. 4509, 1931.)

925   Hafter, E. "Homosexualität und Strafgesetzgeber," in Schweiz.
      Zsch. f. Strafrecht, Vol. 43, 37-71, 1929. (P. A. , Vol. 4,
      No. 4748, 1930.)

926   Henninger, James M. "The Senile Sex Offender," in Mental
      Hygiene, N. Y. , Vol. 23, 436-444, July 1939. (P. A. , Vol.
      14, No. 2430, 1940.)

927   Hirsch, Edwin W. "The Sexual Factor in Prostatic Hypertro-
      phy," in American Journal of Surgery, New Series, Vol. 13,
      No. 1, 34-36, 55, July 1931.

928 Hunt, Bernice, and Hunt, Morton. Prime Time: A Guide to
     the Pleasures and Opportunities of the New Middle Age. New
     York: Stein and Day, 1975.

929 Igari, J.; Hayashi, Y.; and Murase, O. [Clinical and Bacter-
     iological Study of Urinary Tract in Elderly Patients in Nurs-
     ing Home], in Jap. J. Geriat., Vol. 12, 291-297, 1975.

930 Jones, Kenneth Lamar; Shainberg, Louis W.; and Byer, Curtis
     O. Sex. New York: Harper and Row, 1969.

931 Jonsson, G. A. "A Psychiatric Examination of Female Prosti-
     tutes in Sweden," in Acta psychiat., Kbh., Vol. 13, 463-476,
     1938. (P. A., Vol. 13, No. 5209, 1939.)

932 Jovanovic, U. J., and Tan-Eli, B. [Penile Erections During
     Sleep], in Arzneimittel-Forschung, Vol. 4, 393-394, 1969.

933 Kelly, E. L. "Personality As Related to Source and Adequacy
     of Sex Instruction," in McNemar, Q., and Merrill, M. A.
     (eds.), Studies in Personality, pp. 147-158, New York: Mc-
     Graw-Hill, 1942. (P. A., Vol. 16, No. 2732, 1942.)

934 Kleemeier, R. W., and Kantor, M. B. "Methodological Con-
     siderations in the Study of Human Sexual Behavior," in Wino-
     kur, George (ed.), Determinants of Human Sexual Behavior,
     pp. 201-205, Springfield, IL: Charles C. Thomas, 1963.

935 Kline, Milton V. "A Measure of Mental Masculinity and Fem-
     ininity in Relation to Hypnotic Age Progression," in Journal
     of Genetic Psychology (Pedagogical Seminary and Journal of
     Genetic Psychology), Vol. 78, 207-215, 1951. (This was read
     before the Society for Clinical and Experimental Hypnosis,
     November 1949.)

936 Kohoutek, F., and Finková, A. [Treatment of Climacteric
     Symptoms by Folivirin and Its Effects on Sexual Activity (au-
     thor's translation)], in Ceskoslov. Gynaek., Vol. 39, 608-610,
     1974.

937 Koomen, W., and deNiet, R. [Determinants of Sexual Satisfac-
     tion and Frequency of Sexual Intercourse of Married Women
     in the Netherlands], in Mens en Maatsch., Vol. 47, 54-67,
     1972.

938 Kotsovsky, D. "Sexualleben und Alter," in Monatsberichte,
     Vol. 2, 23-36, December 1936.

939 _____. "Sexualleben und Alter [Sex Life and Age]," in Zsch.
     f. Sexualwiss. u. Sex.-pol., Vol. 17, 410-412, 1930-1931.
     (P. A., Vol. 5, No. 2798, 1931.)

940 Krimm, Irwinn F. Sex Power and Health for the Middle-Aged
     And Senior. Seal Beach, CA: Happy Health Publishing, 1974.

941 Kumamoto, E. [Sexual Function and Aging], in Clin. Endocr.,
     Tokyo, Vol. 23, 397-399, 1975.

942 Legros, J. J. "Androgenes et comportement psychosocial chez
     l'homme [Androgens and Psychosocial Behavior in the Human
     Male]," in Revue Medicale de Liege (Liege), Vol. 30, No.
     12, 400-405, 1975.

943 Lehr, U. [On the Problems of Man at a More Mature Adult
     Age--A Sociopsychological Interpretation of the "Climacteric"],
     in Psychiatrie, Neurologie ünd Medizinische Psychologie, Vol.
     18, 59-62, 1966.

944 Lenz, L. L. "Über die Sexualität des alternden Mannes," in
     Zschr. Haut and Geschlkr., Vol. 8, 452-454, 1950.

945 Levie, L. H. [Sex and Old Age], in Ned. Tijdschr. Geneesk.,
     Vol. 121, 1955-1958, 1977.

946 Levine, Lena, and Doherty, Beka. The Menopause. New York:
     Random House, 1952.

947 Lloyd, C. W. "The Climacteric and the Menopause," in his
     Human Reproduction and Sexual Behavior, pp. 304-309, Phila-
     delphia: Lea and Febiger, 1964.

948 Loeb, H. "Untersuchungen über Sexualität beim Manne [Inves-
     tigation of Sexuality of Man]," in Zsch. f. Sexualwiss. u. Sex.-
     pol., Vol. 18, 1-15, 1931. (P. A., Vol. 5, No. 4420, 1931.)

949 Luminet, D. "Aspects psychologiques du vieillissement chez
     l'homme [Psychological Aspects of Aging in the Human Male],"
     in Revue Medicale de Liege (Liege), Vol. 30, No. 12, 396-
     400, 1975.

950 Lunde, A. S. "White-Nonwhite Fertility Differentials in the
     United States," in Health, Education and Welfare Indicators,
     pp. 23-37, Washington, D. C.: U. S. Government Printing
     Office, 1965.

951 Maillard, C. [The Affective and Sexual Life of the Third Age],
     in Revue Française de Gérontologie (Paris), Vol. 17, No. 17,
     19-20, 1971.

952 Mall-Haefeli, M. [Psychosomatic Aspects of the Climacteric--
     Proceedings], in Arch. Gynaek., Vol. 224, 378-381, 1977.

953 Mellgren, Arne. "Aldrandets sexuologi," in Lakartidningen,
     Vol. 67, 3171-3175, July 1970.

954 Menger, P.; Roussin, J. J.; and de Lapouge, G. "Psychose
     ménopausique après un rapport sexuel insolite; problème
     étiologique," in Ann. méd.-psychol., Vol. 116, No. 1, 139-
     144, 1958.

955 Meyers, Robert, et al. Sex, Romance and Marriage After 55.
     Los Angeles: University of Southern California, 1975.

956 Mikorey, M. "Die Problematik der menschlichen Sexualität im
     höheren Alter," in Doberauer, W. (ed.), Alter und Krankheit,
     pp. 59-109, Vienna: Gesellschaft zur Förderung wissenschaft-
     licher Forschung, 1957.

957 Miller, N. E.; Hubert, G.; and Hamilton, J. B. "Mental and
     Behavioral Changes Following Male Hormone Treatment of
     Adult Castration, Hypogonadism, and Psychic Impotence," in
     Proc. Soc. exp. Biol., N. Y., Vol. 38, 538-540, 1938. (P. A.,
     Vol. 12, No. 5250, 1938.)

958 Mohapl, P.; Heczko, P.; and Hyánková, M. [Some Comments
     on Psychosexual Problems in Climacterium (author's transla-
     tion)], in Ceskoslov. Gynaek., Vol. 39, No. 3, 192-193,
     1974.

959 Molinski, Hans, and Kaiser, Eberhard. "Sexuelles Verlangen
     und Hormonstatus [Sexual Desires and Hormone Status]," in
     Zeitschrift für Psychosomatische Medizin und Psychoanalyse,
     Vol. 9, No. 3, 221-223, July-September 1968.

960 Mori, I.; Ikeda, T.; Tsuneyoshi, Y.; et al., [Sexual Function
     and Aging], in Clin. Endocr., Tokyo, Vol. 23, 424-430,
     1975.

961 Motomatsu, T.; Akamine, Y.; Nawata, H.; Wasada, T.; Oma,
     H.; Umeda, F.; Haji, M.; and Muta, K. [Pituitary-Gonadal
     Function in the Aged Male (author's translation)], in Folio
     endocr., japon., Vol. 53, 1300-1309, 1977.

962 Nascher, I. L. "Persistent Sexual Libido in the Aged," in
     American Journal of Urology and Sexology, Vol. 12, 407-415,
     January-December 1916.

963 Okamoto, K. [Sexual Function of Aging Male], in Japanese
     Journal of Geriatrics, Vol. 11, 308-311, 1974.

964 Parrish, Edward. Sex and Love Problems. New York: Psy-
     chology Institute of America, 1935.

965 Patrono, V. "La sessualita negli anziani: aspetti endocrino-
     logici [Sexuality and the Elderly: Endocrinological Aspects],"
     in Giornale di Gerontologia (Florence), Vol. 23, No. 4, 313-
     325, 1975.

966 Pauncz, Arpad. "The Concept of Adult Libido and the Lear
     Complex," in American Journal of Psychotherapy, Vol. 5,
     187-195, 1951. (P. A., Vol. 25, No. 7994, 1951.)

967 Pearl, Raymond. Biology of Population Growth. New York:
     Alfred Knopf, 1925.

968   Pellegrini, R.   "La genitalità del vecchio e la sua vita ses-
      suale," in Gior. Geront., Vol. 4, 569-575, 1956.

969   Peretti, P. O., and Wright, S.   "Effects of Negative Attitudes
      Toward Sexual Intercourse by Retired Aged Males As Inhibi-
      tory Mechanisms of Coital Behavior," in Giornale di Geron-
      tologia, (Florence), Vol. 27, 423-432, 1979.

970   Peruzza, Marino.   "Gli aspetti sociali della sessualità nell'an-
      ziano [Social Aspects of Sexuality in the Elderly]," in Gior-
      nale di Gerontologia (Florence), Vol. 23, No. 4, 326-333, 1975.

971   _____.   "La sessualità nell'anziano, problema psico-biolog-
      ico," in Medicina Geriatrica (Florence), Vol. 11, 94-103, 1979.

972   Pigney, F.   "Sexualité du Troisième Age [Sexuality in Old Age],"
      in Revue de Gerontologie d'Expression Française (Paris), No.
      1, 52-53, 1975.   (A paper presented by G. Abraham at the
      First International Congress of Medical Sexology, Paris, July
      1974.)

973   Pillay, A. P.   "Sex and Senescence," in Med. Bull., Bombay, Vol.
      12, 121-127, April 1, 1944.   (I. M., Vol. 36, No. 669, July-Dec.
      1944.)

974   Pocs, Ollie; Godow, Annette; Tolone, William L.; and Welsh,
      Robert H.   "Is There Sex After 40?" in Psychology Today,
      Vol. 11, No. 1, 54-56, 87, June 1977.

975   Poffenberger, Thomas.   "Husband and Wife Fertility Control,"
      in Indian Journal of Social Research, Vol. 9, No. 1, 36-42,
      April 1968.   (Paper prepared for the Seminar on "Rural
      Change and Planned Development," Simla, May 1967.)

976   Prados, M.   "Marital Problems of the Middle Aged Group,"
      in Journal of the Canadian Psychiatric Association, Vol. 7,
      97-105, 1962.

977   Prill, Hans-Joachim.   "Die Alternde Vita Sexualis," in Sexual-
      medizin, Vol. 6, No. 2, 85-90, February 1977.

978   Raboch, Jan.   [Effects of Age on the Symptomatology of Sexual
      Disorders in Men], in Československa Psychiatrie, Vol. 65, 208-
      210, 1965. No. 5, 305-309, 1969.   (P. A., Vol. 44, No. 16488,
      1970.)

979   _____.   "Der Einfluss des Alterns auf die Symptomatik der
      funtionellen Sexualstörungen," in Andrologie, Vol. 4, No. 1,
      27-36, October 1971.

980   _____.   "Vliv věku na symptomatiku funk-čcnich sexuálnich
      poruch muže," in Československa Psychiatrie, Vol. 65, No.
      5, 305-309, 1969.   (P. A., Vol. 44, No. 16488, 1970.)

981 Robinson, W. J. Woman, Her Sex and Love Life. New York:
     Eugenics Publishing Co. , 1936. (P. A. , Vol. 5, No. 3882,
     1931.)

982 Rozynski, M. [Sexuality in the Aged], in Wiadomosci lek. ,
     Vol. 26, 667-671, 1973.

983 Rubin, Herman H. , and Newman, Benjamin W. Active Sex
     After Sixty. New York: Arco, 1969.

984 Rubin, Isadore. "Sex over 65," in Wiseman, Jacqueline P.
     (ed.), The Social Psychology in Sex, pp. 226-228, New York:
     Harper and Row, 1976.

985 Rucquoy, G. "La sexualité des personnes âgées," in La Revue
     de Gériatrie (Paris), Vol. 4, No. 4, 163-164, April 1979.

986 Ruiz, V. , and Benzecry, L. I. "La líbido durante el clima-
     terio," in Sem. méd. , B. Aires, Vol. 108, 230-231, 1956.

987 Ruskin, Samuel H. "Analysis of Sex Offenses Among Male
     Psychiatric Patients," in American Journal of Psychiatry,
     Vol. 97, No. 4, 955-968, January 1940-1941. (This was
     read at the ninety-sixth annual meeting of The American Psy-
     chiatric Association, Cincinnati, Ohio, May 20-24, 1940.)

988 Ružbarský, V. , and Michal, V. "Morphologic Changes in the
     Arterial Bed of the Penis with Aging. Relationship to the
     Pathogenesis of Impotence," in Invest. Urol. , Vol. 15, 194-
     199, 1977.

989 Sacher, G. A. (ed.) "Aging in Relation to Development and Re-
     production," in Proceedings of the Sixth AUA-ANL Biology
     Symposium, Argonne National Laboratory, 1971. Argonne, IL:
     Argonne National Laboratory, 1971.

990 Sachse, H. [Sexual Disorders Following Prostate Surgery], in
     Münchener Medizinische Wochenschrift, Vol. 108, 1362-1364,
     1966.

991 Schachter, M. "A propos d'une 'flambée' d'erotisme menopaus-
     ique. Contribution à l'étude clinico-psychologique de la meno-
     pause," in Medicina, Madrid, Vol. 18, 438-444, 1950.

992 Schleyer-Saunders, E. "The Climacteric. A Geriatric and
     Social Problem," in Proceedings of the 7th International Con-
     gress of Gerontology. Vienna: Wiener Medizinischen Aka-
     demie, 4, 125-135, 1966.

993 Schmeing, K. "Das Alter als Umkehrung der Jugend," in Zsch.
     f. Sexualwiss. u. Sex. -pol. , Vol. 18, 396-399, December
     1931. (P. A. , Vol. 6, No. 3158, 1932.)

202 Sexuality and Aging

994 Schonfeld, V. [Sexual Problems in Women During the Climacterium and Presenium], in Ceskoslov. Gynaek., Vol. 26,
389-391, 1961.

995 Schulte, W. "Beweggründe für Sexualdelikte im Senium," in
Prax. Psychother., Vol. 4, 37-41, 1959. (Abstract in Excerpta Medica, Vol. 3, [Section 20], No. 1056, 1960.)

996 _____. "Sexualdelikte im Senium," in Doberauer, W. (ed.),
Geriatrie und Fortbildung, pp. 367-381, Vienna: Bergland-
Druckerei Ges. m. b. H., 1960.

997 Schürch, Johannes. "Evolution des déviations sexuelles dans
l'âge avancé: étude catamnestique," in Schweizer archiv für
Neurologie, Neurochirurgie, und Psychiatrie, Vol. 110, No.
2, 331-363, 1972.

998 Sěbek, V. "Difficulties in the Sexual Life of Older Women,"
in Proceedings of the 7th International Congress of Gerontology. Vienna: Wiener Medizinischen Akademie, 3, 131-
134, 1966.

999 Simonin, R. [Sexuality in the Old Person], in Archives Méditerr-
anéennes de Medecine, Vol. 45, 141-150, 1968. (Abstract in
E. M., Vol. 12, [Section 20], No. 678, September 20, 1969.)

1000 Slonaker, James Rollin. "Sex Drive in Rats," in American
Journal of Physiology, Vol. 112, No. 1, 176-181, May 1935.
(P. A., Vol. 9, No. 4181, 1935.)

1001 Solomon, Joan. "Menopause: Rite of Passage," in Ms.,
Vol. 1, 16-18, December 1972.

1002 Somerville, Rose M. Introduction to Family Life and Sex Education. Englewood Cliffs, NJ: Prentice-Hall, Inc., 1972.

1003 Steinhaus, Arthur H. "Sex and the Middle Aged Man," in
Clinical Medicine, Vol. 54, 159-160, May 1947.

1004 Stelzner, H. "Von Klimakterium, Erotik und Sexualität," in
Münch. med. Wschr., Vol. 76, 1974-1977, 1929.

1005 Strakosch, F. M. Factors in the Sex Life of 700 Psychopathic
Women. Utica, N. Y.: State Hospital Press, 1934. (P. A., Vol.
9, No. 1886, 1935.) (Also listed in Doctoral Dissertations Accepted by American Universities, 1934-1935, p. 51, New York:
H. W. Wilson Co., 1935.)

1006 Szewczyk, Hans. "Untersuchungen und Nachuntersuchungen
von Altersitt-lichkeitstätern," in Zeitschrift für Alterfor-
schung, Vol. 26, No. 3, 307-315, 1971.

1007 Tauber, Edward S. "Effects of Castration upon the Sexuality
of the Adult Male: A Review of the Relevant Literature,"

in Psychosomatic Medicine, Vol. 2, No. 1, 74-87, January 1940.

1008 Tavris, Carol, and Sadd, Susan. The Redbook Report on Female Sexuality. New York: Delacorte, 1977.

1009 Tiukov, A. I. [Age Changes in the Vessels of the Cavernous Bodies of the Penis], in Arkhiv Patologii, Vol. 29, 29-34, 1967.

1010 Topiar, A., and Satkova, V. [Children in Sexual Contact with Elderly People], in Československa Psychiatrie (Prague), Vol. 74, 9-12, 1978. (Abstract in Excerpta Medica, Vol. 22, Section 20, No. 516, 1979.)

1011 Torraca, L. "Sessualità e ringiovanimento," in Rif. med., Vol. 39, 252-253, 1923.

1012 Trabucchi, Cherubino. "Aspetti neuropsichiatrici del climacteric femminile [Neuropsychiatric Aspects of the Female Climacteric]," in Sessuologia, Vol. 14, No. 3, 18-24, July-September 1973.

1013 Tümmers, Hannelore. "Umweltvariablen und Sexualität im Alter.," in Aktuelle Gerontologie (Stuttgart), Vol. 9, 99-102, 1979.

1014 _____, and Mertesdorf, Frank. "Anpassung en ein Vorurteil [Adaption to Prejudice]," in Sexualmedizin, Vol. 5, No. 1, 47-50, January 1976.

1015 Ungewitter. "Sexuelle Verfehlungen im Greisenalter," in Arch. KrimAnthrop., Vol. 32, 346-347, 1909.

1016 U. S. Department of Health, Education and Welfare. Public Health Service. "Age at Menopause: United States--1960-1962." U. S. Vital and Health Statistics, Series II, Vol. 19, 1-20, 1966.

1017 _____. "Demographic Characteristics of Persons Married Between January 1955 and June 1958, United States." U. S. Vital and Health Statistics, Series 21, Vol. 2, 1-42, 1965.

1018 Untea, G.; Voinea, R.; and Pirvulescu, I. "Considerations Regarding the Usage of Gerovital-H, During Andropause for Disturbances of Sexual Dynamics," in Giornale di Gerontologia (Florence), Vol. 20, 62-69, 1972.

1019 Války, J., and Pontuch, J. [Histomorphological Changes on the Genitals During Climacterium (author's translation)], in Ceskoslov. Gynaek., Vol. 39, 562-566, 1974.

1020 Valsecchi, A. "Intervento del Teologo [Observations on Sexuality in the Elderly by a Theologian]," in Giornale di Gerontologia (Florence), Vol. 23, No. 4, 334-339, 1975.

1021 van Keep, Pieter A. [Sociological Aspects of the Climacteric Proceedings], in Arch. Gynaek., Vol. 224, 370-377, 1977.

1022 Vecki, Victor G. "Sexual Activity in Old Age," in Robinson, V. (ed.), Encyclopedia Sexualis, pp. 575-576, New York: Dingwall-Rock Ltd., 1936.

1023 _____. "The Sexual Life of Man and Its Relation to Longevity," in The Urologic and Cutaneous Review, Vol. 36, No. 1, 17-19, January 1932. (This was read before the San Francisco County Medical Society, September 29, 1931.)

1024 Veno, M. "The So-Called Coital Death," in Japanese Journal of Legal Medicine, Vol. 17, 333-340, September 1963.

1025 von Schumann, H. J. [Sexuality in the Elderly], in ZFA, Stuttgart, Vol. 52, 1091-1102, 1976.

1026 Vruwink, John, and Popenoe, Paul. "Postoperative Changes in the Libido Following Sterilization," in American Journal of Obstetrics and Gynecology, Vol. 19, No. 1, 72-76, January 1930. (Read at a meeting of the Los Angeles Obstetrical Society, May 14, 1929.) (P.A., Vol. 4, No. 3475, 1930.)

1027 Weinberger, H. "Ein Ausschnitt aus der Sexualkriminalität der Grosstadt," in Arch. KrimAnthrop., Vol. 89, 199-202, 1931. (P.A., Vol. 6, No. 4123, 1932.)

1028 Weller, J. [Sex Behavior and Partnership Problems of the Women in Climacterium with Reference to Her Occupation], in Zentralblatt für Gynaekologie (Leipzig), Vol. 100, 1381-1384, 1978.

1029 Weyrauch, Henry M. Life After Fifty: The Prostatic Age. Los Angeles: Ward Ritchie Press, 1968.

1030 _____. Surgery of the Prostate. Philadelphia: W. B. Saunders Co., 1959.

1031 Wile, Ira Solomon (ed.). The Sex Life of the Unmarried Adult. New York: Vanguard, 1934. (P.A., Vol. 9, No. 351, 1935.)

1032 Wísniewka-Roszkowska, Kinga. "Płeć a proces starzenia się cziowieka," in Polski Tygodnik Lekarski, Vol. 23, No. 10, 361-364, March 4, 1968.

1033 Wójtowicz, M. [Cytological Pattern of the Uterine Cervical Lining Cylindrical Epithelium in Post-Menopausal Subjects], in Gin. polska, Vol. 48, 881-889, 1977.

1034 _____. [Histoclinical Examination of the Uterine Cervix in Postmenopausal Women], in Gin. polska, Vol. 45, 1397-1405, 1974.

1035 Wolf, N. "Sexualdelikte von Greisen," in Münch. med. Wschr., Vol. 99, 256-259, 1957.

1036 Yamauchi, S. [Sexual Function and Aging in Domestic Animals --The Horse and Cattle], in Clin. Endocr., Tokyo, Vol. 23, 419-423, 1975.

1037 Zaĭtsev, M. A. [Simple Method for the Operative Elimination of Prolapse and Ptosis of the Internal Genitalia in Elderly Women], in Pediat. Akush. Ginek., (2), 61-62, 1977.

1038 Zák, K., Martincík, J., Procházka, J., et al. [Venous System of Internal Genitals in Climacteric Women (author's translation)], in Ceskoslov. Gynaek., Vol. 39, 566-567, 1974.

BIBLIOGRAPHIES AND OTHER RESOURCES

1039 Beasley, Ruth (comp.). International Directory of Sex Research and Related Fields. Vol. 2, p. 41, Boston: G. K. Hall, 1976. (two volumes).

1040 Birren, James E., and Moore, Julie L. (eds.). Sexuality and Aging: A Selected Bibliography. Los Angeles: University of Southern California, 1975.

1041 Brooks, Jo Ann, and Hofer, Helen C. Sexual Nomenclature: A Thesaurus. Boston: G. K. Hall, 1976.

1042 Claeys, Russell R. Utilization of College Resources in Gerontology: A Program Guide. Upper Montclair, NJ: Montclair State College Department of Adult Continuing Education, 1976.

1043 Ellis, Albert, and Abarbanel, Albert (eds.). Encyclopedia of Sexual Behavior (2nd edition). New York: Hawthorn Books, 1967.

1044 _____, and _____. Encyclopedia of Sexual Behavior, pp. 75-81, New York: Jason Aronson, Inc., 1973.

1045 Hughes, Marija Matich. The Sexual Barrier: Legal, Medical, Economic and Social Aspects of Sex Discrimination, pp. 1-7, (Aging and Sexual Barriers), Washington, DC: Hughes Press, 1977.

1046 Institute for Sex Research. Aging and Sex Behavior. March 1977, April 1978 addendum and October 1978 addendum. Bloomington, IN: Institute for Sex Research, Indiana University, March 1977.

1047 _____. Catalog of Periodical Literature in the Social and Behavioral Sciences Section, Library of the Institute for Sex Research, Including Supplement to Monographs, 1973-1975. Boston: G. K. Hall, 1976. 4 volumes.

1048 _____. Catalog of the Social and Behavioral Sciences Monograph Section of the Library of the Institute for Sex Research. Boston: G. K. Hall, 1975.

1049 _____. Sources of Information and Materials Relating to

Human Sexuality. Bloomington, IN: Institute for Sex Research, Indiana University, April 1977.

1050   Lewis, Robert A. "Transitions in Middle-Age and Aging Families: A Bibliography from 1940 to 1977," in Family Coordinator, Vol. 27, No. 4, 472-474, October 1978. Contains a section "Sex and Aging" with 104 citations.

1051   Mueller, Jean E., and Kronauer, Margaret L. (comps.). "A Bibliography of Doctoral Dissertations on Aging from American Institutions of Higher Learning, 1975-1977," in Journal of Gerontology, Vol. 33, No. 4, 605-615, 1978.

1052   Rooke, M. Leigh, and Wingrove, C. Ray. Gerontology: An Annotated Bibliography, pp. 231-233, Washington, DC: University of America Press, 1977.

1053   Rutgers University Intra-University Program in Gerontology. A Bibliography of Resources Pertaining to Gerontology in the Camden Area Rutgers Libraries. New Brunswick, NJ: The Program, June 1977.

1054   _____. A Bibliography of Resources Pertaining to Gerontology in the Division on Aging, Department of Community Affairs, State of New Jersey, Trenton. New Brunswick, NJ: The Program, June 1977.

1055   _____. A Bibliography of Works Pertaining to Gerontology in the New Brunswick Area Rutgers Libraries. New Brunswick, NJ: The Program, March 1977.

1056   _____. A Bibliography of Resources Pertaining to Gerontology in the New Jersey State Library, Trenton, New Jersey. New Brunswick, NJ: The Program, June 1977.

1057   _____. A Bibliography of Works Pertaining to Gerontology in the Newark Area Rutgers Libraries. (Dana Library-Rutgers and Rutgers Law Library.) New Brunswick, NJ: The Program, June 1977.

1058   _____. A Bibliography on Sexuality and Aging. New Brunswick, NJ: The Program, June 1978. Library of Congress Catalog Card No. 78-109370. (Compiled by George F. Wharton III.)

1059   Schwartz, Beverly (comp.). Aging Bibliography. Upper Montclair, NJ: National Multimedia Center for Adult Education, Montclair State College, 1977.

1060   Seruya, Flora C.; Losher, Susan; and Ellis, Albert. Sex and Sex Education: A Bibliography. New York: R. R. Bowker Co., 1972.

1061   Sexuality and Aging Bibliography.   Durham, NH: New England
         Gerontology Center, 1977.   (NEGC Order No. 076)
         Included are books, articles and pamphlets on topics includ-
ing behavioral and psychological aspects and medical and social influences.   There are 170 citations listed alphabetically by title. There
are 32 citations from this bibliography excerpted in GeronTopics,
Vol. 3, No. 4, 364, 1979.

1062   "Sexuality and the Aging: A Selective Bibliography," in
         SIECUS Report, Vol. 4, No. 6, 5-8, July 1976.

1063   Shock, Nathan Wetherill.   A Classified Bibliography of Geron-
         tology and Geriatrics.   Stanford, CA: Stanford University
         Press, 1951.

1964   _____. _____. Supplement one, 1949-1955.   Stanford,
         CA: Stanford University Press, 1957.

1065   _____. _____. Supplement two, 1956-1961.   Stanford,
         CA: Stanford University Press, 1963.

1066   _____. "Current Publications in Gerontology and Geriatrics,"
         in Journal of Gerontology, Vol. 29, No. 1, 109-126, 1974.

1067   _____. _____, Vol. 29, No. 2, 240-253, 1974.

1068   _____. _____, Vol. 29, No. 3, 343-358, 1974.

1069   _____. _____, Vol. 29, No. 4, 468-486, 1974.

1070   _____. _____, Vol. 29, No. 5, 591-614, 1974.

1071   _____. _____, Vol. 29, No. 6, 694-714, 1974.

1072. _____. _____, Vol. 30, No. 1, 108-128, 1975.

1073   _____. _____, Vol. 30, No. 2, 239-256, 1975.

1074   _____. _____, Vol. 30, No. 3, 366-384, 1975.

1075   _____. _____, Vol. 30, No. 4, 492-512, 1975.

1076   _____. _____, Vol. 30, No. 5, 619-639, 1975.

1077   _____. _____, Vol. 30, No. 6, 718-738, 1975.

1078   _____. _____, Vol. 31, No. 1, 110-128, 1976.

1079   _____. _____, Vol. 31, No. 2, 231-253, 1976.

1080   _____. _____, Vol. 31, No. 3, 360-382, 1976.

1081   _____. _____, Vol. 31, No. 4, 489-511, 1976.

1082 _____. _____, Vol. 31, No. 5, 619-639, 1976.

1083 _____. _____, Vol. 31, No. 6, 711-737, 1976.

1084 _____. _____, Vol. 32, No. 1, 108-124, 1977.

1085 _____. _____, Vol. 32, No. 2, 237-255, 1977.

1086 _____. _____, Vol. 32, No. 3, 359-382, 1977.

1087 _____. _____, Vol. 32, No. 4, 491-512, 1977.

1088 _____. _____, Vol. 32, No. 5, 613-640, 1977.

1089 _____. _____, Vol. 32, No. 6, 699-731, 1977.

1090 _____. _____, Vol. 33, No. 1, 136-159, 1978.

1091 _____. _____, Vol. 33, No. 2, 299-319, 1978.

1092 _____. _____, Vol. 33, No. 3, 457-479, 1978.

1093 _____. _____, Vol. 33, No. 4, 616-640, 1978.

1094 _____. _____, Vol. 33, No. 5, 775-800, 1978.

1095 _____. _____, Vol. 33, No. 6, 895-921, 1978.

1096 _____. _____, Vol. 34, No. 1, 125-159, 1979.

1097 _____. _____, Vol. 34, No. 2, 286-319, 1979.

1098 _____. _____, Vol. 34, No. 3, 451-480, 1979.

1099 _____. _____, Vol. 34, No. 4, 604-639, July 1979.

1100 _____. _____, Vol. 34, No. 5, 764-800, September
        1979.

1101 _____. _____, Vol. 34, No. 6, 884-912, November
        1979.

1102 _____. _____, Vol. 35, No. 1, 129-159, January 1980.

1103 _____. _____, Vol. 35, No. 2, 284-319, March 1980.

1104 Silverman, Alida G. (comp.). Sexuality in the Later Years
        of Life: An Annotated Bibliography. Ann Arbor, MI: The
        Institute of Gerontology at The University of Michigan, Jan-
        uary 1975.
        Forty references are annotated in this eleven-page bibliog-
raphy. Most of the major works on sexuality and aging are covered.
Twenty one entries from this are listed in a section entitled "Sex-

uality," pp. 23-26 in Hollenshead, Carol; Katz, Carol; and Ingersoll, Berit, Past Sixty: The Older Woman in Print and Film.   Ann Arbor, MI: The Institute of Gerontology, The University of Michigan-Wayne State University, 1977.

1105   University of Southern California.   Catalogs of the Ethel Percy Andrus Gerontology Center.   Volume 1, Author-Title Catalog, Boston, MA: G. K. Hall and Co. , 1976.

1106   _____ . _____ , Volume 2, Subject Catalog, Boston, MA: G. K. Hall and Co. , 1976.

AUTHOR INDEX

Abarbanel, Albert 137, 211,
 1043, 1044
Abraham, Georges 862, 863
Abse, D. Wilfred 796
Acken, Henry S. , Jr. 659,
 719
Adelman, Marcy R. 506
Adelson, Edward T. 34
Afzal, M. 864
Akamine, Y. 961
Akers, Donald S. 797
Albeaux-Fernet, Michel 762
Allen, Andra J. 1
Allen, Gina 2
Allersma, J. 865
Alexander, Mary J. 635
Alpatov, V. V. 866
Alvarez, Walter C. 248
American Association of Sex
 Educators, Counselors, and
 Therapists 430
Amir, M. 254
Amulree, (Lord) B. W. S. 3
Anderson, Barbara G. 4
Anderson, Barrie 747
Anderson, Catherine J. 5
Anderson, Helen C. 6, 660
Anderson, T. W. 630
Angelino, Henry R. 7
Antonovsky, Aaron 718
Arellano, Max G. 540
Aresin, L. 867
Armaingaud 868
Armstrong, Eunice Burton 8
Arony, A. J. 644
Arthur, Mary 716
Atchley, Robert C. 859
Auerbach, Alfred 9
Avant, W. Ray 10, 261
Avioli, Louis V. 661
Ayerst Laboratories 681, 691,
 699, 722

Bablok, Leszek 389
Bakke, J. L. 662
Bakker, Cornelis B. 776
Ballard, Lester A. , Jr. 288
Ballew, John William 720
Baranov, V. G. 869
Barber, Hugh R. K. 693
Barmack, Joseph E. 321
Barnes, Allan C. 663
Barnes, Robert H. 36
Barnett, Donald M. 594
Barnouw, V. 870
Barrai, I. 808
Barrett, J. C. 11
Bart, Pauline B. 664
Barták, V. 871
Baruch, J. Z. 872
Bastani, Jehangir B. 12
Beach, Frank Ambrose 13
Beasley, Ruth 1039
Beck, Aaron T. 549
Bedford, J. R. 665
Beigel, Hugo G. 14, 114, 202
Bellak, Leopold 83, 550, 551
Belliveau, Fred 873
Ben David, Sarah 283
Benedek, Therese 874
Bengston, Vern L. 464
Benjamin, Harry 203, 552,
 553, 875
Benzecry, L. I. 986
Berent, Jerzy 511
Berezin, Martin A. 15, 16
Bergevin, Patrick R. 554
Bergman, S. 254
Berlatsky, Marjorie N. 798
Berlin, Herman 771
Berman, Ellen M. 18
Bernstein, Herbert 155
Berry, Jane 431
Betts, D. 815
Bianchini, M. L. 876

211

Charatan, Fred B.   49
Charles, David   709
Charny, Charles W.   196
Chartham, Robert   50, 51
Chebotarev, Dmitri Fyodoro-
   vich   869
Chen, Pao-Hwei   385
Cherkin, Arthur   631
Chernick, Avinoam   52, 466
Chernick, Beryl   52, 466
Cherry, Sheldon H.   671
Chew, Peter   53
Chilgren, Richard   468
Chin, Y.   891
Chinn, A. B.   880
Chisholm, Lloyd W.   54
Choudhury, Moqbul A.   543
Christ, Jacob   827
Christenson, Cornelia V.   296,
   297, 298
Cilento, Raphael   366
Cislak, I.   892
Claeys, Russell R.   1042
Claman, A. D.   561, 623
Clark, Alexander L.   809, 861
Clark, LeMon   55, 203
Clarkson, Frank E.   804
Clay, Vidal S.   672
Clayton, Paula J.   56
Cleveland, Martha   810
Clistier, Adeline   57
Cocke, W. M.   299
Cohen, Eugene J.   755
Cole, Philip   701
Cole, Sandra S.   562
Cole, Theodore M.   58, 562,
   774
Coley, Silas B., Jr.   406
Coleman, Vernon   563
Comfort, Alex   59, 60, 61, 62,
   63, 64, 65, 66, 99, 257
Connell, Elizabeth   747
Connelly, Richard   177
Cook, W. Leigh, Jr.   793
Cooley, E. E.   258
Coope, Jean   673
Cooper, Allan J.   564
Cooper, Ralph L.   300
Cooper, William H.   674
Correy, J. F.   285
Cory, Thayer   437
Costa, R. L.   275
Costello, Marilyn K.   67

Cote, Paul   6
Cowdry, Edmund Vincent   88,
   268
Cowgill, Ursula M.   515
Cox, Claire   312
Cox, Sue   664
Crawford, Marion P.   675
Crile, George, Jr.   301
Cross, R. R., Jr.   555
Crow, Charles Brandon   220
Crown, Sidney   447
Cuber, John Frank   68
Czaplicki, Maciej   389

Daly, Michael Joseph   676, 748,
   768
Daniel, Ronald S.   69
Datan, Nancy   302
Daut, R. V.   367
Davidson, Janice L.   666
Davidson, William   677
Davies, Leland J.   259
Davis, Glenn C.   168, 183, 184
Davis, M. Edward   547, 678,
   719, 721
Davison, W. Phillips   136
Dean, Stanley R.   70, 71, 260
de Beauvoir, Simone   72
Delaney, Janice   303
de Lapouge, G.   954
De Leon, George   632
De Lora, Joann S.   73
Delore, P.   893
de Niet, R.   326, 937
De Nigola, Pietro   74
de Ridder, Joyce Anna   812
DeMartino, Manfred F.   22, 55,
   164, 426
De Martis, D.   894
Denber, Herman C. B.   565
Derner, Gordon F.   357
Destrem, H.   895
Detre, Thomas   679
Diamond, Milton   516
Dickinson, Peter A.   75
Dietz, J. Herbert, Jr.   306
DiMascio, Alberto   654
Dlin, Barney M.   566
Doberauer, W.   956, 996
Dobrowolski, L. A.   76
Doherty, Beka   946
Dóka, V.   896

Rees, John Rawlings 887
Reichel, William 484
Reichert, Philip 788
Reiff, Theodore R. 190
Reinke, William A. 314
Reiser, Morton F. 776
Reitz, Rosetta 741
Renne, Karen S. 844
Renshaw, Domeena C. 613
Research Group of Gerontology 418
Reuben, David 191, 344
Rhoades, Francis P. 742, 743
Rice, Dabney 744
Richman, Joseph 279
Richter, Lin 873
Ridgeway, James 754
Rizkallah, Tawfik H. 760
Robertson, O. H. 652
Robinson, Jean M. 345
Robinson, V. 1022
Robinson, W. J. 981
Robinson, William J. 614
Rockstein, Morris 395, 626
Rodeheaver, Dean 302
Rodgers, David A. 615
Rodgerson, Eleanor B. 352
Rodstein, Manuel 280
Roff, Lucinda Lee 192
Roff, Merrill 830
Rogers, Joseph 745
Rollins, Boyd C. 845
Rooke, M. Leigh 1052
Rose, Karla 628
Rose, Louise 747
Rosenkrantz, Paul S. 804
Rosenman, Ray H. 776
Rossman, Isadore 84, 194, 195
Roussin, J. J. 954
Rowland, Kay Ford 197
Rozynski, M. 982
Rubenstein, Dan 25
Rubin, Herman H. 983
Rubin, Isadore 122, 198, 199, 200, 201, 202, 203, 204, 281, 616, 617, 652, 984
Rubinstein, Eli Abraham 774
Rucquoy, G. 985
Ruebsaat, Helmut J. 419, 420
Ruhland, W. 900
Ruiz, V. 986
Rummel, Roy LaMar 282

Runciman, Alexander P. 618, 619
Ruskin, Samuel H. 987
Rutgers, Johannes 846
Rutgers University Intra-University Program in Gerontology 1053, 1054, 1055, 1056, 1057, 1058
Rutherford, Jean J. 749
Rutherford, Robert N. 749
Rutledge, Aaron L. 620
Ružbarský, V. 988
Ryan, Kenneth J. 750

Sacher, G. A. 989
Sachse, H. 990
Sachtleben, Marlene R. 518
Sadd, Susan 1008
Sadock, Benjamin J. 278
Safilios-Rothschild, Constantina 355, 847
Sagar, Clifford J. 114, 159
Sagarin, E. 281
Salis, Patricia J. 399, 400
Salisbury, Paul A. 136
Sanchez-Malo de Calvo, P. 886
Sander, Faye 450
Sanville, Jean 205
Sarno, John E. 786
Sarrel, Lorna 206
Sarrel, Philip M. 206
Satkova, V. 1010
Savchenko, O. N. 869
Savitsky, Elias 391
Saxe, Louis P. 421
Scalzi, Cynthia 451
Scarpa-Smith, Clorinda J. 698
Schachter, M. 991
Schaefer, Leah C. 352
Schaffer, Ralph S. 507
Schaie, K. Warner 207
Scheimann, Eugene 789, 790
Scheingold, Lee Dresinger 791
Schiavi, Raul C. 440
Schiller, Patricia 452
Schlesinger, Benjamin 208
Schleyer-Saunders, E. 751, 992
Schmeing, K. 993
Schmitt, Robert C. 848
Schneider, Edward L. 537, 884
Schneider, Jan 538
Schneidman, Barbara 621

224

Watkins, R. A. 285
Watts, Rosalyn Jones 794
Wax, Judith 239, 240
Waxenberg, Sheldon E. 357
Weg, Ruth B. 241, 242, 243,
355, 358, 546, 626
Weideger, Paula 763
Weinberg, Jack 244, 245
Weinberg, Martin S. 508, 509,
510
Weinberger, H. 1027
Weir, J. 58, 258
Weisberg, Martin 246
Weiss, G. 894
Weller, J. 1028
Welsh, Robert H. 974
Wenger, Nanette K. 776
Wesson, Miley B. 656
West, Norman D. 247
Wexler, Harry K. 632
Weyrauch, Henry M. 1029,
1030
Wharton, George F. III 1058
Wharton, Lawrence R. 547
Whiskin, Frederick E. 286
White, Charles B. 489, 490,
491, 492
Whitehead, Tony 627
Whittington, Frank 341
Widholm, Olof 523
Wiendieck, G. 923
Wijsenbeek, Henricus 718
Wikler, Revy 248
Wikström, Juhani 598
Wile, Ira Solomon 1031
Williams, Carroll M. 652
Williams, Colin J. 510
Williams, David 764
Williams, Richard H. 477
Williams, Robert L. 386, 398,
399, 400
Wilson, Charles B. 765
Wilson, Joseph G. 287
Wilson, Robert A. 719, 766,
767
Wilson, Thelma A. 767
Wilson, Thomas A. 721
Wilson, W. Cody 249
Wingrove, C. Ray 1052
Winn, Harold 768
Winokur, George 830, 899,
934
Wirt, Robert D. 830

Wise, D. A. 285
Wiseman, Jacqueline P. 984
Wiseman, R. A. 746
Wísniewka-Roszkowska, Kinga
1032
Witkin, Ruth K. 250
Wójtowicz, M. 1033, 1034
Wood, Robin Young 628
Wood, Vivian 729
Woodruff, Diana S. 251
Woods, Nancy Fugate 252, 360,
361
Wolf, N. 1035
Woolf, Charles M. 548
Woroschbit, A. J. 924
Wray, Jo Ann 540
Wright, Robert Roy 461, 462
Wright, S. 969
Wyon, John B. 536

Yamauchi, S. 1036
Yankowitz, Robert 650
Yannone, Michael E. 769
Yeaworth, Rosalee C. 253
Young, Allen 507
Young, William Caldwell 657,
658

Zaïtsev, M. A. 1037
Zák, K. 1038
Zalar, Marianne 468
Ziegler, Bette 346
Ziegler, Frederick J. 615
Ziel, Harry K. 770
Zimmerman, David 795
Zimring, Joseph G. 629
Zinberg, Norman Earl 16, 17,
429
Zuch, Joseph 378
Zuckerman, H. 526
Zukerman, Henryck 700
Zussman, Leon 463
Zussman, Shirley 463

TITLE INDEX